# AN ESSAY ON THE FOUNDATIONS OF GEOMETRY

*by*

BERTRAND A. W. RUSSELL

WITH A NEW FOREWORD BY

MORRIS KLINE

*Professor of Mathematics*
*at New York University*

DOVER PUBLICATIONS, INC., NEW YORK

Published in Canada by General Publishing Company, Ltd., 30 Lesmill Road, Don Mills, Toronto, Ontario.
Published in the United Kingdom by Constable and Company, Ltd., 10 Orange Street, London WC 2.

This Dover edition, first published in 1956, is an unabridged and unaltered republication of the first (1897) edition. It contains a new Foreword by Professor Morris Kline. It is published through special arrangement with the Cambridge University Press.

*Library of Congress Catalog Card Number: 56-3665*

Manufactured in the United States of America
Dover Publications, Inc.
180 Varick Street
New York, N. Y. 10014

# FOREWORD

The problem Russell analyzes and solves, at least to his satisfaction in 1897, is: What geometrical knowledge must be the logical starting point for a science of space and must also be logically necessary to the experience of any form of externality?

By a form of externality Russell means the space existing outside of our minds, the properties of this space, and the relationships among objects in space. This knowledge, which Russell calls *a priori* because it is independent of experience though perhaps elicited by experience, comprises certain necessary or apodictic principles of geometry and deductions from these principles.

An answer to this problem was given in the late eighteenth century. At that time Euclidean geometry stood forth as the most solidly established body of truths known to man and as the necessary and indubitable geometry of space. When, therefore, Immanuel Kant constructed his epistemology, he affirmed that the laws of Euclidean geometry were necessary, *a priori* judgments. Further, in order to explain how it happens that *a priori* knowledge applies to the physical world, Kant maintained that the space of Euclid is a fundamental intuition, that is, an inborn quality of the mind, and that the mind is constitutionally obliged to organize spatial experiences according to that intuition. For this reason our *a priori* knowledge of space agrees with our experiences of space.

However, geometry underwent a profound revolution in the nineteenth century. The creation of non-Euclidean geometry in the early part of the century cast doubt on the Euclidean character of physical space and certainly showed that the mind is not restricted to thinking about space in Euclidean terms. In particular, it became clear that not all of Euclidean geometry, nor perhaps any of it, is logically necessary to the experience of space. In addition, the nineteenth-century mathematicians built up projective geometry into a full-fledged independent subject; they showed that Euclidean geometry and the several basic non-Euclidean geometries, namely, the hyperbolic geometry of Gauss, Bolyai, and Lobatchevsky, the spherical or double elliptic geometry of Riemann, and the single elliptic geometry of Felix Klein, can be derived as special cases of projective geometry. (Twentieth-century formulations of projective geometry excluded spherical geometry.) Now, projective geometry deals with the descriptive or qualitative properties of space, whereas Euclidean and the basic non-Euclidean geometries deal with metrical or quantitative properties of space. Thus a new set of properties, the qualitative ones, which have no independent existence or recognition in Euclidean geometry, were shown to be logically prior to the Euclidean properties.

The apriority of Euclidean geometry, that is, its necessity for the experience of space, was thus attacked from two directions. It seemed vital to reopen the question of what geometrical knowledge is *a priori* in the sense of preconditions for experience. Thereby Russell was led to review, correct, and complete the transcendental arguments of Kant.

Russell remains a Kantian in that he agrees that the mind must possess some form of externality in order to experience space. Also, to account for the agreement between what is logically *a priori* in a form of externality and what does exist in an objective external world, Russell, like Kant, affirms that owing to the constitution of the *mind*, experience would be impossible unless the *world* accepts certain adjectives. However, as one might expect from the developments in nineteenth-century geometry, Russell finds that the *a priori* properties of any form of externality are not the laws of Euclidean geometry but rather of projective geometry. This geometry, he affirms, deals with the properties common to all spaces; it is wholly *a priori*; and it takes nothing from experience. The mind must know the basic laws of projective geometry and is thereby able to receive and organize perceptions of space.

The fundamental argument for the apriority of projective geometry, as opposed to Euclidean and the non-Euclidean geometries, is that qualitative relations must precede quantitative ones. One can count apples only after noting the qualitative identity of apples. In geometry this doctrine means that qualitative geometry must precede metrical geometry, because metrical geometry is concerned with distance and distance may enter only to measure qualitatively like elements.

Russell then selects those basic principles of projective geometry which he believes to be *a priori*, and from which the theorems of the subject follow. The fundamental projective principles are, first, that all parts of space are qualitatively similar, and are distinguished by the fact that they lie outside of one another (the homogeneity and relativity of space). Secondly, space is continuous and infinitely divisible; the point is the limit of infinite divisibility. Thirdly, two points determine a straight line; three points not on a line determine a plane; and so on to higher figures. Finally, the dimension of space must be finite.

After considering projective geometry, Russell asks whether there are additional *a priori* principles necessary to the experience of metrical geometry. He answers that there are such *a priori* metrical principles, and these prove to be refinements of the projective principles. The homogeneity of space becomes free mobility (which is equivalent analytically to the constant curvature of space). The projective principle that the straight line is determined by two points becomes an axiom about distance: two points determine a distance that is unaltered in any motion of the two points as a single figure (congruence), motion or rigid transformation being an additional *a priori* concept for metrical geometry. The finiteness of dimension remains unaltered.

These metrical principles do not presuppose measurement but are rather the conditions presupposed by measurement. Fortunately for Russell the above metrical properties prove to be common to Euclidean and the basic non-Euclidean geometries, that is, they lie in the domain of metageometry. Hence these geometries may apply to physical space. Moreover, because these geometries are the only mathematically-possible ones whose spaces are homogeneous, they are the only ones that could apply to physical space. In other words, physical space must be Euclidean, hyperbolic, spherical, or single elliptic.

On empirical grounds Russell believes that physical space is Euclidean and three-dimensional. The non-Euclidean geometries, he says, are not likely to be applicable and hence are only of philosophical importance.

Riemann had, however, introduced spaces with a metric or distance-function that varies from point to point in space. Such spaces have nonconstant curvature. Russell proceeds to show that such spaces are only apparently new varieties. One argument is that if geometrical objects changed in size when moving from one position to another in accordance with the variable metric, we could still superpose figures that are congruent in one position in the new position; therefore the change in metric has no significance. A second, deeper argument is that the metric of a space of nonconstant curvature builds up finite distances or lengths on the basis of infinitesimal distances, and in the infinitesimal all surfaces are plane. Thus geometry on the surface of an egg, which has nonconstant curvature, is possible only because we approach it, following Riemann, through infinitesimals. In the plane, of course, the Euclidean distance-function holds and congruence or superposition is available. The denial of the fundamental property of congruence to a space is, according to Russell, logically and philosophically absurd. A variable metric is pointless, senseless, and impossible to know: it may therefore be condemned on *a priori* grounds.

Since Russell lived in the shadow of Arthur Cayley and Felix Klein and, in particular, of Cayley's dictum that projective geometry is all of geometry, one can understand Russell's emphasis on projective geometry. However, just as Russell's philosophical forerunners may have committed errors because they did not know projective geometry, we must be wary of Russell's analysis, because in 1897 he could not have known certain major twentieth-century developments. One of these is a new branch of geometry, topology, which generalizes on projective geometry as projective geometry in turn generalizes on Euclidean and the basic non-Euclidean geometries. Hence the question arises whether Russell would decide today that the *a priori* properties of a form of externality consist of the fundamental principles of projective geometry.

Perhaps the most serious challenge to Russell's analysis of space has come from the now scientifically established theory of relativity. The space of the general theory of relativity is four-dimensional; it is non-Euclidean; finally it is nonhomogeneous, that is, it does not have constant curvature. Russell had rejected all three of these properties, the first two on empirical grounds and the last on logical grounds. He would admit this last one only if the variable metric of the nonhomogeneous space were superposed as a technical convenience on a space whose geometry has constant curvature. But Russell either overlooked or ignored the very suggestion of Riemann that proved to be so momentous for the theory of relativity. Riemann had pointed out that the belief in the homogeneity of space did not take into account the existence of matter. He regarded homogeneous space as an abstraction shorn of matter: when matter is taken into account the homogeneity disappears. This is precisely what occurs in the theory of relativity; the matter in space becomes absorbed by the geometry of space-time so that the nature of space-time varies from one region to another in accordance with the matter in it.

It seems clear, then, that as a consequence of developments of recent years some reconsideration of what is *a priori* in geometry is in order. The question may be asked, what values can one derive from studying questionable theses? First of all, the very reading of this book suggests rethinking through its problem in the light of recent developments. Russell's theses warrant consideration even if only for the purpose of reconsideration. Secondly, in the course of his analysis of the foundations of geometry, Russell reviews and highlights the essential features of the great works in nineteenth-century non-Euclidean geometry. The basic ideas, goals, and philosophical presuppositions of these works are to be obtained here in a manner not possible from reading the works themselves. Not only is there a danger in the latter course of missing the forest for the trees, but the goals and philosophical bases are usually not stated or even clear to the original investigators. Moreover Russell's critique of these works and their philosophical bases is sharp, limpid, and yet profound. With sovereign ease he handles subtleties and ambiguities, disposes of mathematical paradoxes and philosophical paralogisms, refutes errors, and dissipates confusion.

For example, he points out that Riemann and Helmholtz, misled by a quantitative bias, overlooked the qualitative substratum required for any consideration of quantity. He reproaches Helmholtz for subordinating geometry to mechanics. We read with interest and a smug sense of superiority how the nineteenth-century philosophers reacted to, and generally against, non-Euclidean geometry, and how Russell combats the philosophers who denied the possibility of a three-dimensional non-Euclidean space.

He also points out that even in the late nineteenth century the great geometers, notably Klein and Cayley, possessed a decidedly Euclidean bias. They believed that Euclidean geometry was the only really basic geometry; to them the non-Euclidean geometries acquired material significance only through Euclidean interpretations by means of new distance functions. Klein and Cayley missed the philosophical implication in their own work, namely, that Euclidean geometry can no longer be regarded as the fundamental metrical geometry of mathematics or as the only possible geometry for applications to the physical world.

The book also contains an account of the mathematical principles of projective geometry. Though modern axiomatic formulations of projective geometry have improved on Russell's choice of basic principles, in this subject, too, Russell presents analysis, critique, and insight not obtainable from purely technical books.

A larger value lies in the content regarded as history. It is important to recognize our own assumptions and presuppositions and the strengths and weaknesses of current doctrines. We learn these facts by comparing our doctrines with their predecessors. Note how readily we accept a nonhomogeneous, non-Euclidean physical world, whereas the nineteenth century regarded the application of non-Euclidean geometry as only a remote possibility.

We should remember that ideas discarded during one age, if indeed Russell's major theses should be, may reemerge to become all-important in another. Greek atomism is alive today and the Greek controversy as to whether nature is discrete or continuous is a vital current issue. Though the theory of relativity has at the moment cast in doubt beliefs well justified in 1900, there is no telling what dubious or discredited ideas may reign supreme in the year 2000. To obtain suggestions for the proper reconstruction of knowledge we may turn profitably to the best works of earlier generations.

There are, obviously, philosophical presuppositions in this work and therefore some of its conclusions are debatable, for philosophy, unlike mathematics, is dependent upon personal predilections. Those who would like to pursue the arguments initiated by the publication of this work will find stimulating articles in journals such as the *Revue de Métaphysique et de Morale*, *Mind*, *Philosophical Review*, and *Nature* for the years immediately following 1897.

Those who deprecate philosophical works because they do not settle the problems they consider or are tied to their times miss the point of the great Faustian lesson:

> Wer immer strebend sich bemüht,
> Den können wir erlösen.

The insolvable problems continually entice the human mind and the greatest intellectual pleasures are derived from the constant striving after elusive truth. The works of great minds keep the problems before our eyes and prevent us from sinking into mental lethargy. In this respect the works of Bertrand Russell possess supreme value. His admirably clear, precise, and elegantly reasoned analyses provide a stimulus to thought which are of enduring value no matter how much or how little one may see fit to accept of his specific conclusions.

MORRIS KLINE

*Institute of Mathematical Sciences*
*New York University*

# PREFACE.

THE present work is based on a dissertation submitted at the Fellowship Examination of Trinity College, Cambridge, in the year 1895. Section B of the third chapter is in the main a reprint, with some serious alterations, of an article in *Mind* (New Series, No. 17). The substance of the book has been given in the form of lectures at the Johns Hopkins University, Baltimore, and at Bryn Mawr College, Pennsylvania.

My chief obligation is to Professor Klein. Throughout the first chapter, I have found his "Lectures on non-Euclidean Geometry" an invaluable guide; I have accepted from him the division of Metageometry into three periods, and have found my historical work much lightened by his references to previous writers. In Logic, I have learnt most from Mr Bradley, and next to him, from Sigwart and Dr Bosanquet. On several important points, I have derived useful suggestions from Professor James's "Principles of Psychology."

My thanks are due to Mr G. F. Stout and Mr A. N. Whitehead for kindly reading my proofs, and helping me by many useful criticisms. To Mr Whitehead I owe, also, the inestimable assistance of constant criticism and suggestion throughout the course of construction, especially as regards the philosophical importance of projective Geometry.

HASLEMERE.
*May*, 1897.

TO

JOHN McTAGGART ELLIS McTAGGART

TO WHOSE DISCOURSE AND FRIENDSHIP IS OWING

THE EXISTENCE OF THIS BOOK.

# TABLE OF CONTENTS.

## INTRODUCTION.

### OUR PROBLEM DEFINED BY ITS RELATIONS TO LOGIC, PSYCHOLOGY AND MATHEMATICS.



## CHAPTER I.

### A SHORT HISTORY OF METAGEOMETRY.

## CHAPTER II.

### CRITICAL ACCOUNT OF SOME PREVIOUS PHILOSOPHICAL THEORIES OF GEOMETRY.

# CHAPTER III.

## SECTION A. THE AXIOMS OF PROJECTIVE GEOMETRY.

## SECTION B. THE AXIOMS OF METRICAL GEOMETRY.



### I. *The Axiom of Free Mobility.*

## II. *The Axiom of Dimensions.*



## III. *The Axiom of Distance.*

## CHAPTER IV.

### PHILOSOPHICAL CONSEQUENCES.

# INTRODUCTION.

### OUR PROBLEM DEFINED BY ITS RELATIONS TO LOGIC, PSYCHOLOGY AND MATHEMATICS.

**1.** GEOMETRY, throughout the 17th and 18th centuries, remained, in the war against empiricism, an impregnable fortress of the idealists. Those who held—as was generally held on the Continent—that certain knowledge, independent of experience, was possible about the real world, had only to point to Geometry: none but a madman, they said, would throw doubt on its validity, and none but a fool would deny its objective reference. The English Empiricists, in this matter, had, therefore, a somewhat difficult task; either they had to ignore the problem, or if, like Hume and Mill, they ventured on the assault, they were driven into the apparently paradoxical assertion that Geometry, at bottom, had no certainty of a different *kind* from that of Mechanics—only the perpetual presence of spatial impressions, they said, made our experience of the truth of the axioms so wide as to *seem* absolute certainty.

Here, however, as in many other instances, merciless logic drove these philosophers, whether they would or no, into glaring opposition to the common sense of their day. It was only through Kant, the creator of modern Epistemology, that the geometrical problem received a modern form. He reduced the question to the following hypotheticals: If Geometry has apodeictic certainty, its matter, *i.e.* space, must be *à priori*, and as such must be purely subjective; and conversely, if space is purely subjective, Geometry must have apodeictic certainty. The latter hypothetical has more weight with Kant, indeed it is ineradicably bound up with his whole Epistemology; nevertheless it has, I think, much less force than the former. Let us accept, however, for the moment, the Kantian formulation, and endeavour to give precision to the terms *à priori* and *subjective*.

**2.** One of the great difficulties, throughout this controversy, is the extremely variable use to which these words, as well as the word *empirical*, are put by different authors. To Kant, who was nothing of a psychologist, *à priori* and *subjective* were almost interchangeable terms[1]; in modern usage there is, on the whole, a tendency to confine the word *subjective* to Psychology, leaving *à priori* to do duty for Epistemology. If we accept this differentiation, we may set up, corresponding to the problems of these two sciences, the following provisional definitions: *à priori* applies to any piece of knowledge which, though perhaps elicited by experience, is *logically* presupposed in experience: *subjective* applies to any mental state whose immediate cause lies, not in the external world, but within the limits of the subject. The latter definition, of course, is framed exclusively for Psychology: from the point of view of physical Science all mental states are subjective. But for a Science whose matter, strictly speaking, is *only* mental states, we require, if we are to use the word to any purpose, some differentia among mental states, as a mark of a more special subjectivity on the part of those to which this term is applied.

Now the only mental states whose immediate causes lie in the external world are *sensations*. A pure sensation is, of course, an impossible abstraction—we are never wholly passive under the action of an external stimulus—but for the purposes of Psychology the abstraction is a useful one. Whatever, then, is not sensation, we shall, in Psychology, call subjective. It is in sensation alone that we are directly affected by the external world, and only here does it give us direct information about itself.

**3.** Let us now consider the epistemological question, as to the sort of knowledge which can be called *à priori*. Here we have nothing to do—in the first instance, at any rate—with the cause or genesis of a piece of knowledge; we accept knowledge as a datum to be analysed and classified. Such analysis will reveal a formal and a material element in

[1] Cf. Erdmann, Axiome der Geometrie, p. 111: "Für Kant sind Apriorität und ausschliessliche Subjectivität allerdings Wechselbegriffe."

knowledge. The formal element will consist of postulates which are required to make knowledge possible at all, and of all that can be deduced from these postulates; the material element, on the other hand, will consist of all that comes to fill in the form given by the formal postulates—all that is contingent or dependent on experience, all that might have been otherwise without rendering knowledge impossible. We shall then call the formal element *à priori*, the material element empirical.

**4.** Now what is the connection between the subjective and the *à priori*? It is a connection, obviously—if it exists at all—from the outside, *i.e.* not deducible directly from the nature of either, but provable—if it can be proved—only by a general view of the conditions of both. The question, what knowledge is *à priori*, must, on the above definition, depend on a logical analysis of knowledge, by which the conditions of possible experience may be revealed; but the question, what elements of a cognitive state are subjective, is to be investigated by pure Psychology, which has to determine what, in our perceptions, belongs to sensation, and what is the work of thought or of association. Since, then, these two questions belong to different sciences, and can be settled independently, will it not be wise to conduct the two investigations separately? To decree that the *à priori* shall always be subjective, seems dangerous, when we reflect that such a view places our results, as to the *à priori*, at the mercy of empirical psychology. How serious this danger is, the controversy as to Kant's pure intuition sufficiently shows.

**5.** I shall, therefore, throughout the present Essay, use the word *à priori* without any psychological implication. My test of apriority will be purely logical: Would experience be impossible, if a certain axiom or postulate were denied? Or, in a more restricted sense, which gives apriority only within a particular science: Would experience as to the subject-matter of that science be impossible, without a certain axiom or postulate? My results also, therefore, will be purely logical. If Psychology declares that some things, which I have declared *à priori*, are not subjective, then, failing an error of detail in my proofs, the connection of the *à priori* and the subjective, so far as those things are concerned, must be given up. There will be no discussion, accordingly, throughout this Essay, of the relation of the *à priori* to the subjective—a relation which cannot determine what pieces of knowledge are *à priori*, but rather depends on that determination, and belongs, in any case, rather to Metaphysics than to Epistemology.

**6**. As I have ventured to use the word *à priori* in a slightly unconventional sense, I will give a few elucidatory remarks of a general nature.

The *à priori*, since Kant at any rate, has generally stood for the necessary or apodeictic element in knowledge. But modern logic has shown that necessary propositions are always, in one aspect at least, hypothetical. There may be, and usually is, an implication that the connection, of which necessity is predicated, has some existence, but still, necessity always points beyond itself to a *ground* of necessity, and asserts this ground rather than the actual connection. As Bradley points out, "arsenic poisons" remains true, even if it is poisoning no one. If, therefore, the *à priori* in knowledge be primarily the necessary, it must be the necessary on some hypothesis, and the *ground* of necessity must be included as *à priori*. But the ground of necessity is, so far as the necessary connection in question can show, a mere fact, a merely categorical judgment. Hence necessity alone is an insufficient criterion of apriority.

To supplement this criterion, we must supply the hypothesis or ground, on which alone the necessity holds, and this ground will vary from one science to another, and even, with the progress of knowledge, in the same science at different times. For as knowledge becomes more developed and articulate, more and more necessary connections are perceived, and the merely categorical truths, though they remain the foundation of apodeictic judgments, diminish in relative number. Nevertheless, in a fairly advanced science such as Geometry, we can, I think, pretty completely supply the appropriate ground, and establish, within the limits of the isolated science, the distinction between the necessary and the merely assertorical.

**7**. There are two grounds, I think, on which necessity may be sought within any science. These may be (very roughly) distinguished as the ground which Kant seeks in the

*Prolegomena*, and that which he seeks in the *Pure Reason*. We may start from the existence of our science as a fact, and analyse the reasoning employed with a view to discovering the fundamental postulate on which its logical possibility depends; in this case, the postulate, and all which follows from it alone, will be *à priori*. *Or* we may accept the existence of the subject-matter of our science as our basis of fact, and deduce dogmatically whatever principles we can from the essential nature of this subject-matter. In this latter case, however, it is not the whole empirical nature of the subject-matter, as revealed by the subsequent researches of our science, which forms our ground; for if it were, the whole science would, of course, be *à priori*. Rather it is that element, in the subject-matter, which makes *possible* the branch of experience dealt with by the science in question[1]. The importance of this distinction will appear more clearly as we proceed[2].

**8**. These two grounds of necessity, in ultimate analysis, fall together. The *methods* of investigation in the two cases differ widely, but the *results* cannot differ. For in the first case, by analysis of the science, we discover the postulate on which alone its reasonings are possible. Now if reasoning in the science is impossible without some postulate, this postulate must be essential to experience of the subject-matter of the science, and thus we get the second ground. Nevertheless, the two methods are useful as supplementing one another, and the first, as starting from the actual science, is the safest and easiest method of investigation, though the second seems the more convincing for exposition.

**9**. The course of my argument, therefore, will be as follows: In the first chapter, as a preliminary to the logical analysis of Geometry, I shall give a brief history of the rise and development of non-Euclidean systems. The second chapter will prepare the ground for a constructive theory of Geometry, by a criticism of some previous philosophical views; in this chapter, I shall

[1] I use "experience" here in the widest possible sense, the sense in which the word is used by Bradley.

[2] Where the branch of experience in question is essential to all experience, the resulting apriority may be regarded as absolute; where it is necessary only to some special science, as relative to that science.

endeavour to exhibit such views as partly true, partly false, and so to establish, by preliminary polemics, the truth of such parts of my own theory as are to be found in former writers. A large part of this theory, however, cannot be so introduced, since the whole field of projective Geometry, so far as I am aware, has been hitherto unknown to philosophers. Passing, in the third chapter, from criticism to construction, I shall deal first with projective Geometry. This, I shall maintain, is necessarily true of any form of externality, and is, since some such form is necessary to experience, completely *à priori*. In metrical Geometry, however, which I shall next consider, the axioms will fall into two classes: (1) Those common to Euclidean and non-Euclidean spaces. These will be found, on the one hand, essential to the possibility of measurement in any continuum, and on the other hand, necessary properties of any form of externality with more than one dimension. They will, therefore, be declared *à priori*. (2) Those axioms which distinguish Euclidean from non-Euclidean spaces. These will be regarded as wholly empirical. The axiom that the number of dimensions is three, however, though empirical, will be declared, since small errors are here impossible, exactly and certainly true of our actual world; while the two remaining axioms, which determine the value of the space-constant, will be regarded as only approximately known, and certain only within the errors of observation[1]. The fourth chapter, finally, will endeavour to prove, what was assumed in Chapter III., that some form of externality is necessary to experience, and will conclude by exhibiting the logical impossibility, if knowledge of such a form is to be freed from contradictions, of wholly abstracting this knowledge from all reference to the matter contained in the form.

I shall hope to have touched, with this discussion, on all the main points relating to the Foundations of Geometry.

[1] I have given no account of these empirical proofs, as they seem to be constituted by the whole body of physical science. Everything in physical science, from the law of gravitation to the building of bridges, from the spectroscope to the art of navigation, would be profoundly modified by any considerable inaccuracy in the hypothesis that our actual space is Euclidean. The observed truth of physical science, therefore, constitutes overwhelming empirical evidence that this hypothesis is very approximately correct, even if not rigidly true.

# CHAPTER I.

## A SHORT HISTORY OF METAGEOMETRY.

**10.** WHEN a long established system is attacked, it usually happens that the attack begins only at a single point, where the weakness of the established doctrine is peculiarly evident. But criticism, when once invited, is apt to extend much further than the most daring, at first, would have wished.

> "First cut the liquefaction, what comes last,
> But Fichte's clever cut at God himself?"

So it has been with Geometry. The liquefaction of Euclidean orthodoxy is the axiom of parallels, and it was by the refusal to admit this axiom without proof that Metageometry began. The first effort in this direction, that of Legendre[1], was inspired by the hope of deducing this axiom from the others—a hope which, as we now know, was doomed to inevitable failure. Parallels are defined by Legendre as lines in the same plane, such that, if a third line cut them, it makes the sum of the interior and opposite angles equal to two right angles. He proves without difficulty that such lines would not meet, but is unable to prove that non-parallel lines in a plane must meet. Similarly he can prove that the sum of the angles of a triangle cannot exceed two right angles, and that if any one triangle has a sum equal to two right angles, all triangles have the same sum; but he is unable to prove the existence of this one triangle.

**11.** Thus Legendre's attempt broke down; but mere failure

[1] V. Mémoires de l'Académie royale des Sciences de l'Institut de France, T. XII. 1833, for a full statement of his results, with references to former writings.

could prove nothing. A bolder method, suggested by Gauss, was carried out by Lobatchewsky and Bolyai[1]. If the axiom of parallels is logically deducible from the others, we shall, by denying it and maintaining the rest, be led to contradictions. These three mathematicians, accordingly, attacked the problem indirectly: they denied the axiom of parallels, and yet obtained a logically consistent Geometry. They inferred that the axiom was logically independent of the others, and essential to the Euclidean system. Their works, being all inspired by this motive, may be distinguished as forming the first period in the development of Metageometry.

The second period, inaugurated by Riemann, had a much deeper import: it was largely philosophical in its aims and constructive in its methods. It aimed at no less than a logical analysis of all the essential axioms of Geometry, and regarded space as a particular case of the more general conception of a *manifold*. Taking its stand on the methods of analytical metrical Geometry, it established two non-Euclidean systems, the first that of Lobatchewsky, the second—in which the axiom of the straight line, in Euclid's form, was also denied—a new variety, by analogy called spherical. The leading conception in this period is the *measure of curvature*, a term invented by Gauss, but applied by him only to surfaces. Gauss had shown that free mobility on surfaces was only possible when the measure of curvature was constant; Riemann and Helmholtz extended this proposition to $n$ dimensions, and made it the fundamental property of space.

In the third period, which begins with Cayley, the philosophical motive, which had moved the first pioneers, is less apparent, and is replaced by a more technical and mathematical spirit. This period is chiefly distinguished from the second, in a mathematical point of view, by its method, which is projective instead of metrical. The leading mathematical conception here

[1] This bolder method, it appears, had been suggested, nearly a century earlier, by an Italian, Saccheri. His work, which seems to have remained completely unknown until Beltrami rediscovered it in 1889, is called "Euclides ab omni naevo vindicatus, etc." Mediolani, 1733. (See Veronese, Grundzüge der Geometrie, German translation, Leipzig, 1894, p. 636.) His results included spherical as well as hyperbolic space; but they alarmed him to such an extent that he devoted the last half of his book to disproving them.

is the Absolute (*Grundgebild*), a figure by relation to which all metrical properties become projective. Cayley's work, which was very brief, and attracted little attention, has been perfected and elaborated by F. Klein, and through him has found general acceptance. Klein has added to the two kinds of non-Euclidean Geometry already known, a third, which he calls elliptic; this third kind closely resembles Helmholtz's spherical Geometry, but is distinguished by the important difference that, in it, two straight lines meet in only one point[1]. The distinctive mark of the spaces represented by both is that, like the surface of a sphere, they are finite but unbounded. The reduction of metrical to projective properties, as will be proved hereafter, has only a technical importance; at the same time, projective Geometry is able to deal directly with those purely descriptive or qualitative properties of space which are common to Euclid and Metageometry alike. The third period has, therefore, great philosophical importance, while its method has, mathematically, much greater beauty and unity than that of the second; it is able to treat all kinds of space at once, so that every symbolic proposition is, according to the meaning given to the symbols, a proposition in whichever Geometry we choose. This has the advantage of proving that further research cannot lead to contradictions in non-Euclidean systems, unless it at the same moment reveals contradictions in Euclid. These systems, therefore, are logically as sound as that of Euclid himself.

After this brief sketch of the characteristics of the three periods, I will proceed to a more detailed account. It will be my aim to avoid, as far as possible, all technical mathematics, and bring into relief only those fundamental points in the

[1] Klein's first account of elliptic Geometry, as a result of Cayley's projective theory of distance, appeared in two articles entitled "Ueber die sogenannte Nicht-Euklidische Geometrie, I, II," Math. Annalen 4, 6 (1871—2). It was afterwards independently discovered by Newcomb, in an article entitled "Elementary Theorems relating to the geometry of a space of three dimensions, and of uniform positive curvature in the fourth dimension," Crelle's Journal für die reine und angewandte Mathematik, Vol. 83 (1877). For an account of the mathematical controversies concerning elliptic Geometry, see Klein's "Vorlesungen über Nicht-Euklidische Geometrie," Göttingen 1893, I. p. 284 ff. A bibliography of the relevant literature up to the year 1878 was given by Halsted in the American Journal of Mathematics, Vols. 1, 2.

mathematical development, which seem of logical or philosophical importance.

### First Period.

**12.** The originator of the whole system, *Gauss*, does not appear, as regards strictly non-Euclidean Geometry, in any of his hitherto published papers, to have given more than results; his proofs remain unknown to us. Nevertheless he was the first to investigate the consequences of denying the axiom of parallels[1], and in his letters he communicated these consequences to some of his friends, among whom was Wolfgang Bolyai. The first mention of the subject in his letters occurs when he was only 18; four years later, in 1799, writing to W. Bolyai, he enunciates the important theorem that, in hyperbolic Geometry, there is a maximum to the area of a triangle. From later writings it appears that he had worked out a system nearly, if not quite, as complete as those of Lobatchewsky and Bolyai[2].

It is important to remember, however, that Gauss's work on curvature, which *was* published, laid the foundation for the whole method of the second period, and was undertaken, according to Riemann and Helmholtz[3], with a view to an (unpublished) investigation of the foundations of Geometry. His work in this direction will, owing to its method, be better treated of under the second period, but it is interesting to observe that he stood, like many pioneers, at the head of two tendencies which afterwards diverged.

**13.** *Lobatchewsky*, a professor in the University of Kasan, first published his results, in their native Russian, in the proceedings of that learned body for the years 1829—1830. Owing to this double obscurity of language and place, they attracted little attention, until he translated them into French[4]

[1] Veronese (op. cit. p. 638) denies the priority of Gauss in the invention of a non-Euclidean system, though he admits him to have been the first to regard the axiom of parallels as indemonstrable. His grounds for the former assertion seem scarcely adequate: on the evidence against it, see Klein, Nicht-Euklid, I. pp. 171–174.

[2] V. Briefwechsel mit Schumacher, Bd. II. p. 268.

[3] Cf. Helmholtz, Wiss. Abh. II. p. 611.

[4] Crelle's Journal, 1837.

and German[1]; even then, they do not appear to have obtained the notice they deserved, until, in 1868, Beltrami unearthed the article in Crelle, and made it the theme of a brilliant interpretation.

In the introduction to his little German book, Lobatchewsky laments the slight interest shown in his writings by his compatriots, and the inattention of mathematicians, since Legendre's abortive attempt, to the difficulties in the theory of parallels. The body of the work begins with the enunciation of several important propositions which hold good in the system proposed as well as in Euclid: of these, some are in any case independent of the axiom of parallels, while others are rendered so by substituting, for the word "parallel," the phrase "not intersecting, however far produced." Then follows a definition, intentionally framed so as to contradict Euclid's: With respect to a given straight line, all others in the same plane may be divided into two classes, those which cut the given straight line, and those which do not cut it; a line which is the limit between the two classes is called *parallel* to the given straight line. It follows that, from any external point, two parallels can be drawn, one in each direction. From this starting-point, by the Euclidean synthetic method, a series of propositions are deduced; the most important of these is, that in a triangle the sum of the angles is always less than, or always equal to two right angles, while in the latter case the whole system becomes orthodox. A certain analogy with spherical Geometry—whose meaning and extent will appear later—is also proved, consisting roughly in the substitution of hyperbolic for circular functions.

**14.** Very similar is the system of *Johann Bolyai*, so similar, indeed, as to make the independence of the two works, though a well-authenticated fact, seem all but incredible. Johann Bolyai first published his results in 1832, in an appendix to a work by his father Wolfgang, entitled; "Appendix, scientiam spatii absolute veram exhibens: a veritate aut falsitate Axiomatis XI. Euclidei (a priori haud unquam decidenda) independentem; adjecta ad casum falsitatis, quadratura circuli geometrica." Gauss, whose bosom friend he became at college

[1] Theorie der Parallellinien, Berlin, 1840. Republished, Berlin, 1887. Translated by Halsted, Austin, Texas, U.S.A. 4th edition, 1892.

and remained through life, was, as we have seen, the inspirer of Wolfgang Bolyai, and used to say that the latter was the only man who appreciated his philosophical speculations on the axioms of Geometry; nevertheless, Wolfgang appears to have left to his son Johann the detailed working out of the hyperbolic system. The works of both the Bolyai are very rare, and their method and results are known to me only through the renderings of Frischauf and Halsted[1]. Both as to method and as to results, the system is very similar to Lobatchewsky's, so that neither need detain us here. Only the initial postulates, which are more explicit than Lobatchewsky's, demand a brief attention. Frischauf's introduction, which has a philosophical and Newtonian air, begins by setting forth that Geometry deals with absolute (empty) space, obtained by abstracting from the bodies in it, that two figures are called congruent when they differ only in position, and that the axiom of Congruence is indispensable in all determination of spatial magnitudes. Congruence was to refer to geometrical bodies, with none of the properties of ordinary bodies except impenetrability (Erdmann, Axiome der Geometrie, p. 26). A straight line is defined as determined by two of its points[2], and a plane as determined by three. These premisses, with a slight exception as to the straight line, we shall hereafter find essential to every Geometry. I have drawn attention to them, as it is often supposed that non-Euclideans deny the axiom of Congruence, which, here and elsewhere, is never the case. The stress laid on this axiom by Bolyai is probably due to the influence of Gauss, whose work on the curvature of surfaces laid the foundation for the use made of congruence by Helmholtz.

**15.** It is important to remember that, throughout the period we have just reviewed, the purpose of hyperbolic Geometry is indirect: not the truth of the latter, but the logical independence of the axiom of parallels from the rest, is

[1] Frischauf, Absolute Geometrie, nach Johann Bolyai, Leipzig, 1872. Halsted, The Science Absolute of Space, translated from the Latin, 4th edition, Austin, Texas, U.S.A. 1896.

[2] Both Lobatchewsky and Bolyai, as Veronese remarks, start rather from the point-pair than from distance. See Frischauf, Absolute Geometrie, Anhang.

the guiding motive of the work. If, by denying the axiom of parallels while retaining the rest, we can obtain a system free from logical contradictions, it follows that the axiom of parallels cannot be implicitly contained in the others. If this be so, attempts to dispense with the axiom, like Legendre's, cannot be successful; Euclid must stand or fall with the suspected axiom. Of course, it remained possible that, by further development, latent contradictions might have been revealed in these systems. This possibility, however, was removed by the more direct and constructive work of the second period, to which we must now turn our attention.

### Second Period.

**16.** The work of Lobatchewsky and Bolyai remained, for nearly a quarter of a century, without issue—indeed, the investigations of Riemann and Helmholtz, when they came, appear to have been inspired, not by these men, but rather by Gauss[1] and Herbart. We find, accordingly, very great difference, both of aim and method, between the first period and the second. The former, beginning with a criticism of one point in Euclid's system, preserved his synthetic method, while it threw over one of his axioms. The latter, on the contrary, being guided by a philosophical rather than a mathematical spirit, endeavoured to classify the conception of space as a species of a more general conception: it treated space algebraically, and the properties it gave to space were expressed in terms, not of intuition, but of algebra. The aim of Riemann and Helmholtz was to show, by the exhibition of logically possible alternatives, the empirical nature of the received axioms. For this purpose, they conceived space as a particular case of a manifold, and showed that various relations of magnitude (*Massverhältnisse*) were mathematically possible in an extended manifold. Their philosophy, which seems to me not always irreproachable, will be discussed in Chapter II.; here, while it is important to remember the philosophical motive of Riemann and Helmholtz, we shall confine our attention to the mathematical side of their work. In so doing, while we shall, I fear, somewhat maim the system of their thoughts, we shall secure a closer unity of subject, and

[1] Compare Stallo, Concepts of Modern Physics, p. 248.

a more compact account of the purely mathematical development. But there is, in my opinion, a further reason for separating their philosophy from their mathematics. While their philosophical purpose was, to prove that all the axioms of Geometry are empirical, and that a different content of our experience might have changed them all, the unintended result of their mathematical work was, if I am not mistaken, to afford material for an *à priori* proof of certain axioms. These axioms, though they believed them to be unnecessary, were always introduced in their mathematical works, before laying the foundations of non-Euclidean systems. I shall contend, in Chapter III., that this retention was logically inevitable, and was not merely due, as they supposed, to a desire for conformity with experience. If I am right in this, there is a divergence between Riemann and Helmholtz the philosophers, and Riemann and Helmholtz the mathematicians. This divergence makes it the more desirable to trace the mathematical development apart from the accompanying philosophy.

**17.** *Riemann's* epoch-making work, "*Ueber die Hypothesen, welche der Geometrie zu Grunde liegen*[1]", was written, and read to a small circle, in 1854; owing, however, to some changes which he desired to make in it, it remained unpublished till 1867, when it was published by his executors. The two fundamental conceptions, on whose invention rests the historic importance of this dissertation, are that of a *manifold*, and that of the *measure of curvature* of a manifold. The former conception serves a mainly philosophical purpose, and is designed, principally, to exhibit space as an instance of a more general conception. On this aspect of the manifold, I shall have much to say in Chapter II.; its mathematical aspect, which alone concerns us here, is less complicated and less fruitful of controversy. The latter conception also serves a double purpose, but its mathematical use is the more prominent. We will consider these two conceptions successively.

**18.** (1) *Conception of a manifold*[2]. The general purpose of Riemann's dissertation is, to exhibit the axioms as successive

[1] Gesammelte Werke, pp. 255–268.

[2] On the history of this word, see Stallo, Concepts of Modern Physics, p. 258. It was used by Kant, and adapted by Herbart to almost the same

steps in the classification of the species space. The axioms of Geometry, like the marks of a scholastic definition, appear as successive determinations of class-conceptions, ending with Euclidean space. We have thus, from the analytical point of view, about as logical and precise a formulation as can be desired—a formulation in which, from its classificatory character, we seem certain of having nothing superfluous or redundant, and obtain the axioms explicitly in the most desirable form, namely as adjectives of the conception of space. At the same time, it is a pity that Riemann, in accordance with the metrical bias of his time, regarded space as primarily a magnitude[1], or assemblage of magnitudes, in which the main problem consists in assigning quantities to the different elements or points, without regard to the qualitative nature of the quantities assigned. Considerable obscurity thus arises as to the whole nature of magnitude[2]. This view of Geometry underlies the definition of the manifold, as the general conception of which space forms a special case. This definition, which is not very clear, may be rendered as follows.

**19.** Conceptions of magnitude, according to Riemann, are possible there only, where we have a general conception, capable of various determinations (*Bestimmungsweisen*). The various determinations of such a conception together form a *manifold*, which is continuous or discrete, according as the passage from one determination to another is continuous or discrete. Particular bits of a manifold, or quanta, can be compared by counting when discrete, and by measurement when continuous. "Measurement consists in a superposition of the magnitudes to be compared. If this be absent, magnitudes can only be compared when one is part of another, and then only the more or less, not the how much, can be decided" (p. 256). We thus reach the general conception of a manifold of several dimensions, of which space and colours are mentioned as special cases.

meaning as it bears in Riemann. Herbart, however, also uses the word *Reihenform* to express a similar idea. See Psychologie als Wissenschaft, I. § 100 and II. § 139, where Riemann's analogy with colours is also suggested.

[1] Compare Erdmann's "Grössenbegriff vom Raum."

[2] Compare Veronese, op. cit. p. 642: "Riemann ist in seiner Definition des Begriffs Grösse dunkel." See also Veronese's whole following criticism.

To the absence of this conception Riemann attributes the "obscurity" which, on the subject of the axioms, "lasted from Euclid to Legendre" (p. 254). And Riemann certainly has succeeded, from an algebraic point of view, in exhibiting, far more clearly than any of his predecessors, the axioms which distinguish spatial quantity from other quantities with which mathematics is conversant. But by the assumption, from the start, that space can be regarded as a quantity, he has been led to state the problem as: What sort of magnitude is space? rather than: What must space be in order that we may be able to regard it as a magnitude at all? He does not realise, either—indeed in his day there were few who realized—that an elaborate Geometry is possible which does not deal with space as a quantity at all. His definition of space as a species of manifold, therefore, though for analytical purposes it defines, most satisfactorily, the nature of spatial magnitudes, leaves obscure the true ground for this nature, which lies in the nature of space as a system of relations, and is anterior to the possibility of regarding it as a system of magnitudes at all.

But to proceed with the mathematical development of Riemann's ideas. We have seen that he declared measurement to consist in a superposition of the magnitudes to be compared. But in order that this may be a possible means of determining magnitudes, he continues, these magnitudes must be independent of their position in the manifold (p. 259). This can occur, he says, in several ways, as the simplest of which, he assumes that the lengths of lines are independent of their position. One would be glad to know what other ways are possible: for my part, I am unable to imagine any other hypothesis on which magnitude would be independent of place. Setting this aside, however, the problem, owing to the fact that measurement consists in superposition, becomes identical with the determination of the most general manifold in which magnitudes are independent of place. This brings us to Riemann's other fundamental conception, which seems to me even more fruitful than that of a manifold.

**20.** (2) *Measure of curvature.* This conception is due to Gauss, but was applied by him only to surfaces; the novelty in Riemann's dissertation was its extension to a manifold of $n$

dimensions. This extension, however, is rather briefly and obscurely expressed, and has been further obscured by Helmholtz's attempts at popular exposition. The term *curvature*, also, is misleading, so that the phrase has been the source of more misunderstanding, even among mathematicians, than any other in Pangeometry. It is often forgotten, in spite of Helmholtz's explicit statement[1], that the "measure of curvature" of an $n$-dimensional manifold is a purely analytical expression, which has only a symbolic affinity to ordinary curvature. As applied to three-dimensional space, the implication of a four-dimensional "plane" space is wholly misleading; I shall, therefore, generally use the term space-constant instead[2]. Nevertheless, as the conception grew, historically, out of that of curvature, I will give a very brief exposition of the historical development of theories of curvature.

Just as the notion of *length* was originally derived from the straight line, and extended to other curves by dividing them into infinitesimal straight lines, so the notion of *curvature* was derived from the circle, and extended to other curves by dividing them into infinitesimal circular arcs. Curvature may be regarded, originally, as a measure of the amount by which a curve departs from a straight line; in a circle, which is similar throughout, this amount is evidently constant, and is measured by the reciprocal of the radius. But in all other curves, the amount of curvature varies from point to point, so that it cannot be measured without infinitesimals. The measure which at once suggests itself is, the curvature of the circle most nearly coinciding with the curve at the point considered. Since a circle is determined by three points, this circle will pass through three consecutive points of the curve. We have thus defined the curvature of any curve, plane or tortuous; for, since any three points lie in a plane, such a circle can always be described.

If we now pass to a surface, what we want is, by analogy, a measure of its departure from a plane. The curvature, as above defined, has become indeterminate, for through any point of the surface we can draw an infinite number of arcs, which

[1] Vorträge und Reden, Vol. II. p. 18. [2] Cf. Klein, Nicht-Euklid, I. p. 160.

will not, in general, all have the same curvature. Let us, then, draw all the geodesics joining the point in question to neighbouring points of the surface in all directions. Since these arcs form a singly infinite manifold, there will be among them, if they have not all the same curvature, one arc of maximum, and one of minimum curvature[1]. The product of these maximum and minimum curvatures is called the *measure of curvature* of the surface at the point under consideration. To illustrate by a few simple examples: on a sphere, the curvatures of all such lines are equal to the reciprocal of the radius of the sphere, hence the measure of curvature everywhere is the square of the reciprocal of the radius of the sphere. On any surface, such as a cone or a cylinder, on which straight lines can be drawn, these have no curvature, so that the measure of curvature is everywhere zero—this is the case, in particular, with the plane. In general, however, the measure of curvature of a surface varies from point to point.

Gauss, the inventor of this conception[2], proved that, in order that two surfaces may be developable upon each other —*i.e.* may be such that one can be bent into the shape of the other without stretching or tearing—it is necessary that the two surfaces should have equal measures of curvature at corresponding points. When this is the case, every figure which is possible on the one is, in general, possible on the other, and the two have practically the same Geometry[3]. As a corollary, it follows that a necessary condition, for the free mobility of figures on any surface, is the constancy of the

[1] Since we are considering the curvature at a point, we are only concerned with the first infinitesimal elements of the geodesics that start from such a point.

[2] Disquisitiones generales circa superficies curvas, Werke, Bd. IV. SS. 219–258, 1827.

[3] Nevertheless, the Geometries of different surfaces of equal curvature are liable to important differences. For example, the cylinder is a surface of zero curvature, but since its lines of curvature in one direction are finite, its Geometry coincides with that of the plane only for lengths smaller than the circumference of its generating circle (see Veronese, op. cit. p. 644). Two geodesics on a cylinder may meet in many points. For surfaces of zero curvature on which this is not possible, the identity with the plane may be allowed to stand. Otherwise, the identity extends only to the properties of figures not exceeding a certain size.

measure of curvature[1]. This condition was proved to be sufficient, as well as necessary, by Minding[2].

**21.** So far, all has been plain sailing—we have been dealing with purely geometrical ideas in a purely geometrical manner—but we have not, as yet, found any sense of the measure of curvature, in which it can be extended to space, still less to an $n$-dimensional manifold. For this purpose, we must examine Gauss's method, which enables us to determine the measure of curvature of a surface at any point as an inherent property, quite independent of any reference to the third dimension.

The method of determining the measure of curvature from within is, briefly, as follows: If any point on the surface be determined by two coordinates, $u$, $v$, then small arcs of the surface are given by the formula

$$ds^2 = Edu^2 + 2Fdu\,dv + Gdv^2,$$

where $E$, $F$, $G$ are, in general, functions of $u$, $v$.[3] From this formula alone, without reference to any space outside the surface, we can determine the measure of curvature at the point $u$, $v$, as a function of $E$, $F$, $G$ and their differentials with respect to $u$ and $v$. Thus we may regard the measure of curvature of a surface as an inherent property, and the above geometrical definition, which involved a reference to the third dimension, may be dropped. But at this point a caution is necessary. It will appear in Chap. III. (§ 176), that it is logically impossible to set up a precise coordinate system, in which the coordinates represent spatial magnitudes, without the axiom of Free Mobility, and this axiom, as we have just seen, holds on surfaces only when the measure of curvature is constant. Hence our definition of the measure of curvature will only be *really* free from reference to the third dimension, when we are dealing with a surface of constant measure of curvature—a point which

[1] For we may consider two different parts of the same surface as corresponding parts of different surfaces; the above proposition then shows that a figure can be reproduced in one part when it has been drawn in another, if the measures of curvature correspond in the two parts.

[2] Crelle, Vols. XIX., XX., 1839–40.

[3] In this formula, $u$, $v$ may be the lengths of lines, or the angles between lines, drawn on the surface, and having thus no necessary reference to a third dimension.

Riemann entirely overlooks. This caution, however, applies only in space, and if we take the coordinate system as presupposed in the conception of a manifold, we may neglect the caution altogether—while remembering that the possibility of a coordinate system in space involves axioms to be investigated later. We can thus see how a meaning might be found, without reference to any higher dimension, for a constant measure of curvature of three-dimensional space, or for any measure of curvature of an $n$-dimensional manifold in general.

**22.** Such a meaning is supplied by Riemann's dissertation, to which, after this long digression, we can now return. We may define a continuous manifold as any continuum of elements, such that a single element is defined by $n$ continuously variable magnitudes. This definition does not really include space, for coordinates in space do not define a point, but its relations to the origin, which is itself arbitrary. It includes, however, the analytical conception of space with which Riemann deals, and may, therefore, be allowed to stand for the moment. Riemann then assumes that the difference—or distance, as it may be loosely called—between any two elements is comparable, as regards magnitude, to the difference between any other two. He assumes further, what it is Helmholtz's merit to have proved, that the difference $ds$ between two consecutive elements can be expressed as the square root of a quadratic function of the differences of the coordinates: *i.e.*

$$ds^2 = \Sigma_1^n \, \Sigma_1^n \, a_{ik} \, dx_i \, . \, dx_k,$$

where the coefficients $a_{ik}$ are, in general, functions of the coordinates $x_1 \, x_2 \ldots x_n$.[1] The question is: How are we to obtain a definition of the measure of curvature out of this formula? It is noticeable, in the first place, that, just as in a surface we found an infinite number of *radii* of curvature at a point, so in a manifold of three or more dimensions we must find an infinite number of *measures* of curvature at a point, one for every two-dimensional manifold passing through the point, and contained in the higher manifold. What we have first to do, therefore, is

[1] In what follows, I have given rather Klein's exposition of Riemann, than Riemann's own account. The former is much clearer and fuller, and not substantially different in any way. V. Klein, Nicht-Euklid, I. pp. 206 ff.

to define such two-dimensional manifolds. They must consist, as we saw on the surface, of a singly infinite series of geodesics through the point. Now a geodesic is completely determined by one point and its direction at that point, or by one point and the next consecutive point. Hence a geodesic through the point considered is determined by the ratios of the increments of coordinates, $dx_1\, dx_2 \ldots dx_n$. Suppose we have two such geodesics, in which the $i$'th increments are respectively $d'x_i$ and $d''x_i$. Then all the geodesics given by

$$dx_i = \lambda' d'x_i + \lambda'' d''x_i$$

form a singly infinite series, since they contain one parameter, namely $\lambda' : \lambda''$. Such a series of geodesics, therefore, must form a two-dimensional manifold, with a measure of curvature in the ordinary Gaussian sense. This measure of curvature can be determined from the above formula for the elementary arc, by the help of Gauss's general formula alluded to above. We thus obtain an infinite number of measures of curvature at a point, but from $\frac{n.(n-1)}{2}$ of these, the rest can be deduced (Riemann, Gesammelte Werke, p. 262). When all the measures of curvature at a point are constant, and equal to all the measures of curvature at any other point, we get what Riemann calls a manifold of constant curvature. In such a manifold free mobility is possible, and positions do not differ intrinsically from one another. If $a$ be the measure of curvature, the formula for the arc becomes, in this case,

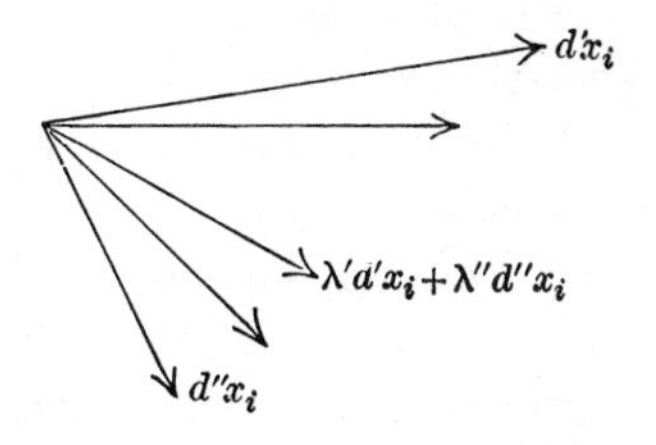


$$ds^2 = \Sigma dx^2 \left(1 + \frac{a}{4}\Sigma x^2\right)^2.$$

In this case only, as I pointed out above, can the term "measure of curvature" be properly applied to space without reference to a higher dimension, since free mobility is logically indispensable to the existence of quantitative or metrical Geometry.

**23.** The mathematical result of Riemann's dissertation

may be summed up as follows. Assuming it possible to apply magnitude to space, *i.e.* to determine its elements and figures by means of algebraical quantities, it follows that space can be brought under the conception of a manifold, as a system of quantitatively determinable elements. Owing, however, to the peculiar nature of spatial measurement, the quantitative determination of space demands that magnitudes shall be independent of place—in so far as this is not the case, our measurement will be necessarily inaccurate. If we now assume, as the quantitative relation of distance between two elements, the square root of a quadratic function of the coordinates—a formula subsequently proved by Helmholtz and Lie—then it follows, since magnitudes are to be independent of place, that space must, within the limits of observation, have a constant measure of curvature, or must, in other words, be homogeneous in all its parts. In the infinitesimal, Riemann says (p. 267), observation could not detect a departure from constancy on the part of the measure of curvature; but he makes no attempt to show how Geometry could remain possible under such circumstances, and the only Geometry he has constructed is based entirely on Free Mobility. I shall endeavour to prove, in Chapter III., that any metrical Geometry, which should endeavour to dispense with this axiom, would be logically impossible. At present I will only point out that Riemann, in spite of his desire to prove that all the axioms can be dispensed with, has nevertheless, in his mathematical work, retained three fundamental axioms, namely, Free Mobility, the finite integral number of dimensions, and the axiom that two points have a unique relation, namely distance. These, as we shall see hereafter, are retained, in actual mathematical work, by all metrical Metageometers, even when they believe, like Riemann and Helmholtz, that no axioms are philosophically indispensable.

**24.** *Helmholtz*, the historically nearest follower of Riemann, was guided by a similar empirical philosophy, and arrived independently at a very similar method of formulating the axioms. Although Helmholtz published nothing on the subject until after Riemann's death, he had then only just seen Riemann's dissertation (which was published posthumously), and had worked out his results, so far as they were then completed, in entire independence both of Riemann and of Lobatchewsky. Helmholtz is by far the most widely read of all writers on Metageometry, and his writings, almost alone, represent to philosophers the modern mathematical standpoint on this subject. But his importance is much greater, in this domain, as a philosopher than as a mathematician; almost his only original mathematical result, as regards Geometry, is his proof of Riemann's formula for the infinitesimal arc, and even this proof was far from rigid, until Lie reformed it by his method of continuous groups. In this chapter, therefore, only two of his writings need occupy us, namely the two articles in the *Wissenschaftliche Abhandlungen*, Vol. II., entitled respectively "Ueber die thatsächlichen Grundlagen der Geometrie," 1866 (p. 610 ff.), and "Ueber die Thatsachen, die der Geometrie zum Grunde liegen," 1868 (p. 618 ff.).

**25.** In the first of these, which is chiefly philosophical, Helmholtz gives hints of his then uncompleted mathematical work, but in the main contents himself with a statement of results. He announces that he will prove Riemann's quadratic formula for the infinitesimal arc; but for this purpose, he says, we have to *start* with Congruence, since without it spatial measurement is impossible. Nevertheless, he maintains that Congruence is proved by experience. How we could, without the help of measurement, discover lapses from Congruence, is a point which he leaves undiscussed. He then enunciates the four axioms which he considers essential to Geometry, as follows:

(1) *As regards continuity and dimensions.* In a space of $n$ dimensions, a point is uniquely determined by the measurement of $n$ continuous variables (coordinates).

(2) *As regards the existence of moveable rigid bodies.* Between the $2n$ coordinates of any point-pair of a rigid body, there exists an equation which is the same for all congruent point-pairs. By considering a sufficient number of point-pairs, we get more equations than unknown quantities: this gives us a method of determining the form of these equations, so as to make it possible for them all to be satisfied.

(3) *As regards free mobility.* Every point can pass freely and continuously from one position to another. From (2) and

(3) it follows, that if two systems $A$ and $B$ can be brought into congruence in any one position, this is also possible in every other position.

(4) *As regards independence of rotation in rigid bodies* (Monodromy). If $(n-1)$ points of a body remain fixed, so that every other point can only describe a certain curve, then that curve is closed.

These axioms, says Helmholtz, suffice to give, with the axiom of three dimensions, the Euclidean and non-Euclidean systems as the only alternatives. That they *suffice*, mathematically, cannot be denied, but they seem, in some respects, to go too far. In the first place, there is no necessity to make the axiom of Congruence apply to actual rigid bodies—on this subject I have enlarged in Chapter II.[1] Again, Free Mobility, as distinct from Congruence, hardly needs to be specially formulated: what barrier could empty space offer to a point's progress? The axiom is involved in the homogeneity of space, which is the same thing as the axiom of Congruence. Monodromy, also, has been severely criticized; not only is it evident that it might have been included in Congruence, but even from the purely analytical point of view, Sophus Lie has proved it to be superfluous[2]. Thus the axiom of Congruence, rightly formulated, includes Helmholtz's third and fourth axioms and part of his second axiom. All the four, or rather, as much of them as is relevant to Geometry, are consequences, as we shall see hereafter, of the one fundamental principle of the relativity of position.

**26.** The second article, which is mainly mathematical, supplies the promised proof of the arc-formula, which is Helmholtz's most important contribution to Geometry. Riemann had *assumed* this formula, as the simplest of a number of alternatives: Helmholtz proved it to be a necessary consequence of his axioms. The present paper begins with a short repetition of the first, including the statement of the axioms, to which, at the end of the paper, two more are added, (5) that space has three dimensions, and (6) that space is infinite. It

[1] See §§ 69–73.

[2] Grundlagen der Geometrie, I. and II., Leipziger Berichte, 1890; v. end of present chapter, § 45.

is supposed in the text, as also in the first paper, that the measure of curvature cannot be negative, and, consequently, that an infinite space must be Euclidean. This error in both papers is corrected in notes, added after the appearance of Beltrami's paper on negative curvature. It is a sample of the slightly unprofessional nature of Helmholtz's mathematical work on this subject, which elicits from Klein the following remarks[1]: "Helmholtz is not a mathematician by profession, but a physicist and physiologist....From this non-mathematical quality of Helmholtz, it follows naturally that he does not treat the mathematical portion of his work with the thoroughness which one would demand of a mathematician by trade (*von Fach*)." He tells us himself that it was the physiological study of vision which led him to the question of the axioms, and it is as a physicist that he makes his axioms refer to actual rigid bodies. Accordingly, we find errors in his mathematics, such as the axiom of Monodromy, and the assumption that the measure of curvature must be positive. Nevertheless, the proof of Riemann's arc-formula is extremely able, and has, on the whole, been substantiated by Lie's more thorough investigations.

**27.** Helmholtz's other writings on Geometry are almost wholly philosophical, and will be discussed at length in Chapter II. For the present, we may pass to the only other important writer of the second period, *Beltrami*. As his work is purely mathematical, and contains few controverted points, it need not, despite its great importance, detain us long.

The "Saggio di Interpretazione della Geometria non-Euclidea[2]," which is principally confined to two dimensions, interprets Lobatchewsky's results by the characteristic method of the second period. It shows, by a development of the work of Gauss and Minding[3], that all the propositions in plane Geometry, which Lobatchewsky had set forth, hold, within ordinary Euclidean space, on surfaces of constant negative

[1] Nicht-Euklid, I. pp. 258–9.

[2] Giornale di Matematiche, Vol. VI., 1868. Translated into French by J. Hoüel in the "Annales Scientifiques de l'École Normale Supérieure," Vol. VI. 1869.

[3] Crelle's Journal, Vols. XIX. XX., 1839–40.

curvature. It is strange, as Klein points out[1], that this interpretation, which was known to Riemann and perhaps even to Gauss, should have remained so long without explicit statement. This is the more strange, as Lobatchewsky's "Géométrie Imaginaire" had appeared in Crelle, Vol. XVII.[2], and Minding's article, from which the interpretation follows at once, had appeared in Crelle, Vol. XIX. Minding had shewn that the Geometry of surfaces of constant negative curvature, in particular as regards geodesic triangles, could be deduced from that of the sphere by giving the radius a purely imaginary value $ia$.[3] This result, as we have seen, had also been obtained by Lobatchewsky for his Geometry, and yet it took thirty years for the connection to be brought to general notice.

**28.** In Beltrami's Saggio, straight lines are, of course, replaced by geodesics; his coordinates are obtained through a point-by-point correspondence with an auxiliary plane, in which straight lines correspond to geodesics on the surface. Thus geodesics have linear equations, and are always uniquely determined by two points. Distances on the surface, however, are not equal to distances on the plane; thus while the surface is infinite, the corresponding portion of the plane is contained within a certain finite circle. The distance of two points on the surface is a certain function of the coordinates, not the ordinary function of elementary Geometry. These relations of plane and surface are important in connection with Cayley's theory of distance, which we shall have to consider next. If we were to define distance on the plane as that function of the coordinates which gives the corresponding distance on the surface, we should obtain what Klein calls "a plane with a hyperbolic system of measurement (*Massbestimmung*)," in which Cayley's theory of distance would hold. It is evident, however, that the ordinary notion of distance has been presupposed in setting up the coordinate system, so that we do not really

[1] Nicht-Euklid, I. p. 190.

[2] This article is more trigonometrical and analytical than the German book, and therefore makes the above interpretation peculiarly evident.

[3] Such surfaces are by no means particularly remote. One of them, for example, is formed by the revolution of the common Tractrix

$$x = a \sin \phi, \qquad y = a\left(\log \tan \frac{\phi}{2} + \cos \phi\right).$$

get alternative Geometries on one and the same plane. The bearing of these remarks will appear more fully when we come to consider Cayley and Klein.

**29**. The value of Beltrami's Saggio, in his own eyes, lies in the intelligible Euclidean sense which it gives to Lobatchewsky's planimetry: the corresponding system of Solid Geometry, since it has no meaning for Euclidean space, is barely mentioned in this work. In a second paper[1], however, almost contemporaneous with the first, he proceeds to consider the general theory of $n$-dimensional manifolds of constant negative curvature. This paper is greatly influenced by Riemann's dissertation; it begins with the formula for the linear element, and proves from this first, that Congruence holds for such spaces, and next, that they have, according to Riemann's definition, a constant negative measure of curvature. (It is instructive to observe, that both in this and in the former Essay, great stress is laid on the necessity of the Axiom of Congruence.)

This work has less philosophical interest than the former, since it does little more than repeat, in a general form, the results which the Saggio had obtained for two dimensions—results which sink, when extended to $n$ dimensions, to the level of mere mathematical constructions. Nevertheless, the paper is important, both as a restoration of negative curvature, which had been overlooked by Helmholtz, and as an analytical treatment of Lobatchewsky's results—a treatment which, together with the Saggio, at last restored to them the prominence they deserved.

### Third Period.

**30**. The third period differs radically, alike in its methods and aims, and in the underlying philosophical ideas, from the period which it replaced. Whereas everything, in the second period, turned on measurement, with its apparatus of Congruence, Free Mobility, Rigid Bodies, and the rest, these vanish completely in the third period, which, swinging to the opposite extreme, regards quantity as a perfectly irrelevant

[1] "Teoria fondamentale degli spazii di curvatura costanta," Annali di Matematica, II. Vol. 2, 1868–9. Also translated by J. Hoüel, *loc. cit.*

category in Geometry, and dispenses with congruence and the method of superposition. The ideas of this period, unfortunately, have found no exponent so philosophical as Riemann or Helmholtz, but have been set forth only by technical mathematicians. Moreover the change of fundamental ideas, which is immense, has not brought about an equally great change in actual procedure; for though spatial quantity is no longer a part of projective Geometry, quantity is still employed, and we still have equations, algebraic transformations, and so on. This is apt to give rise to confusion, especially in the mind of the student, who fails to realise that the quantities used, so far as the propositions are really projective, are mere names for points, and not, as in metrical Geometry, actual spatial magnitudes.

Nevertheless, the fundamental difference between this period and the former must strike any one at once. Whereas Riemann and Helmholtz dealt with metrical ideas, and took, as their foundations, the measure of curvature and the formula for the linear element—both purely metrical—the new method is erected on the formulae for transformation of coordinates required to express a given collineation. It begins by reducing all so-called metrical notions—distance, angle, etc.—to projective forms, and obtains, from this reduction, a methodological unity and simplicity before impossible. This reduction depends, however, except where the space-constant is negative, upon imaginary figures—in Euclid, the circular points at infinity; it is moreover purely symbolic and analytical, and must be regarded as philosophically irrelevant. As the question concerning the import of this reduction is of fundamental importance to our theory of Geometry, and as Cayley, in his Presidential Address to the British Association in 1883, formally challenged philosophers to discuss the use of imaginaries, on which it depends, I will treat this question at some length. But first let us see how, as a matter of mathematics, the reduction is effected.

**31.** We shall find, throughout this period, that almost every important proposition, though misleading in its obvious interpretation, has nevertheless, when rightly interpreted, a wide philosophical bearing. So it is with the work of *Cayley*, the pioneer of the projective method.

The projective formula for angles, in Euclidean Geometry, was first obtained by Laguerre, in 1853. This formula had, however, a perfectly Euclidean character, and it was left for Cayley to generalize it so as to include both angles and distances in Euclidean and non-Euclidean systems alike[1].

*Cayley* was, to the last, a staunch supporter of Euclidean *space*, though he believed that non-Euclidean *Geometries* could be applied, within Euclidean space, by a change in the definition of distance[2]. He has thus, in spite of his Euclidean orthodoxy, provided the believers in the possibility of non-Euclidean spaces with one of their most powerful weapons. In his "Sixth Memoir upon Quantics" (1859), he set himself the task of "establishing the notion of distance upon purely descriptive principles." He showed that, with the ordinary notion of distance, it can be rendered projective by reference to the circular points and the line at infinity, and that the same is true of angles[3]. Not content with this, he suggested a new definition of distance, as the inverse sine or cosine of a certain function of the coordinates; with this definition, the properties usually known as metrical become projective properties, having reference to a certain conic, called by Cayley the Absolute. (The circular points are, analytically, a degenerate conic, so that ordinary Geometry forms a particular case of the above.) He proves that, when the Absolute is an *imaginary* conic, the Geometry so obtained for two dimensions is spherical Geometry. The correspondence with Lobatchewsky, in the case where the Absolute is *real*, is not worked out: indeed there is, throughout, no evidence of acquaintance with non-Euclidean systems. The importance of the memoir, to Cayley, lies entirely in its proof that metrical is only a branch of descriptive Geometry.

**32.** The connection of Cayley's Theory of Distance with Metageometry was first pointed out by Klein[4]. Klein showed in detail that, if the Absolute be real, we get Lobatchewsky's

[1] See Klein, Nicht-Euklid, I. p. 47 ff., and the references there given.

[2] See quotation below, from his British Association Address.

[3] Compare the opening sentence, due to Cayley, of Salmon's Higher Plane Curves.

[4] V. Nicht-Euklid, I. Chaps. I. and II.

(hyperbolic) system; if it be imaginary, we get either spherical Geometry or a new system, analogous to that of Helmholtz, called by Klein elliptic; if the Absolute be an imaginary point-pair, we get parabolic Geometry, and if, in particular, the point-pair be the circular points, we get ordinary Euclid. In elliptic Geometry, two straight lines in the same plane meet in only one point, not two as in Helmholtz's system. The distinction between the two kinds of Geometry is difficult, and will be discussed later.

**33.** Since these systems are all obtained from a Euclidean plane, by a mere alteration in the definition of distance, Cayley and Klein tend to regard the whole question as one, not of the nature of space, but of the definition of distance. Since this definition, on their view, is perfectly arbitrary, the philosophical problem vanishes—Euclidean *space* is left in undisputed possession, and the only problem remaining is one of convention and mathematical convenience[1]. This view has been forcibly expressed by Poincaré: "What ought one to think," he says, "of this question: Is the Euclidean Geometry true? The question is nonsense." Geometrical axioms, according to him, are mere conventions: they are "definitions in disguise[2]." Thus Klein blames Beltrami for regarding his auxiliary plane as merely auxiliary, and remarks that, if he had known Cayley's Memoir, he would have seen the relation between the plane and the pseudosphere to be far more intimate than he supposed[3]. A view which removes the problem entirely from the arena of philosophy demands, plainly, a full discussion. To this discussion we will now proceed.

**34.** The view in question has arisen, it would seem, from a natural confusion as to the nature of the coordinates employed. Those who hold the view have not adequately realised, I believe, that their coordinates are not *spatial* quantities, as in metrical Geometry, but mere conventional signs, by which different points can be distinctly designated. There is no reason, therefore, until we already have metrical Geometry,

[1] See p. 9 of Cayley's address to the Brit. Ass. 1883. Also a quotation from Klein in Erdmann's Axiome der Geometrie, p. 124 note.

[2] Nature, Vol. XLV. p. 407.

[3] Nicht-Euklid, I. p. 200.

for regarding one function of the coordinates as a better expression of distance than another, so long as the fundamental addition-equation[1] is preserved. Hence, if our coordinates are regarded as adequate for all Geometry, an indeterminateness arises in the expression of distance, which can only be avoided by a convention. But projective coordinates—so our argument will contend—though perfectly adequate for all projective properties, and entirely free from any metrical presupposition, are inadequate to express metrical properties, just because they have no metrical presupposition. Thus where metrical properties are in question, Beltrami remains justified as against Klein; the reduction of metrical to projective properties is only apparent, though the independence of these last, as against metrical Geometry, is perfectly real.

**35.** But what are projective coordinates, and how are they introduced? This question was not touched upon in Cayley's Memoir, and it seemed, therefore, as if a logical error were involved in using coordinates to define distance. For coordinates, in all previous systems, had been deduced from distance; to use any existing coordinate system in defining distance was, accordingly, to incur a vicious circle. Cayley mentions this difficulty in a note, where he only remarks, however, that he had regarded his coordinates as numbers arbitrarily assigned, on some system not further investigated, to different points. The difficulty has been treated at length by Sir R. Ball (Theory of the Content, Trans. R. I. A. 1889), who urges that if the values of our coordinates already involve the usual measure of distance, then to give a new definition, while retaining the usual coordinates, is to incur a contradiction. He says (op. cit. p. 1): "In the study of non-Euclidean Geometry I have often felt a difficulty which has, I know, been shared by others. In that theory it seems as if we try to replace our ordinary notion of distance between two points by the logarithm of a certain anharmonic ratio[2]. But this ratio itself involves the notion of distance measured in the ordinary way. How, then,

[1] I.e. the equation $AB + BC = AC$, for three points in one straight line.

[2] The formula substituted by Klein for Cayley's inverse sine or cosine. The two are equivalent, but Klein's is mathematically much the more convenient.

can we supersede our old notion of distance by the non-Euclidean notion, inasmuch as the very definition of the latter involves the former?"

**36.** This objection is valid, we must admit, so long as anharmonic ratio is defined in the ordinary metrical manner. It would be valid, for example, against any attempt to found a new definition of distance on Cremona's account of anharmonic ratio[1], in which it appears as a metrical property unaltered by projective transformation. If a logical error is to be avoided, in fact, all reference to spatial magnitude of any kind must be avoided; for all spatial magnitude, as will be shown hereafter[2], is logically dependent on the fundamental magnitude of distance. Anharmonic ratio and coordinates must alike be defined by purely descriptive properties, if the use afterwards made of them is to be free from metrical presuppositions, and therefore from the objections of Sir R. Ball.

Such a definition has been satisfactorily given by Klein[3], who appeals, for the purpose, to v. Staudt's quadrilateral construction[4]. By this construction, which I have reproduced in outline in Chapter III. Section A, § 112 ff., we obtain a purely descriptive definition of harmonic and anharmonic ratio, and, given a pair of points, we can obtain the harmonic conjugate to any third point on the same straight line. On this construction, the introduction of projective coordinates is based. Starting with any three points on a straight line, we assign to them arbitrarily the numbers $0, 1, \infty$. We then find the harmonic conjugate to the first with respect to $1, \infty$, and assign to it the number 2. The object of assigning this number rather than any other, is to obtain the value $-1$ for the anharmonic ratio of the four numbers corresponding to the four points[5]. We then find the harmonic conjugate to the point 1, with respect to $2, \infty$, and assign to it the number 3; and so on. Klein has shown that by this construction, we can obtain any number of points, and

[1] Elements of Projective Geometry, Second Edition, Oxford, 1893, Chap. IX.

[2] Chap. III. Section B.

[3] See Nicht-Euklid, I. p. 338 ff.

[4] See his Geometrie der Lage, § 8, Harmonische Gebilde.

[5] The anharmonic ratio of four numbers, $p, q, r, s$, is defined as

$$(p-q).(r-s)/(p-r).(q-s).$$

can construct a point corresponding to any given number, fractional or negative. Moreover, when two sets of four points have the same anharmonic ratio, descriptively defined[1], the corresponding numbers also have the same anharmonic ratio. By introducing such a numerical system on two straight lines, or on three, we obtain the coordinates of any point in a plane, or in space. By this construction, which is of fundamental importance to projective Geometry, the logical error, upon which Sir R. Ball bases his criticism, is satisfactorily avoided. Our coordinates are introduced by a purely descriptive method, and involve no presupposition whatever as to the measurement of distance.

**37.** With this coordinate system, then, to define distance as a certain function of the coordinates is not to be guilty of a vicious circle. But it by no means follows that the definition of distance is arbitrary. All reference to distance has been hitherto excluded, to avoid metrical ideas; but when distance is introduced, metrical ideas inevitably reappear, and we have to remember that our coordinates give no information, *primâ facie*, as to any of these metrical ideas. It is open to us, of course, if we choose, to continue to exclude distance in the ordinary sense, as the quantity of a finite straight line, and to define the *word* distance in any way we please. But the conception, for which the word has hitherto stood, will then require a new name, and the only result will be a confusion between the *apparent* meaning of our propositions, to those who retain the associations belonging to the old sense of the word, and the *real* meaning, resulting from the new sense in which the word is used.

This confusion, I believe, has actually occurred, in the case of those who regard the question between Euclid and Metageometry as one of the definition of distance. Distance is a quantitative relation, and as such presupposes identity of quality. But projective Geometry deals only with quality—for which reason it is called descriptive—and cannot distinguish between two figures which are qualitatively alike. Now the meaning of qualitative likeness, in Geometry, is the possibility

[1] *I.e.* as transformable into each other by a collineation. See Chap. III. Sec. A, § 110.

of mutual transformation by a collineation[1]. Any two pairs of points on the same straight line, therefore, are qualitatively alike; their only qualitative relation is the straight line, which both pairs have in common; and it is exactly the qualitative identity of the relations of the two pairs, which enables the difference of their relations to be exhaustively dealt with by quantity, as a difference of distance. But where quantity is excluded, any two pairs of points on the same straight line appear as alike, and even any two sets of three: for any three points on a straight line can be projectively transformed into any other three. It is only with *four* points in a line that we acquire a projective property distinguishing them from other sets of four, and this property is anharmonic ratio, descriptively defined. The projective Geometer, therefore, sees no reason to give a name to the relation between two points, in so far as this relation is anything over and above the unlimited straight line on which they lie; and when he introduces the notion of distance, he defines it, in the only way in which projective principles allow him to define it, as a relation between *four* points. As he nevertheless wishes the word to give him the power of distinguishing between different *pairs* of points, he agrees to take two out of the four points as fixed. In this way, the only variables in distance are the two remaining points, and distance appears, therefore, as a function of *two* variables, namely the coordinates of the two variable points. When we have further defined our function so that distance may be additive, we have a function with many of the properties of distance in the ordinary sense. This function, therefore, the projective Geometer regards as the only proper definition of distance.

We can see, in fact, from the manner in which our projective coordinates were introduced, that *some* function of these coordinates must express distance in the ordinary sense. For they were introduced serially, so that, as we proceeded from the zero-point towards the infinity-point, our coordinates continually grew. To every point, a definite coordinate corresponded: to the distance between two variable points, therefore, as a function dependent on no other variables, must correspond

[1] See Chap. III. Sec. A.

some definite function of the coordinates, since these are themselves functions of their points. The function discussed above, therefore, must certainly include distance in the ordinary sense.

But the arbitrary and conventional nature of distance, as maintained by Poincaré and Klein, arises from the fact that the two fixed points, required to determine our distance in the projective sense, may be arbitrarily chosen, and although, when our choice is once made, any two points have a definite distance, yet, according as we make that choice, distance will become a different function of the two variable points. The ambiguity thus introduced is unavoidable on projective principles; but are we to conclude, from this, that it is really unavoidable? Must we not rather conclude that projective Geometry cannot adequately deal with distance? If $A$, $B$, $C$, be three different points on a line, there must be *some* difference between the relation of $A$ to $B$ and of $A$ to $C$, for otherwise, owing to the qualitative identity of all points, $B$ and $C$ could not be distinguished. But such a difference involves a relation, between $A$ and $B$, which is independent of other points on the line; for unless we have such a relation, the other points cannot be distinguished as different. Before we can distinguish the two fixed points, therefore, from which the projective definition starts, we must already suppose some relation, between any two points on our line, in which they are independent of other points; and this relation is distance in the ordinary sense[1]. When we have measured this quantitative relation by the ordinary methods of metrical Geometry, we can proceed to decide what base-points must be chosen, on our line, in order that the projective function discussed above may have the same value as ordinary distance. But the choice of these base-points, when we are discussing distance in the ordinary sense, is not arbitrary, and their introduction is only a technical device. Distance, in the ordinary sense, remains a relation between *two* points, not between *four;* and it is the failure to perceive that the projective sense differs from, and cannot

[1] It follows from this, that the reduction of metrical to projective properties, even when, as in hyperbolic Geometry, the Absolute is real, is only apparent, and has a merely technical validity.

supersede, the ordinary sense, which has given rise to the views of Klein and Poincaré. The question is not one of convention, but of the irreducible metrical properties of space. To sum up: Quantities, as used in projective Geometry, do not stand for spatial magnitudes, but are conventional symbols for purely qualitative spatial relations. But distance, *quâ* quantity, presupposes identity of quality, as the condition of quantitative comparison. Distance in the ordinary sense is, in short, that quantitative relation, between two points on a line, by which their difference from other points can be defined. The projective definition, however, being unable to distinguish a collection of less than four points from any other on the same straight line, makes distance depend on two other points besides those whose relation it defines. No name remains, therefore, for distance in the ordinary sense, and many projective Geometers, having abolished the name, believe the thing to be abolished also, and are inclined to deny that *two* points have a unique relation at all. This confusion, in projective Geometry, shows the importance of a name, and should make us chary of allowing new meanings to obscure one of the fundamental properties of space.

**38.** It remains to discuss the manner in which non-Euclidean Geometries result from the projective definition of distance, as also the true interpretation to be given to this view of Metageometry. It is to be observed that the projective methods which follow Cayley deal throughout with a Euclidean plane, on which they introduce different measures of distance. Hence arises, in any interpretation of these methods, an apparent subordination of the non-Euclidean spaces, as though these were less self-subsistent than Euclid's. This subordination is not intended in what follows; on the contrary, the correlation with Euclidean space is regarded as valuable, first, because Euclidean space has been longer studied and is more familiar, but secondly, because this correlation proves, when truly interpreted, that the other spaces are self-subsistent. We may confine ourselves chiefly, in discussing this interpretation, to distances measured along a single straight line. But we must be careful to remember that the metrical definition of distance—which, according to the view here advocated, is the only adequate definition—is the same in Euclidean and in non-Euclidean spaces; to argue in its favour is not, therefore, to argue in favour of Euclid.

The projective scheme of coordinates consists of a series of numbers, of which each represents a certain anharmonic ratio and denotes one and only one point, and which increase uniformly with the distance from a fixed origin, until they become infinite on reaching a certain point. Now Cayley showed that, in Euclidean Geometry, distance may be expressed as the limit of the logarithm of the anharmonic ratio of the two points and the (coincident) points at infinity on their straight line; while, if we assumed that the points at infinity were distinct, we obtained the formula for distance in hyperbolic or spherical Geometry, according as these points were real or imaginary. Hence it follows that, with the projective definition of distance, we shall obtain precisely the formulae of hyperbolic, parabolic or spherical Geometry, according as we choose the point, to which the value $+\infty$ is assigned, at a finite, infinite or imaginary distance (in the ordinary sense) from the point to which we assign the value 0. Our straight line remains, all the while, an ordinary Euclidean straight line. But we have seen that the projective definition of distance fits with the true definition only when the two fixed points to which it refers are suitably chosen. Now the ordinary meaning of distance is required in non-Euclidean as in Euclidean Geometries—indeed, it is only in metrical properties that these Geometries differ. Hence our *Euclidean* straight line, though it may serve to illustrate other Geometries than Euclid's, can only be dealt with correctly by Euclid. Where we give a different definition of distance from Euclid's, we are still in the domain of purely projective properties, and derive no information as to the metrical properties of our straight line. But the importance, to Metageometry, of this new interpretation, lies in the fact that, having independently established the metrical formulae of non-Euclidean spaces, we find, as in Beltrami's Saggio, that these spaces can be related, by a homographic correspondence, with the points of Euclidean space; and that this can be effected in such a manner as to give, for the distance between two points of our non-Euclidean space, the hyperbolic or spherical measure of distance for the corresponding points of Euclidean space.

**39.** On the whole, then, a modification of Sir R. Ball's view, which is practically a generalized statement of Beltrami's method, seems the most tenable. He imagines what, with Grassmann, he calls a Content, *i.e.* a perfectly general three-dimensional manifold, and then correlates its elements, one by one, with points in Euclidean space. Thus every element of the Content acquires, as its coordinates, the ordinary Euclidean coordinates of the corresponding point in Euclidean space. By means of this correlation, our calculations, though they refer to the Content, are carried on, as in Beltrami's Saggio, in ordinary Euclidean space. Thus the confusion disappears, but with it, the supposed Euclidean interpretation also disappears. Sir R. Ball's Content, if it is to be a space at all, must be a space radically different from Euclid's[1]; to speak, as Klein does, of ordinary planes with hyperbolic or elliptic measures of distance, is either to incur a contradiction, or to forego any metrical meaning of distance. Instead of ordinary planes, we have surfaces like Beltrami's, of constant measure of curvature; instead of Euclid's space, we have hyperbolic or spherical space. At the same time, it remains true that we can, by Klein's method, give a Euclidean meaning to every symbolic proposition in non-Euclidean Geometry. For by substituting, for distance, the logarithm above alluded to, we obtain, from the non-Euclidean result, a result which follows from the ordinary Euclidean axioms. This correspondence removes, once for all, the possibility of a lurking contradiction in Metageometry, since, to a proposition in the one, corresponds one and only one proposition in the other, and contradictory results in one system, therefore, would correspond to contradictory results in the other. Hence Metageometry cannot lead to contradictions, unless Euclidean Geometry, at the same moment, leads to corresponding contradictions. Thus the Euclidean plane with hyperbolic or elliptic measure of distance, though either contradictory or not metrical

[1] Sir R. Ball does not regard his non-Euclidean content as a possible space (*v. op. cit.* p. 151). In this important point I disagree with his interpretation, holding such a content to be a space as possible, *à priori*, as Euclid's, and perhaps actually true within the margin due to errors of observation.

as an independent notion, has, as a help in the interpretation of non-Euclidean results, a very high degree of utility.

**40.** We have still to discuss Klein's third kind of non-Euclidean Geometry, which he calls elliptic. The difference between this and spherical Geometry is difficult to grasp, but it may be illustrated by a simpler example. A plane, as every one knows, can be wrapped, without stretching, on a cylinder, and straight lines in the plane become, by this operation, geodesics on the cylinder. The Geometries of the plane and the cylinder, therefore, have much in common. But since the generating circle of the cylinder, which is one of its geodesics, is finite, only a portion of the plane is used up in wrapping it once round the cylinder. Hence, if we endeavour to establish a point-to-point correspondence between the plane and the cylinder, we shall find an infinite series of points on the plane for a single point on the cylinder. Thus it happens that geodesics, though on the plane they have only one point in common, may on the cylinder have an infinite number of intersections. Somewhat similar to this is the relation between the spherical and elliptic Geometries. To any one point in elliptic space, two points correspond in spherical space. Thus geodesics, which in spherical space may have two points in common, can never, in elliptic space, have more than one intersection.

But Klein's method can only prove that elliptic Geometry holds of the ordinary Euclidean plane with elliptic measure of distance. Klein has made great endeavours to enforce the distinction between the spherical and elliptic Geometries[1], but it is not immediately evident that the latter, as distinct from the former, is valid.

In the first place, Klein's elliptic Geometry, which arises as one of the alternative metrical systems on a Euclidean plane or in a Euclidean space, does not by itself suffice, if the above discussion has been correct, to prove the possibility of an elliptic space, *i.e.* of a space having a point-to-point correspondence with the Euclidean space, and having as the ordinary distance between two of its points the elliptic definition of the distance between corresponding points of the Euclidean space. To prove this possibility, we must adopt the direct method of

[1] See Nicht-Euklid, I. p. 97 ff. and p. 292 ff.

Newcomb (Crelle's Journal, Vol. 83). Now in the first place Newcomb has not proved that his postulates are self-consistent; he has only failed to prove that they are contradictory[1]. This would leave elliptic space in the same position in which Lobatchewsky and Bolyai left hyperbolic space. But further there seems to be, at first sight, in *two*-dimensional elliptic space, a positive contradiction. To explain this, however, some account of the peculiarities of the elliptic plane will be necessary.

The elliptic plane, regarded as a figure in three-dimensional elliptic space, is what is called a double surface[2], *i.e.* as Newcomb says (*loc. cit.* p. 298): "The two sides of a complete plane are not distinct, as in a Euclidean surface.... If...a being should travel to distance $2D$, he would, on his return, find himself on the opposite surface to that on which he started, and would have to repeat his journey in order to return to his original position without leaving the surface." Now if we imagine a

[1] Newcomb says (*loc. cit.* p. 293): "The system here set forth is founded on the following three postulates.

"1. I assume that space is triply extended, unbounded, without properties dependent either on position or direction, and possessing such planeness in its smallest parts that both the postulates of the Euclidean Geometry, and our common conceptions of the relations of the parts of space are true for every indefinitely small region in space.

"2. I assume that this space is affected with such curvature that a right line shall always return into itself at the end of a finite and real distance $2D$ without losing, in any part of its course, that symmetry with respect to space on all sides of it which constitutes the fundamental property of our conception of it.

"3. I assume that if two right lines emanate from the same point, making the indefinitely small angle $a$ with each other, their distance apart at the distance $r$ from the point of intersection will be given by the equation

$$s = \frac{2aD}{\pi} \sin \frac{r\pi}{2D}.$$

The right line thus has this property in common with the Euclidean right line that two such lines intersect only in a single point. It may be that the number of points in which two such lines can intersect admit of being determined from the laws of curvature, but not being able so to determine it, I assume as a postulate the fundamental property of the Euclidean right line."

It is plain that in the absence of the determination spoken of, the possibility of elliptic space is not established. It may be possible, for example, to prove that, in a space where there is a maximum to distance, there must be an infinite number of straight lines joining two points of maximum distance. In this event, elliptic space would become impossible.

[2] For an elucidation of this term, see Klein, Nicht-Euklid, I. p. 99 ff.

*two*-dimensional elliptic space, the distinction between the sides of a plane becomes unmeaning, since it only acquires significance by reference to the third dimension. Nevertheless, some such distinction would be forced upon us. Suppose, for example, that we took a small circle provided with an arrow, as in the figure, and moved this circle once round the universe. Then the sense of the arrow would be reversed. We should thus be forced, either to regard the new position as distinct from the former, which transforms our plane into a spherical plane, or to attribute the reversal of the arrow to the action of a motion which restores our circle to its original place. It is to be observed that nothing short of moving round the universe would suffice to reverse the sense of the arrow. This reversal *seems* like an action of empty space, which would force us to regard the points which, from a three-dimensional point of view, are coincident though opposite, as really distinct, and so reduce the elliptic to the spherical plane. But motion, not space, really causes the change, and the elliptic plane is therefore not proved to be impossible. The question is not, however, of any great philosophic importance.

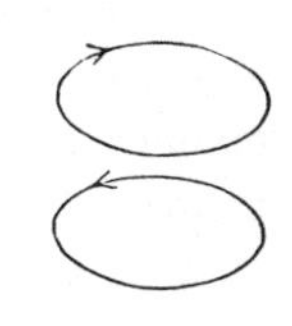

**41.** In connection with the reduction of metrical to projective Geometry, we have one more topic for discussion. This is the geometrical use of imaginaries, by means of which, except in the case of hyperbolic space, the reduction is effected. I have already contended, on other grounds, that this reduction, in spite of its immense technical importance, and in spite of the complete logical freedom of projective Geometry from metrical ideas, is *purely* technical, and is not philosophically valid. The same conclusion will appear, if we take up Cayley's challenge at the British Association, in his Presidential Address of 1883.

In this address, Professor Cayley devoted most of his time to non-Euclidean systems. Non-Euclidean *spaces*, he declared, seemed to him mistaken *à priori*[1]; but non-Euclidean *Geometries*,

[1] Cf. p. 9 of Report: "My own view is that Euclid's twelfth axiom, in Playfair's form of it, does not need demonstration, but is part of our notion of space, of the physical space of our experience, but which is the representation lying at the bottom of all external experience."

here as in his mathematical works, were accepted as flowing from a change in the definition of distance. This view has been already discussed, and need not, therefore, be further criticised here. What I wish to speak about, is the question with which Cayley himself opened his address, namely, the geometrical use and meaning of imaginary quantities. From the manner in which he spoke of this question, it becomes imperative to treat it somewhat at length. For he said (pp. 8–9):

"...The notion which is the really fundamental one (and I cannot too strongly emphasize the assertion) underlying and pervading the whole notion of modern analysis and Geometry, [is] that of imaginary magnitude in analysis, and of imaginary space (or space as the *locus in quo* of imaginary points and figures) in Geometry: I use in each case the word imaginary as including real.... Say even the conclusion were that the notion belongs to mere technical mathematics, or has reference to nonentities in regard to which no science is possible, still it seems to me that (as a subject of philosophical discussion) the notion ought not to be thus ignored; it should at least be shown that there is a right to ignore it."

**42.** This right it is now my purpose to demonstrate. But for fear non-mathematicians should miss the point of Cayley's remark (which has sometimes been erroneously supposed to refer to non-Euclidean spaces), I may as well explain, at the outset, that this question is radically distinct from, and only indirectly connected with, the validity or import of Metageometry. An imaginary quantity is one which involves $\sqrt{-1}$: its most general form is $a+\sqrt{-1}\,b$ where $a$ and $b$ are real; Cayley uses the word imaginary so as to include real, in order to cover the special case where $b=0$. It will be convenient, in what follows, to exclude this wider meaning, and assume that $b$ is not zero. An imaginary point is one whose coordinates involve $\sqrt{-1}$, *i.e.* whose coordinates are imaginary quantities. An imaginary curve is one whose points are imaginary—or, in some special uses, one whose equation contains imaginary coefficients. The mathematical subtleties to which this notion leads need not be here discussed; the reader who is interested in them will find an excellent elementary account of their geometrical uses in Klein's Nicht-Euklid, II. pp. 38–46.

But for our present purpose, we may confine ourselves to imaginary points. If these are found to have a merely technical import, and to be destitute of any philosophical meaning, then the same will hold of any collection of imaginary points, *i.e.* of any imaginary curve or surface.

That the notion of imaginary points is of supreme importance in Geometry, will be seen by any one who reflects that the circular points are imaginary, and that the reduction of metrical to projective Geometry, which is one of Cayley's greatest achievements, depends on these points. But to discuss adequately their philosophical import is difficult to me, since I am unacquainted with any satisfactory philosophy of imaginaries in pure Algebra. I will therefore adopt the most favourable hypothesis, and assume that no objection can be successfully urged against this use. Even on this hypothesis, I think, no case can be made out for imaginary points in Geometry.

In the first place, we must exclude, from the imaginary points considered, those whose coordinates are only imaginary with certain special systems of coordinates. For example, if one of a point's coordinates be the tangent from it to a sphere, this coordinate will be imaginary for any point inside the sphere, and yet the point is perfectly real. A point, then, is only to be called imaginary, when, whatever real system of coordinates we adopt, one or more of the quantities expressing these coordinates remains imaginary. For this purpose, it is mathematically sufficient to suppose our coordinates Cartesian—a point whose Cartesian coordinates are imaginary, is a true imaginary point in the above sense.

To discuss the meaning of such a point, it is necessary to consider briefly the fundamental nature of the correspondence between a point and its coordinates. Assuming that elementary Geometry has proved—what I think it does satisfactorily prove—that spatial relations are susceptible of quantitative measurement, then a given point will have, with a suitable system of coordinates, in a space of $n$ dimensions, $n$ quantitative relations to the fixed spatial figure forming the axes of coordinates, and these $n$ quantitative relations will, under certain reservations, be unique—*i.e.*, no other point will have the same quantities assigned to it. (With many possible coordinate systems, this latter condition is not realized: but for that very reason they are inconvenient, and employed only in special problems.) Thus given a coordinate system, and given any set of quantities, these quantities, *if they determine a point at all*, determine it uniquely. But, by a natural extension of the method, the above reservation is dropped, and it is assumed that to *every* set of quantities some point must correspond. For this assumption there seems to me no vestige of evidence. As well might a postman assume that, because every house in a street is uniquely determined by its number, therefore there must be a house for every imaginable number. We must know, in fact, that a given set of quantities can be the coordinates of some point in space, before it is legitimate to give any spatial significance to these quantities: and this knowledge, obviously, cannot be derived from operations with coordinates alone, on pain of a vicious circle. We must, to return to the above analogy, know the number of houses in Piccadilly, before we know whether a given number has a corresponding house or not; and arithmetic alone, however subtly employed, will never give us this information.

Thus the distinction which is important is, not the distinction between real and imaginary quantities, but between quantities to which points correspond and quantities to which no points correspond. We can conventionally agree to denote real points by imaginary coordinates, as in the Gaussian method of denoting by the single quantity $(a + \sqrt{-1}\, b)$ the point whose ordinary coordinates are $a$, $b$. But this does not touch Cayley's meaning. Cayley means that it is of great utility in mathematics to regard, as points with a real existence in space, the assumed spatial correlates of quantities which, with the coordinate system employed, have no correlates in every-day space; and that this utility is supposed, by many mathematicians, to indicate the validity of so fruitful an assumption. To fix our ideas, let us consider Cartesian axes in three-dimensional Euclidean space. Then it appears, by inspection, that a point may be situated at any distance to right or left of any of the three coordinate planes; taking this distance as a coordinate, therefore, it appears that real points correspond to all quantities from $-\infty$ to $+\infty$. The same appears for the other two coordinates; and since elementary Geometry proves their variations mutually independent, we know that one and only one real point corresponds to any three real quantities. But we also know, from the exhaustive method pursued, that all space is covered by the range of these three variable quantities: a fresh set of quantities, therefore, such as is introduced by the use of imaginaries, possesses no spatial correlate, and can be supposed to possess one only by a convenient fiction.

**43**. The fact that the fiction *is* convenient, however, may be thought to indicate that it is more than a fiction. But this presumption, I think, can be easily explained away. For all the fruitful uses of imaginaries, in Geometry, are those which begin and end with real quantities, and use imaginaries only for the intermediate steps. Now in all such cases, we have a real spatial interpretation at the beginning and end of our argument, where alone the spatial interpretation is important: in the intermediate links, we are dealing in a purely algebraical manner with purely algebraical quantities, and may perform any operations which are algebraically permissible. If the quantities with which we end are capable of spatial interpretation, then, and only then, our result may be regarded as geometrical. To use geometrical language, in any other case, is only a convenient help to the imagination. To speak, for example, of projective properties which refer to the circular points, is a mere *memoria technica* for purely algebraical properties; the circular points are not to be found in space, but only in the auxiliary quantities by which geometrical equations are transformed. That no contradictions arise from the geometrical interpretation of imaginaries, is not wonderful: for they are interpreted solely by the rules of Algebra, which we may admit as valid in their application to imaginaries. The perception of space being wholly absent, Algebra rules supreme, and no inconsistency can arise. Wherever, for a moment, we allow our ordinary spatial notions to intrude, the grossest absurdities do arise—every one can see that a circle, being a closed curve, cannot get to infinity. The metaphysician, who should invent anything so preposterous as the circular points, would be hooted from the field. But the mathematician may steal the horse with impunity.

Finally, then, only a knowledge of space, not a knowledge of Algebra, can assure us that any given set of quantities will have a spatial correlate, and in the absence of such a correlate, operations with these quantities have no geometrical import. This is the case with imaginaries in Cayley's sense, and their use in Geometry, great as are its technical advantages, and rigid as is its technical validity, is wholly destitute of philosophical importance.

**44.** We have now, I think, discussed most of the questions concerning the scope and validity of the projective method. We have seen that it is independent of all metrical presuppositions, and that its use of coordinates does not involve the assumption that spatial magnitudes are measured or expressed by them. We have seen that it is able to deal, by its own methods alone, with the question of the qualitative likeness of geometrical figures, which is logically prior to any comparison as to quantity, since quantity presupposes qualitative likeness. We have seen also that, so far as its legitimate use extends, it applies equally to all homogeneous spaces, and that its criterion of an independently possible space—the determination of a straight line by two points[1]—is not subject to the qualifications and limitations which belong, as we have seen in the case of the cylinder, to the metrical criterion of constant curvature. But we have also seen that, when projective Geometry endeavours to grapple with spatial magnitude, and bring distance and the measurement of angles beneath its sway, its success, though technically valid and important, is philosophically an apparent success only. Metrical Geometry, therefore, if quantity is to be applied to space at all, remains a separate, though logically subsequent branch of Mathematics.

**45.** It only remains to say a few words about *Sophus Lie.* As a mathematician, as the inventor of a new and immensely powerful method of analysis, he cannot be too highly praised. Geometry is only one of the numerous subjects to which his

[1] The exception to this axiom, in spherical space, presupposes metrical Geometry, and does not destroy the validity of the axiom for projective Geometry. See Chap. III. Sec. B, § 171.

theory of continuous groups applies, but its application to Geometry has made a revolution in method, and has rendered possible, in such problems as Helmholtz's, a treatment infinitely more precise and exhaustive than any which was possible before.

The general definition of a group is as follows: If we have any number of independent variables $x_1\ x_2 \ldots x_n$, and any series of transformations of these into new variables—the transformations being defined by equations of specified forms, with parameters varying from one transformation to another—then the series of transformations form a *group*, if the successive application of any two is equivalent to a single member of the original series of transformations. The group is *continuous*, when we can pass, by infinitesimal gradations within the group, from any one of the transformations to any other.

Now, in Geometry, the result of two successive motions or collineations of a figure can always be obtained by a single motion or collineation, and any motion or collineation can be built up of a series of infinitesimal motions or collineations. Moreover the analytical expression of either is a certain transformation of the coordinates of all the points of the figure[1]. Hence the transformations determining a motion or a collineation are such as to form a continuous group. But the question of the projective equivalence of two figures, to which all projective Geometry is reducible, must always be dealt with by a collineation; and the question of the equality of two figures, to which all metrical Geometry is reducible, must always be decided by a motion such as to cause superposition; hence the whole subject of Geometry may be regarded as a theory of the continuous groups which define all possible collineations and motions.

Now Sophus Lie has developed, at great length, the purely analytical theory of groups; he has therefore, by this method of formulating the problem, a very powerful weapon ready for

[1] Mathematicians of Lie's school have a habit, at first somewhat confusing, of speaking of motions of space instead of motions of bodies, as though space as a whole could move. All that is meant is, of course, the equivalent motion of the coordinate axes, *i.e.* a change of axes in the usual elementary sense.

the attack. In two papers "On the foundations of Geometry[1]," undertaken at Klein's urgent request, he takes premisses which roughly correspond to those of Helmholtz, omitting Monodromy, and applies the theory of groups to the deduction of their consequences[2]. Helmholtz's work, he says, can hardly be looked upon as *proving* its conclusions, and indeed the more searching analysis of the group-theory reveals several possibilities unknown to Helmholtz. Nevertheless, as a pioneer, devoid of Lie's machinery, Helmholtz deserves, I think, more praise than Lie is willing to give him[3].

Lie's method is perfectly exhaustive; omitting the premiss of Monodromy, the others show that a body has six degrees of freedom, *i.e.* that the group giving all possible motions of a body will have six independent members; if we keep one point fixed, the number of independent members is reduced to three. He then, from his general theory, enumerates all the groups which satisfy this condition. In order that such a group should

[1] "Ueber die Grundlagen der Geometrie," Leipziger Berichte, 1890. The problem of these two papers is really metrical, since it is concerned, not with collineations in general, but with motions. The problem, however, is dealt with by the projective method, motions being regarded as collineations which leave the Absolute unchanged. It seemed impossible, therefore, to discuss Lie's work, until some account had been given of the projective method.

[2] Lie's premisses, to be accurate, are the following:

Let

$$x_1 = f(x, y, z, a_1, a_2 \ldots)$$
$$x_2 = \phi(x, y, z, a_1, a_2 \ldots)$$
$$x_3 = \psi(x, y, z, a_1, a_2 \ldots)$$

give an infinite family of real transformations of space, as to which we make the following hypotheses:

A. The functions $f$, $\phi$, $\psi$, are *analytical* functions of

$$x, y, z, a_1, a_2 \ldots.$$

B. Two points $x_1 y_1 z_1$, $x_2 y_2 z_2$ possess an invariant, *i.e.*

$$\Omega(x_1, y_1, z_1, x_2, y_2, z_2) = \Omega(x_1', y_1', z_1', x_2', y_2', z_2')$$

where $x_1' \ldots$, $x_2' \ldots$ are the transformed coordinates of the two points.

C. Free Mobility: *i.e.*, any point can be moved into any other position; when one point is fixed, any other point of general position can take up $\infty^2$ positions; when two points are fixed, any other of general position can take up $\infty^1$ positions; when three, no motion is possible—these limitations being results of the equations given by the invariant $\Omega$.

[3] On this point, cf. Klein, Höhere Geometrie, Göttingen, 1893, II. pp. 225–244, especially pp. 230–1.

give possible motions, it is necessary, by Helmholtz's second axiom, that it should leave invariant some function of the coordinates of any two points. This eliminates several of the groups previously enumerated, each of which he discusses in turn. He is thus led to the following results:

I. *In two dimensions*, if free mobility is to hold *universally*, there are no groups satisfying Helmholtz's first three axioms, except those which give the ordinary Euclidean and non-Euclidean motions; but if it is to hold only *within a certain region*, there is also a possible group in which the curve described by any point in a rotation is not closed, but an equiangular spiral. To exclude this possibility, Helmholtz's axiom of Monodromy is required.

II. *In three dimensions*, the results go still more against Helmholtz. Assuming free mobility only *within a certain region*, we have to distinguish two cases: *Either* free mobility holds, within that region, absolutely without exception, *i.e.* when one point is held fast, *every* other point within the region can move freely over a surface: in this case the axiom of Monodromy is unnecessary, and the first three axioms suffice to define our group as that of Euclidean and non-Euclidean motions. *Or* free mobility, within the specified region, holds only of every point *of general position*, while the points of a certain line, when one point is fixed, are only able to move on that line, not on a surface; when this is the case, other groups are possible, and can only be excluded by Helmholtz's fourth axiom.

Having now stated the purely mathematical results of Lie's investigations, we may return to philosophical considerations, by which Helmholtz's work was mainly motived. It becomes obvious, not only that exceptions within a certain region, but also that limitation to a certain region, of the axiom of Free Mobility, are philosophically quite impossible and inconceivable. How can a certain line, or a certain surface, form an impassable barrier in space, or have any mobility different in kind from that of all other lines or surfaces? The notion cannot, in philosophy, be permitted for a moment, since it destroys that most fundamental of all the axioms, the homogeneity of space. We not only may, therefore, but must take Helmholtz's axiom of Free Mobility in its very strictest sense; the axiom of Monodromy thus becomes mathematically, as well as philosophically, superfluous. This is, from a philosophical standpoint, the most important of Lie's results.

**46.** I have now come to the end of my history of Metageometry. It has not been my aim to give an exhaustive account of even the important works on the subject—in the third period, especially, the names of Poincaré, Pasch, Cremona, Veronese, and others who might be mentioned, would have cried shame upon me, had I had any such object. But I have tried to set forth, as clearly as I could, the principles at work in the various periods, the motives and results of successive theories. We have seen how the philosophical motive, at first predominant, has been gradually extruded by the purely mathematical and technical spirit of most recent Geometers. At first, to discredit the Transcendental Aesthetic seemed, to Metageometers, as important as to advance their science; but from the works of Cayley, Klein or Lie, no reader could gather that Kant had ever lived. We have also seen, however, that as the interest *in* philosophy waned, the interest *for* philosophy increased: as the mathematical results shook themselves free from philosophical controversies, they assumed gradually a stable form, from which further development, we may reasonably hope, will take the form of growth, rather than transformation. The same gradual development out of philosophy might, I believe, be traced in the infancy of most branches of mathematics; when philosophical motives cease to operate, this is, in general, a sign that the stage of uncertainty as to premisses is past, so that the future belongs entirely to mathematical technique. When this stable stage has been attained, it is time for Philosophy to borrow of Science, accepting its final premisses as those imposed by a real necessity of fact or logic.

**47.** Now in discussing the systems of Metageometry, we have found two kinds, radically distinct and subject to different axioms. The historically prior kind, which deals with metrical ideas, discusses, to begin with, the conditions of Free Mobility, which is essential to all measurement of space. It finds the analytical expression of these conditions in the existence of a space-constant, or constant measure of curvature, which is equivalent to the homogeneity of space. This is its first axiom.

Its second axiom states that space has a finite integral number of dimensions, *i.e.* in metrical terms, that the position of a point, relative to any other figure in space, is uniquely determined by a finite number of spatial magnitudes, called coordinates.

The third axiom of metrical Geometry may be called, to distinguish it from the corresponding projective axiom, the axiom of distance. There exists one relation, it says, between any two points, which can be preserved unaltered in a combined motion of both points, and which, in any motion of a system as one rigid body, is always unaltered. This relation we call distance.

The above statement of the three essential axioms of metrical Geometry is taken from Helmholtz as amended by Lie. Lie's own statement of the axioms, as quoted above, has been too much influenced by projective methods to give a historically correct rendering of the spirit of the second period; Helmholtz's statement, on the other hand, requires, as Lie has shewn, very considerable modifications. The above compromise may, therefore, I hope be taken as accepting Lie's corrections while retaining Helmholtz's spirit.

**48.** But metrical Geometry, though it is historically prior, is logically subsequent to projective Geometry. For projective Geometry deals directly with that qualitative likeness, which the judgment of quantitative comparison requires as its basis. Now the above three axioms of metrical Geometry, as we shall see in Chapter III. Section B, do not presuppose measurement, but are, on the contrary, the conditions presupposed by measurement. Without these axioms, which are common to all three spaces, measurement would be impossible; with them, so I shall contend, measurement is able, though only empirically, to decide approximately which of the three spaces is valid of our actual world. But if these three axioms themselves express, not results, but conditions, of measurement, must they not be equivalent to the statement of that qualitative likeness on which quantitative comparison depends? And if so, must we not expect to find the same axioms, though perhaps under a different form, in projective Geometry?

**49.** This expectation will not be disappointed. The above three axioms, as we shall see hereafter, are one and all philosophically equivalent to the homogeneity of space, and this in turn is equivalent to the axioms of projective Geometry. The axioms of projective Geometry, in fact, may be roughly stated thus:

I. Space is continuous and infinitely divisible; the zero of extension, resulting from infinite division, is called a Point. All points are qualitatively similar, and distinguished by the mere fact that they lie outside one another.

II. Any two points determine a unique figure, the straight line; two straight lines, like two points, are qualitatively similar, and distinguished by the mere fact that they are mutually external.

III. Three points not in one straight line determine a unique figure, the plane, and four points not in one plane determine a figure of three dimensions. This process may, so far as can be seen *à priori*, be continued, without in any way interfering with the possibility of projective Geometry, to five or to $n$ points. But projective Geometry requires, as an axiom, that the process should stop with some positive integral number of points, after which, any fresh point is contained in the figure determined by those already given. If the process stops with $(n+1)$ points, our space is said to have $n$ dimensions.

These three axioms, it will be seen, are the equivalents of the three axioms of metrical Geometry[1], expressed without reference to quantity. We shall find them to be deducible, as before, from the homogeneity of space, or, more generally still, from the possibility of experiencing externality. They will therefore appear as *à priori*, as essential to the existence of any Geometry and to experience of an external world as such.

**50.** That some logical necessity is involved in these axioms might, I think, be inferred as probable, from their historical development alone. For the systems of Metageometry have not, in general, been set up as more likely to fit facts than the

[1] Axiom II. of the metrical triad corresponds to Axiom III. of the projective, and *vice versâ*.

system of Euclid; with the exception of Zöllner, for example, I know of no one who has regarded the fourth dimension as required to explain phenomena. As regards the space-constant again, though a *small* space-constant is regarded as empirically possible, it is not usually regarded as probable; and the finite space-constants, with which Metageometry is equally conversant, are not usually thought even possible, as explanations of empirical fact[1]. Thus the motive has been throughout not one of fact, but one of logic. Does not this give a strong presumption, that those axioms which are retained, are retained because they are logically indispensable? If this be so, the axioms common to Euclid and Metageometry will be *à priori*, while those peculiar to Euclid will be empirical. After a criticism of some differing theories of Geometry, I shall proceed, in Chapters III. and IV., to the proof and consequences of this thesis, which will form the remainder of the present work.

[1] Cf. Helmholtz, Wiss. Abh. Vol. II. p. 640, note: "Die Bearbeiter der Nicht-Euklidischen Geometrie (haben) deren objective Wahrheit nie behauptet."

# CHAPTER II.

## CRITICAL ACCOUNT OF SOME PREVIOUS PHILOSOPHICAL THEORIES OF GEOMETRY.

**51.** WE have now traced the mathematical development of the theory of geometrical axioms, from the first revolt against Euclid to the present day. We may hope, therefore, to have at our command the technical knowledge required for the philosophy of the subject. The importance of Geometry, in the theories of knowledge which have arisen in the past, can scarcely be exaggerated. In Descartes, we find the whole theory of method dominated by analytical Geometry, of whose fruitfulness he was justly proud. In Spinoza, the paramount influence of Geometry is too obvious to require comment. Among mathematicians, Newton's belief in absolute space was long supreme, and is still responsible for the current formulation of the laws of motion. Against this belief on the one hand, and against Leibnitz's theory of space on the other, and not, as Caird has pointed out[1], against Hume's empiricism, was directed that keystone of the Critical Philosophy, the Kantian doctrine of space. Thus Geometry has been, throughout, of supreme importance in the theory of knowledge.

But in a criticism of representative modern theories of Geometry, which is designed to be, not a history of the subject, but an introduction to, and defence of, the views of the author, it will not be necessary to discuss any more ancient theory than that of Kant. Kant's views on this subject, true or false, have so dominated subsequent thought, that whether they were

[1] The Critical Philosophy of Kant, Vol. I. p. 287.

accepted or rejected, they seemed equally potent in forming the opinions, and the manner of exposition, of almost all later writers.

### Kant.

**52.** It is not my purpose, in this chapter, to add to the voluminous literature of Kantian criticism, but only to discuss the bearing of Metageometry on the argument of the Transcendental Aesthetic, and the aspect under which this argument must be viewed in a discussion of Geometry[1]. On this point several misunderstandings seem to me to have had wide prevalence, both among friends and foes, and these misunderstandings I shall endeavour, if I can, to remove.

In the first place, what does Kant's doctrine mean for Geometry? Obviously not the aspect of the doctrine which has been attacked by psychologists, the "Kantian machine-shop" as James calls it—at any rate, if this can be clearly separated from the logical aspect. The question whether space is given in sensation, or whether, as Kant maintained, it is given by an intuition to which no external matter corresponds, may for the present be disregarded. If, indeed, we held the view which seems crudely to sum up the standpoint of the Critique, the view that all certain knowledge is self-knowledge, then we should be committed, if we had decided that Geometry was apodeictic, to the view that space is subjective. But even then, the psychological question could only arise when the epistemological question had been solved, and could not, therefore, be taken into account in our first investigation. The question before us is precisely the question whether, or how far, Geometry is apodeictic, and for the moment we have only to investigate this question, without fear of psychological consequences.

**53.** Now on this question, as on almost all questions in the Aesthetic or the Analytic, Kant's argument is twofold. On the one hand, he says, Geometry is known to have apodeictic certainty: therefore space must be *à priori* and subjective. On the other hand, it follows, from grounds independent of

[1] For a discussion of Kant from a less purely mathematical standpoint, see Chap. IV.

Geometry, that space is subjective and *à priori*; therefore Geometry must have apodeictic certainty. These two arguments are not clearly distinguished in the Aesthetic, but a little analysis, I think, will disentangle them. Thus in the first edition, the first two arguments deduce, from non-geometrical grounds, the apriority of space; the third deduces the apodeictic certainty of Geometry, and maintains, conversely, that no other view can account for this certainty[1]; the last two arguments only maintain that space is an intuition, not a concept. In the second edition, the double argument is clearer, the apriority of space being proved independently of Geometry in the metaphysical deduction, and deduced from the certainty of Geometry, as the only possible explanation of this, in the transcendental deduction. In the Prolegomena, the latter argument alone is used, but in the Critique both are employed.

**54.** Now it must be admitted, I think, that Metageometry has destroyed the legitimacy of the argument from Geometry to space; we can no longer affirm, on purely geometrical grounds, the apodeictic certainty of Euclid. But unless Metageometry has done more than this—unless it has proved, what I believe it alone cannot prove, that Euclid has *not* apodeictic certainty—then Kant's other line of argument retains what force it may ever have had. The actual space we know, it may say, is admittedly Euclidean, and is proved, without any reference to Geometry, to be *à priori; hence* Euclid has apodeictic certainty, and non-Euclid stands condemned. To this it is no answer to urge, with the Metageometers, that non-Euclidean systems are *logically* self-consistent; for Kant is careful to argue that geometrical reasoning, by virtue of our intuition of space, is synthetic, and cannot, though *à priori*, be upheld by the principle of contradiction alone[2]. Unless non-Euclideans can prove, what they have certainly failed to prove up to the present, that we can frame an *intuition* of non-Euclidean spaces,

[1] Cf. Vaihinger's Commentar, II. pp. 202, 265. Also p. 336 ff.

[2] E.g. second edition, p. 39: "So werden auch alle geometrischen Grundsätze, z. B. dass in einem Triangel zwei Seiten zusammen grösser sind als die dritte, niemals aus allgemeinen Begriffen von Linie und Triangel, sondern aus der Anschauung, und zwar *à priori* mit apodiktischer Gewissheit abgeleitet."

Kant's position cannot be upset by Metageometry alone, but must also be attacked, if it is to be successfully attacked, on its purely philosophical side.

**55.** For such an attack, two roads lie open: either we may disprove the first two arguments of the Aesthetic, or we may criticize, from the standpoint of general logic, the Kantian doctrine of synthetic *à priori* judgments and their connection with subjectivity. Both these attacks, I believe, could be conducted with some success; but if we are to disprove the apodeictic certainty of Geometry, one or other is essential, and both, I believe, will be found only partially successful. It will be my aim to prove, in discussing these two lines of attack, (1) that the distinction of synthetic and analytic judgments is untenable, and further, that the principle of contradiction can only give fruitful results on the assumption that experience in general, or, in a particular science, some special branch of experience, is to be formally possible; (2) that the first two arguments of the Transcendental Aesthetic suffice to prove, not Euclidean space, but *some* form of externality—which may be sensational or intuitional, but not merely conceptual—a necessary prerequisite of experience of an external world. In the third and fourth chapters, I shall contend, as a result of these conclusions, that those axioms, which Euclid and Metageometry have in common, coincide with those properties of any form of externality which are deducible, by the principle of contradiction, from the possibility of experience of an external world. These properties, then, may be said, though not quite in the Kantian sense, to be *à priori* properties of space, and as to these, I think, a modified Kantian position may be maintained. But the question of the subjective or objective nature of space may be left wholly out of account during the course of this discussion, which will gain by dealing exclusively with logical, as opposed to psychological points of view.

**56.** (1) *Kant's logical position.* The doctrine of synthetic and analytic judgments—at any rate if this is taken as the corner-stone of Epistemology—has been so completely rejected by most modern logicians[1], that it would demand little attention

[1] Cf. Bradley's Logic, Bk. III. Pt. I. Chap. VI.; Bosanquet's Logic, Bk. I. Chap. I. pp. 97–103.

here, but for the fact that an enthusiastic French Kantian, M. Renouvier, has recently appealed to it, with perfect confidence, on the very question of Geometry[1]. And it must be owned, with M. Renouvier, that if such judgments existed, in the Kantian sense, non-Euclidean Geometry, which makes no appeal to intuition, could have nothing to say against them. M. Renouvier's contention, therefore, forces us briefly to review the arguments against Kant's doctrine, and briefly to discuss what logical canon is to replace it.

Every judgment—so modern logic contends—is both synthetic and analytic; it combines parts into a whole, and analyses a whole into parts[2]. If this be so, the distinction of analysis and synthesis, whatever may be its importance in pure Logic, can have no value in Epistemology. But such a doctrine, it must be observed, allows full scope to the principle of contradiction: this criterion, since all judgments, in one aspect at least, are analytic, is applicable to all judgments alike. On the other hand, the whole which is analysed must be supposed already given, before the parts can be mutually contradictory: for only by connection in a given whole can two parts or adjectives be incompatible. Thus the principle of contradiction remains barren until we already have some judgments, and even some inference: for the parts may be regarded, to some extent, as an inference from the whole, or *vice versâ*. When once the arch of knowledge is constructed, the parts support one another, and the principle of contradiction is the keystone: but until the arch is built, the keystone remains suspended, unsupported and unsupporting, in the empty air. In other words, knowledge once existent can be analysed, but knowledge which should have to win every inch of the way against a critical scepticism, could never begin, and could never attain that circular condition in which alone it can stand.

But Kant's doctrine, if true, is designed to restrain a critical scepticism even where it might be effective. Certain fundamental propositions, he says, are not deducible from logic,

[1] Philosophie de la Règle et du Compas, Année Philosophique, II. pp. 1–66.

[2] I have stated this doctrine dogmatically, as a proof would require a whole treatise on Logic. I accept the proofs offered by Bradley and Bosanquet, to which the reader is referred.

*i.e.* their contradictories are not self-contradictory; they combine a subject and predicate which cannot, in any purely logical way, be shewn to have any connection, and yet these judgments have apodeictic certainty. But concerning such judgments, Kant is generally careful not to rely upon the mere subjective conviction that they are undeniable: he proves, with every precaution, that without them experience would be impossible. Experience consists in the combination of terms which formal logic leaves apart, and presupposes, therefore, certain judgments by which a framework is made for bringing such terms together. Without these judgments—so Kant contends—all synthesis and all experience would be impossible. If, therefore, the detail of the Kantian reasoning be sound, his results may be obtained by the principle of contradiction *plus* the possibility of experience, as well as by his distinction of synthetic and analytic judgments.

Logic, at the present day, arrogates to itself at once a wider and a narrower sphere than Kant allowed to it. Wider, because it believes itself capable of condemning any false principle or postulate; narrower, because it believes that its law of contradiction, without a given whole or a given hypothesis, is powerless, and that two terms, *per se*, though they may be different, cannot be contradictories, but acquire this relation only by combination in a whole about which something is known, or by connection with a postulate which, for some reason, must be preserved. Thus no judgment, *per se*, is either analytic or synthetic, for the severance of a judgment from its context robs it of its vitality, and makes it not truly a judgment at all. But in its proper context it is neither purely synthetic nor purely analytic; for while it is the further determination of a given whole, and thus in so far analytic, it also involves the emergence of *new* relations within this whole, and is so far synthetic.

**57.** We may retain, however, a distinction roughly corresponding to the Kantian *à priori* and *à posteriori*, though less rigid, and more liable to change with the degree of organisation of knowledge. Kant usually endeavoured to prove, as observed above, that his synthetic *à priori* propositions were necessary prerequisites of experience; now although we cannot retain the term synthetic, we can retain the term *à priori*, for those assumptions, or those postulates, from which alone the possibility of experience follows. Whatever can be deduced from these postulates, without the aid of the matter of experience, will also, of course, be *à priori*. From the standpoint of general logic, the laws of thought and the categories, with the indispensable conditions of their applicability, will be alone *à priori*; but from the standpoint of any special science, we may call *à priori* whatever renders possible the experience which forms the subject-matter of our science. In Geometry, to particularize, we may call *à priori* whatever renders possible experience of externality as such.

It is to be observed that this use of the term is at once more rationalistic and less precise than that of Kant. Kant would seem to have supposed himself immediately aware, by inspection, that some knowledge was apodeictic, and its subject-matter, therefore, *à priori*: but he did not always deduce its apriority from any further principle. Here, however, it is to be shown, before admitting apriority, that the falsehood of the judgment in question would not be effected by a mere change in the *matter* of experience, but only by a change which should render some branch of experience formally impossible, *i.e.* inaccessible to our methods of cognition. The above use is also less precise, for it varies according to the specialization of the experience we are assuming possible, and with every progress of knowledge some new connection is perceived, two previously isolated judgments are brought into logical relation, and the *à priori* may thus, at any moment, enlarge its sphere, as more is found deducible from fundamental postulates.

**58.** (2) *Kant's arguments for the apriority of space.* Having now discussed the logical canon to be used as regards the *à priori*, we may proceed to test Kant's arguments as regards space. The argument from Geometry, as remarked above, is upset by Metageometry, at least so far as those properties are concerned, which belong to Euclid but not to non-Euclidean spaces; as regards the common properties of both kinds of space, we cannot decide on their apriority till we have discussed the consequences of denying them, which will be done in Chapter III. As regards the two arguments which prove that space is an intuition, not a concept, they would call for much discussion in a special criticism of Kant, but here they may be passed by with the obvious comment that infinite homogeneous Euclidean space is a concept, not an intuition—a concept invented to explain an intuition, it is true, but still a pure concept[1]. And it is this pure concept which, in all discussions of Geometry, is primarily to be dealt with; the intuition need only be referred to where it throws light on the functions or the nature of the concept. The second of Kant's arguments, that we can imagine empty space, though not the absence of space, is false if it means a space without matter anywhere, and irrelevant if it merely means a space between matters and regarded as empty[2]. The only argument of importance, then, is the first argument. But I must insist, at the outset, that our problem is purely logical, and that all psychological implications must be excluded to the utmost possible extent. Moreover, as will be proved in Chapter IV., the proper function of space is to distinguish between different presented things, not between the Self and the object of sensation or perception. The argument then becomes the following: consciousness of a world of mutually external things demands, in presentations, a cognitive but non-inferential element leading to the discrimination of the objects presented. This element must be non-inferential, for from whatever number or combination of presentations, which did not of themselves demand diversity in their objects, I could never be led to infer the mutual externality of their objects. Kant says: "In order that sensations may be ascribed to something external to me...and similarly in order that I may be able to present them as outside and beside one another,... the presentation of space must be already present." But this goes rather too far: in the first place, the question should be only as to the mutual externality of presented things, not as to their externality to the Self[3]; and in the second place, things will appear mutually external if I have the presentation of *any* form of externality, whether Euclidean

[1] For a further discussion of this point, see Chaps. III. and IV.

[2] See Chap. IV. for a discussion of this argument.

[3] See Chap. IV. § 185.

or non-Euclidean. Whatever may be true of the *psychological* scope of this argument—whose validity is here irrelevant—the *logical* scope extends, not to Euclidean space, but only to any form of externality which could exist intuitively, and permit knowledge, in beings with our laws of thought, of a world of diverse but interrelated things.

Moreover externality, to render the scope of the argument wholly logical, must not be left with a sensational or intuitional meaning, though it must be supposed given in sensation or intuition. It must mean, in this argument, the fact of Otherness[1], the fact of being different from some other thing: it must involve the distinction between different things, and must be that element, in a cognitive state, which leads us to discriminate constituent parts in its object. So much, then, would appear to result from Kant's argument, that experience of diverse but interrelated things demands, as a necessary prerequisite, some sensational or intuitional element, in perception, by which we are led to attribute complexity to objects of perception[2]; that this element, in its isolation may be called a form of externality; and that those properties of this form, if any such be found, which can be deduced from its mere function of rendering experience of interrelated diversity possible, are to be regarded as *à priori*. What these properties are, and how the various lines of argument here suggested converge to a single result, we shall see in Chapters III. and IV.

**59.** In the philosophers who followed Kant, Metaphysics, for the most part, so predominated over Epistemology, that little was added to the theory of Geometry. What was added, came indirectly from the one philosopher who stood out against the purely ontological speculations of his time, namely *Herbart*. Herbart's actual views on Geometry, which are to be found chiefly in the first section of his *Synechologie*, are not of any great value, and have borne no great fruit in the development of the subject. But his psychological theory of space, his construction of extension out of series of points, his comparison of space with the tone and colour-series, his general preference

[1] An Otherness of substance, rather than of attribute, is here intended; an Otherness which may perhaps be called real as opposed to logical diversity.

[2] This proposition will be argued at length in Chap. IV.

for the discrete above the continuous, and finally his belief in the great importance of classifying space with other forms of series (*Reihenformen*[1]), gave rise to many of Riemann's epoch-making speculations, and encouraged the attempt to explain the nature of space by its analytical and quantitative aspect alone[2]. Through his influence on Riemann, he acquired, indirectly, a great importance in geometrical philosophy. To Riemann's dissertation, which we have already discussed in its mathematical aspect, we must now return, considering, this time, only its philosophical views.

## Riemann.

**60**. The aim of Riemann's dissertation, as we saw in Chapter I., was to define space as a species of manifold, *i.e.* as a particular kind of collection of magnitudes. It was thus assumed, to begin with, that spatial figures could be regarded as magnitudes, and the axioms which emerged, accordingly, determined only the particular place of these among the many algebraically possible varieties of magnitudes. The resulting formulation of the axioms—while, from the mathematical standpoint of metrical Geometry, it was almost wholly laudable—must, from the standpoint of philosophy, be regarded, in my opinion, as a *petitio principii*. For when we have arrived at regarding spatial figures as magnitudes, we have already traversed the most difficult part of the ground. The axioms of metrical Geometry—and it is metrical Geometry, exclusively, which is considered in Riemann's Essay—will appear, in Chapter III., to be divisible into two classes. Of these, the first class—which contains the axioms common to Euclid and Metageometry, the only axioms seriously discussed by Riemann—are not the results of measurement, nor of any conception of magnitude, but are conditions to be fulfilled before measurement becomes possible. The second class only—those which express the difference between Euclidean and non-

[1] See Psychologie als Wissenschaft, I. Section III. Chap. VII.; II. Section I. Chap. III. and Section II. Chap. III. Compare also Synechologie, Section I. Chaps. II. and III.

[2] On the influence of Herbart on Riemann, compare Erdmann, Die Axiome der Geometrie, p. 30.

Euclidean spaces—can be deduced as results of measurement or of conceptions of magnitude. As regards the first class, on the contrary, we shall see that the relativity of position—by which space is distinguished from all other known manifolds, except time—leads logically to the necessity of three of the most distinctive axioms of Geometry, and yet this relativity cannot be called a deduction from conceptions of magnitude. In analytical Geometry, owing to the fact that coordinate systems start from points, and hence build up lines and surfaces, it is easy to suppose that points can be given independently of lines and of each other, and thus the relativity of position is lost sight of. The error thus suggested by mathematics was probably reinforced by Herbart's theory of space, which, by its serial character, as we have seen, appeared to him to facilitate a construction out of successive points, and to which Riemann acknowledges his indebtedness both in his Dissertation and elsewhere. The same error reappears in Helmholtz, in whom it is probably due wholly to the methods of analytical Geometry. It is a striking fact that, throughout the writings of these two men, there is not, so far as I know, one allusion to the relativity of position, that property of space from which, as our next chapter will shew, the richest quarry of consequences can be extracted. This is not a result of any conception of magnitude, but follows from the nature of our space-intuition; yet no one, surely, could call it empirical, since it is bound up in the very possibility of locating things *there* as opposed to *here*.

**61.** Indeed we can see, from a purely logical consideration of the judgment of quantity, that Riemann's manner of approaching the problem can never, by legitimate methods, attain to a philosophically sound formulation of the axioms. For quantity is a result of comparison of two qualitatively similar objects, and the judgment of quantity neglects altogether the qualitative aspect of the objects compared. Hence a knowledge of the essential properties of space can never be obtained from judgments of quantity, which neglect these properties, while they yet presuppose them. As well might one hope to learn the nature of man from a census. Moreover, the judgment of quantity is the result of comparison, and therefore presupposes the possibility of comparison. To know whether, or by what means, comparison is possible, we must know the qualities of the things compared and of the medium in which comparison is effected; while to know that *quantitative* comparison is possible, we must know that there is a qualitative identity between the things compared, which again involves a previous qualitative knowledge. When spatial figures have once been reduced to quantity, their quality has already been neglected, as known and similar to the quality of other figures. To hope, therefore, for the qualities of space, from a comparison of its expression as pure quantity with other pure quantities, is an error natural to an analytical geometer, but an error, none the less, from which there is no return to the qualitative basis of spatial quantity.

**62.** We must entirely dissent, therefore, from the disjunction which underlies Riemann's philosophy of space. Either the axioms must be consequences of general conceptions of magnitude, he thinks, or else they can only be proved by experience (p. 255). Whatever *can* be derived from general conceptions of magnitude, we may retort, cannot be an *à priori* adjective of space: for all the necessary adjectives of space are presupposed in any judgment of spatial quantity, and cannot, therefore, be consequences of such a judgment. Riemann's disjunction, accordingly, since one of its alternatives is obviously impossible, really begs the question. In formulating the axioms of metrical Geometry, our question should be: What axioms, *i.e.* what adjectives of space, must be presupposed, in order that quantitative comparison of the parts of space may be possible at all? And only when we have determined these conditions, which are *à priori* necessary to any quantitative science of space, does the second question arise: what inferences can we draw, as to space, from the observed results of this quantitative science, *i.e.* of this measurement of spatial figures? The conditions of measurement themselves, though not results of any conception of magnitude, will be *à priori*, if it can be shown that, without them, experience of externality would be impossible.

After this initial protest against Riemann's general philosophical position, let us proceed to examine, in detail, his use of the notion of a manifold.

**63.** In the first place there is, if I am not mistaken, considerable obscurity in the definition of a manifold, of which an almost verbal rendering was given in Chapter I. What is meant, to begin with, by a general conception capable of various determinations? Does not this property belong to all conceptions? It affords, certainly, a basis for counting, but if continuous quantity is to arise, we must, surely, have some less discrete formulation. It might afford a basis, for example, for the distinction of points in projective Geometry, but projective Geometry has nothing to do with quantity. Something more fluid and flexible than a conception, one would think, is necessary as the basis of continua. Then, again, what is meant by a quantum of a manifold? In space, the answer is obvious: what is meant is a piece of volume. But how about Riemann's other continuous manifold, colour? Does a quantum of colour mean a single line in the spectrum, or a band of finite thickness? In either case, what are the magnitudes to be compared? And how is superposition necessary, or even possible? A colour is fixed by its position in the spectrum: two lines in the same spectrum cannot be superposed, and two lines in different spectra need not be—their positions in their respective spectra suffice, or even, roughly, their immediate sense-quality. The fact is, Riemann had space in his mind from the start, and many of the properties, which he enunciates as belonging to all manifolds, belong, as a matter of fact, only to space. It is far from clear what the magnitudes are which the various determinations make possible. Do these magnitudes measure the elements of the manifold, or the relations between elements? This is surely a very fundamental point, but it is one which Riemann never touches on. In the former case, the superposition which he speaks of becomes unnecessary, since the magnitude is inherent in the element considered. We do not require superposition to measure quantities corresponding to different tones or colours; these can be discovered by analysis of single tones or colours. With space, on the other hand, if we seek for elements, we can find none except points, and no analysis of a point will find magnitudes inherent in it—such magnitudes are a fiction of coordinate Geometry. The magnitudes which space deals with, as we shall see in Chapter III., are relations between points, and it is for this reason that superposition is essential to space-measurement. There is no inherent quality in a single point, as there is in a single colour, by which it can be quantitatively distinguished from another. Thus the conception of a manifold, as defined by Riemann, either does not include colours, or does not involve superposition as the only means of measurement. From this dilemma there is no escape.

**64**. But if "measurement *consists* in a superposition of the magnitudes compared" (p. 256), does it not follow immediately that measurement is logically possible *only* where such superposition leaves the magnitudes unchanged? And therefore that measurement, as above defined, involves, as an *à priori* condition, that magnitudes are unchanged by motion? This consequence is not drawn by Riemann; indeed he proceeds immediately (pp. 256–7) to consider what he calls a general portion of the doctrine of magnitude (*Grössenlehre*), independent of measurement. But how is any doctrine of magnitude possible, in which the magnitudes cannot be measured? The reason of the confusion is, that Riemann's definition of measurement is applicable to no single manifold except space, since it depends on the noteworthy property that what we measure in Geometry is not points, but relations between points, and the latter, though not the former, may of course be unaltered by motion. Let us try, in illustration, to apply Riemann's definition of measurement to colours. We must remember that motion, in dealing with the colour manifold, means—not motion in space but—motion in the colour manifold itself. Now since every point of the colour manifold is completely determined by three magnitudes, which are given in fact, and cannot be arbitrarily chosen, it is plain that measurement by superposition—involving, as it does, motion, and therefore change in these determining magnitudes—is totally out of the question. The superposition of one colour on another, as a means of measurement, is sheer nonsense. And yet measurement is possible in the colour-manifold, by means of Helmholtz's law of mixture (*Mischungsgesetz*); but the measurement is of every separate element, not of the relations between elements, and is thus radically different from space-measurement[1]. The elements are not, like points in space, qualitatively

[1] I do not mean that measurement of colours is effected without reference to

alike, and distinguished by the mere fact of their mutual externality. What we have, in colours, is three fundamental qualitatively distinct elements, out of certain proportions of which we can build up all the other elements of the manifold—each of the resulting elements having the same combination of qualitative diversity and similarity as the three original elements. But in space, what could we make of such a procedure? Given three points, how are we to combine them in certain proportions? The phrase is meaningless. If some one makes the obvious retort, that we have to combine lines, not points, my rejoinder is equally obvious. To begin with, lines are not elements. Metaphysically, space has *no* elements, being, as the sequel will show, mere relations between non-spatial elements. Mathematically, this fact exhibits itself in the self-contradictory notion of the point, or zero magnitude in space, as the limit in our vain search for spatial elements. But even if we allow the line to pass as the spatial element, what does the combination of three lines in definite proportions give us? It gives us, simply, the coordinates of a *point*. Here again we see a great difference between the colour and space-manifolds. In colours, the combination of magnitudes gives a new magnitude of the same kind; in space, it defines, not a magnitude at all, but a would-be element of a different kind from the defining magnitudes. In the tone-manifold, we should find still different conditions. Here, no one of the measuring magnitudes can vanish without the tone vanishing too, and all three are so bound up together, in the single resulting sensation, that none can exist without a finite quantity of the others. They are all qualitatively different, both from each other, and from any possible tone, being constituents of it, as mass and velocity are constituents of momentum. All these different conditions require to be examined, before a manifold can be completely defined; and until we have conducted such an examination in detail, we cannot pronounce as to the *à priori* or empirical nature of the laws of the manifold. As regards space, I have attempted such an examination in the third and fourth chapters of this Essay.

their relations, since all measurement is essentially comparison. But in colours, it is the elements which are compared, while in space, it is the relations between elements.

**65**. I do not wish to deny, however, the great value of the conception of space as a manifold. On the contrary, this conception seems to have become essential to any treatment of the question. I only wish to urge that the purely algebraical treatment of any manifold, important as it may be in deducing fresh consequences from known premisses, tends rather to conceal than to make clear the basis of the premisses themselves, and is therefore misleading in a philosophical investigation. For mathematics, where quantity reigns supreme, Riemann's conception has proved itself abundantly fruitful; for philosophy, on the contrary, where quantity appears rather as a cloak to conceal the qualities it abstracts from, the conception seems to me more productive of error and confusion than of sound doctrine.

We are thus brought back to the point from which we started, namely, the falsity of Riemann's initial disjunction, and the consequent fallacy in his proof of the empirical nature of the axioms. His philosophy is chiefly vitiated, to my mind, by this fallacy, and by the uncritical assumption that a metrical coordinate system can be set up independently of any axioms as to space-measurement[1]. Riemann has failed to observe, what I have endeavoured to prove in the next chapter, that, unless space had a strictly constant measure of curvature, Geometry would become impossible; also that the absence of constant measure of curvature involves absolute position, which is an absurdity. Hence he is led to the conclusion that all geometrical axioms are empirical, and may not hold in the infinitesimal, where observation is impossible. Thus he says (p. 267): "Now the empirical conceptions, on which spatial measurements are based, the conceptions of the rigid body and the light-ray, appear to lose their validity in the infinitesimal: it is therefore quite conceivable that the relations of spatial magnitudes in the infinitesimal do not correspond to the presuppositions of Geometry, and this would, in fact, have to be assumed, as soon as it would enable us to explain the phenomena more simply." From this conclusion I must entirely dissent. In very large spaces, there might be a departure from Euclid; for they depend upon the axiom of

[1] For a discussion of this point, see Chap. III. Sec. B, § 176.

parallels, which is not contained in the axiom of Free Mobility; but in the infinitesimal, departures from Euclid could only be due to the absence of Free Mobility, which, as I hope my third chapter will show, is once for all impossible.

## Helmholtz.

**66.** Helmholtz, like Riemann, was important both in the mathematics and in the philosophy of Geometry. From the mathematical point of view, his work has been already considered in Chapter I.; the consideration of his philosophy, which must occupy us here, will be a more serious task. Like Riemann, he endeavoured to prove that all the axioms are empirical, and like Riemann, he based his proof chiefly on Metageometry. He had an additional resource, however, in the physiology of the senses, which first led him to reject the Transcendental Aesthetic, and enabled him to attack Kant from the psychological as well as the mathematical side[1].

The principal topics, for a criticism of Helmholtz, are three: First, his criterion of the *à priori*; second, his discussion with Land as to the "imaginability" of non-Euclidean spaces; third —and this is by far the most important of the three—his

[1] The works of Helmholtz on geometrical philosophy comprise, in addition to the articles quoted in Chap. I., the following articles: "Ursprung und Sinn der geometrischen Axiome, gegen Land," Wiss. Abh. Vol. II. p. 640, 1878. (Also Mind, Vol. III.: an answer to Land in Mind, Vol. II.) "Ursprung und Bedeutung der geometrischen Axiome," 1870, Vorträge und Reden, Vol. II. p. 1. (Also Mind, Vol. I.) Two Appendices to "Die Thatsachen in der Wahrnehmung," entitled: II. "Der Raum kann transcendental sein, ohne dass es die Axiome sind"; and III. "Die Anwendbarkeit der Axiome auf die physische Welt," 1878, Vorträge und Reden, Vol. II. p. 256 ff.

The two Appendices last mentioned are popularizings and expansions of the article in Mind, Vol. III. The most widely read, though also, to my mind, the least valuable, of all Helmholtz's writings on Geometry, is the article in Mind, Vol. I. This contains the famous and much misunderstood analogies of Flatland and Sphereland, which will be discussed, and as far as possible defended, in answering Lotze's attack on Metageometry—an attack based, apparently, almost entirely on this one popular article. The present discussion, therefore, may be confined almost entirely to Mind, Vol. III., and the philosophical portions of the two papers quoted in Chap. I., *i.e.* to the articles in Wiss. Abh. Vol. II. pp. 610–660. His other works are popular, and important only because of the large public to which they appeal.

theory of the dependence of Geometry on Mechanics. Let us discuss these three points successively.

**67.** Helmholtz's criterion of apriority is difficult to discover, as he never, to my knowledge, gives a precise statement of it. From his discussion of physical and transcendental Geometry[1], however, it would appear that he regards as empirical whatever applies to empirical matter. For he there maintains, that even if space were an *à priori* form, yet any Geometry, which aimed at an application to Physics, would, since the actual places of bodies are not known *à priori,* be necessarily empirical[2]. It seems the more probable that he regards this as a possible criterion, as it is adopted, in several passages, by his disciple Erdmann[3], and so strange a test could hardly be accepted by a philosopher, unless he had found it in his master. I have called this a strange test, because it seems to me completely to ignore the work of the Critical Philosophy. For if there is one thing which, one might have hoped, had been made sufficiently clear by Kant's Critique, it is this, that knowledge which is *à priori,* being itself the condition of possible experience, applies—and in Kant's view, applies only—to empirical matter. Helmholtz and Erdmann, therefore, in setting up this test without discussion, simply ignore the existence of Kant and the possibility of a transcendental argument. Helmholtz assumes always that empirical knowledge must be wholly empirical, that there can be no *à priori* conditions of the experience in question, that experience will always be possible, and may give any kind of result. Thus in discussing "physical" Geometry, he assumes that the possibility of empirical measurement involves no *à priori* axioms, and that no *à priori* element can be contained in the process. This assumption, as we shall see in Chapter III., is quite unwarrantable: certain properties of *space,* in fact, are involved in the possibility of measuring *matter.* In spite of the fact, therefore, that we apply measurement to empirical matter, and that our results are therefore empirical, there

[1] In the answer to Land, Mind, Vol. III. and Wiss. Abh. II. p. 640.

[2] See also Die Thatsachen in der Wahrnehmung, Zusatz II., Der Raum kann transcendental sein, ohne dass es die Axiome sind. Vorträge und Reden, Vol. II.

[3] See below, criticism of Erdmann, § 84.

may well be an *à priori* element in measurement, which is presupposed in its possibility. Such a criterion, therefore, must pronounce everything empirical, but must itself be pronounced worthless.

Another and a better criterion, it is true, is also to be found in Helmholtz, and has also been adopted by Erdmann. Whatever might, by a different experience, have been rendered different—so this criterion contends—must itself be dependent on experience, and so empirical. This criterion seems perfectly sound, but Helmholtz's use of it is usually vitiated by his neglecting to prove the possibility of the different experience in question. He says, for example, that if our experience showed us only bodies which changed their shapes in motion, we should not arrive at the axiom of Congruence, which he pronounces accordingly to be empirical. But I shall endeavour to prove, in Chapter III., that without the axiom of Congruence, experience of spatial magnitude would be impossible. If my proof be correct, it follows that no experience can ever reveal spatial magnitudes which contradict this axiom—a possibility which Helmholtz nowhere discusses, in setting up his hypothetical experience. Thus this second criterion, though perfectly sound, requires always an accompanying transcendental argument, as to the conditions of possible experience. But this accompaniment is seldom to be found in Helmholtz.

**68.** One of the few cases, in which Helmholtz has attempted such an accompaniment, occurs in connection with our second point, the imaginability of non-Euclidean spaces. The argument on this point was elicited by Helmholtz's Kantian opponents, who maintained that the merely logical possibility of these spaces was irrelevant, since the basis of Geometry was not logic, but intuition. The axioms, they said, are synthetic propositions, and their contraries are, therefore, not self-contradictory; they are nevertheless apodeictic propositions, since no other *intuition* than the Euclidean is possible to us[1]. I have already criticized this line of argument in the beginning of the present chapter. Helmholtz's criticism, however, was different: admitting the internal consistency of the argument, he denied one of its premisses. We *can* imagine non-Euclidean spaces,

[1] See Prof. Land, in Mind, Vol. II.

he said, though their unfamiliarity makes this difficult. From this view it followed, of course, that Kant's argument, even if it were formally valid, could not prove the apriority of Euclidean space in particular, but only of that general space which included Euclid and non-Euclid alike[1].

Although I agree with Helmholtz in thinking the distinction between Euclidean and non-Euclidean spaces empirical, I cannot think his argument on the "imaginability" of the latter a very happy one. The validity of any proof must turn, obviously, on the definition of imaginability. The definition which Helmholtz gives in his answer to Land is as follows: Imaginability requires "die vollständige Vorstellbarkeit derjenigen Sinneseindrücke, welche das betreffende Object in uns nach den bekannten Gesetzen unserer Sinnesorgane unter allen denkbaren Bedingungen der Beobachtung erregen, und wodurch es sich von anderen ähnlichen Objecten unterscheiden würde" (Wiss. Abh. II. p. 644). This definition is not very clear, owing to the ambiguity of the word "*Vorstellbarkeit*." The following definition seems less ambiguous: "Wenn die Reihe der Sinneseindrücke vollständig und eindeutig angegeben werden kann, muss man m. E. die Sache für *anschaulich vorstellbar* erklären" (Vorträge und Reden, II. p. 234). This makes clear, what also appears from his manner of proof, that he regards things as imaginable which can be *described* in conceptual terms. Such, as Land remarks (Mind, Vol. II. p. 45), "is not the sense required for argumentation in this case." That Land's criticism is just, is shown by Helmholtz's proof for non-Euclidean spaces, for it consists only in an analogy to the volume inside a sphere, which is mathematically obtained thus: We take the symbols representing magnitudes in "pseudo-spherical" (hyperbolic) space, and give them a new Euclidean meaning; thus all our symbolic propositions become capable of two interpretations, one for pseudo-spherical space, and one for the volume inside a sphere. It is, however, sufficiently obvious that this procedure, though it enables us to *describe* our new space, does not enable us to *imagine* it, in the sense of calling up images of the way things would look in it. We really derive, from this analogy, no more knowledge than a man born blind may derive, as to light, from

[1] See concluding paragraph of Helmholtz's article in Mind, Vol. III.

an analogy with heat. The dictum "Nihil est in intellectu quod non fuerit ante in sensu," would unquestionably be true, if for *intellect* we were to substitute *imagination*; it is vain, therefore, *if* our actual space be Euclidean, to hope for a power of *imagining* a non-Euclidean space. What Helmholtz might, I believe with perfect truth, have urged against Land, is that the image we actually have of space is not sufficiently accurate to exclude, in the actual space we know, all possibility of a slight departure from the Euclidean type. But in maintaining that we cannot imagine, though we can conceive and describe, a space different from that we actually have, Land is, in my opinion, unquestionably in the right. For a pure Kantian, who maintains, with Land, that none of the axioms can be proved, this question is of great importance. But if, as I have maintained, some of the axioms are susceptible of a transcendental proof, while the others can be verified empirically, the question is freed from psychological implications, and the imaginability or non-imaginability of metageometrical spaces becomes unimportant.

**69.** We come now to the third and most important question, the relation of Geometry to Mechanics. There are three senses in which Helmholtz's appeal to rigid bodies may be taken: the first, I think, is the sense in which he originally intended it; the second seems to be the sense which he adopted in his defence against Land; while the third is admitted by Land, and will be admitted in the following argument. These three senses are as follows:

(1) It may be asserted that the actual meaning of the axiom of Free Mobility lies in the assertion of empirical rigid bodies, and that the two propositions are equivalent to one another. This is certainly false.

(2) The axiom of Free Mobility, it may be said, is logically distinguishable from the assertion of rigid bodies, and may even be not empirical; but it is barren, even for pure Geometry, without the aid of measures, which must themselves be empirical rigid bodies. This sense is more plausible than the first, but I believe we can show that, in this sense also, the proposition is false.

(3) For pure Geometry and the abstract study of space,

it may be said, Free Mobility, as applied to an abstract geometrical matter, gives a sufficient possibility of quantitative comparison; but the moment we extend our results to mixed mathematics, and apply them to empirically given matter, we require also, as measures, empirically given rigid bodies, or bodies, at least, whose departures from rigidity are empirically known. In this sense, I admit, the proposition is correct[1].

In discussing these three meanings, I shall not confine myself strictly to the text of Helmholtz or Land: if I endeavoured to do so, I should be met by the difficulty that neither of them defines the *à priori*, and that each is too much inclined, in my opinion, to test it by psychological criteria. I shall, therefore, take the three meanings in turn, without laying stress on their historical adequacy to the views of Land or Helmholtz.

**70.** (1) Congruence may be taken to mean—as Helmholtz would certainly seem to desire—that we find actual bodies, in our mechanical experience, to preserve their shapes with approximate constancy, and that we infer, from this experience, the homogeneity of space. This view, in my opinion, radically misconceives the nature of measurement, and of the axioms involved in it. For what is meant by the non-rigidity of a body? We mean, simply, that it has changed its shape. But this involves the possibility of comparison with its former shape, in other words, of measurement. In order, therefore, that there may be any question of rigidity or non-rigidity, the measurement of spatial magnitudes must be already possible. It follows that measurement cannot, without a vicious circle, be itself derived from experience of rigid bodies. Geometrical measurement, in fact, is the comparison of spatial magnitudes, and such comparison involves, as will be proved at length in Chapter III., the homogeneity of space. This is, therefore, the logical prerequisite of all experience of rigid bodies, and cannot be the result of such experience. Without the homogeneity of space, the very notion of rigidity or non-rigidity could not exist, since these mean, respectively, the constancy or inconstancy of spatial magnitude in pieces of

[1] Cf. Veronese, Grundzüge der Geometrie (German translation), p. ix. Also pp. xxxiv, 304, and Note II. pp. 692–4.

matter, and both alike, therefore, presuppose the possibility of spatial measurement. From the homogeneity of space, we learn that a body, when it moves, will not change its shape without some physical cause; that it actually does not change its shape, is never asserted, and is indeed known to be false. As soon as measurement is possible, actual changes of shape can be estimated, and their empirical causes can be sought. But if space were not homogeneous, measurement would be impossible, constant shape would be a meaningless phrase, and rigidity could never be experienced. Congruence asserts, in short, that a body can, so far as mere space is concerned, move without change of shape; rigidity asserts that it actually does so move—a very different proposition, involving obviously, as its logical prius, the former geometrical proposition.

This argument may be summed up by the following disjunction: If bodies change their shapes in motion—and to some extent, since no body is perfectly rigid, they must all do so—then one of two cases must occur. *Either* the changes of shape, as bodies move from place to place, follow no geometrical law, are not, for instance, functions of the amount or direction of motion; in which case the law of causation requires that they should not be effects of the change of place, but of some simultaneous non-geometrical change, such as temperature. *Or* the changes are regular, and the shape $S$ becomes, in a new position $p$, $Sf(p)$. In this case, the law of concomitant variations leads us to attribute the change of shape to the mere motion, and shape thus becomes a function of absolute position. But this is absurd, for position *means* merely a relation or set of relations; it is impossible, therefore, that mere position should be able to effect changes in a body. Position is one term in a relation, not a thing *per se*; it cannot, therefore, act on a thing, nor exist by itself, apart from the other terms of the relation. Thus Helmholtz's view, that Congruence depends on the existence of rigid bodies, must, since it involves absolute position, be condemned as a logical fallacy. Congruence, in fact, as I shall prove more fully in Chapter III., is an *à priori* deduction from the relativity of position.

**71.** (2) The above argument seems to me to answer satisfactorily Helmholtz's contention in the precise form which he first gave it. The axiom of Congruence, we must agree, is logically distinguishable from the existence of rigid bodies. Nevertheless some reference to matter is logically involved in Geometry[1], but whether this reference makes Geometry empirical, or does not, rather, show an *à priori* element in dynamics, is a further question.

The reference to matter is necessitated by the homogeneity of empty space. For so long as we leave matter out of account, one position is perfectly indistinguishable from another, and a science of the relations of positions is impossible. Indeed, before spatial relations can arise at all, the homogeneity of empty space must be destroyed, and this destruction must be effected by matter. The blank page is useless to the geometer until he defaces its homogeneity by lines in ink or pencil. No spatial figures, in short, are conceivable, without a reference to a not purely spatial matter. Again, if Congruence is ever to be used, there must be motion: but a purely geometrical point, being defined solely by its spatial attributes, cannot be supposed to move without a contradiction in terms. What moves, therefore, must be matter. Hence, in order that motion may afford a test of equality, we must have some *matter* which is known to be unaffected throughout the motion, that is, we must have some rigid bodies. And the difficulty is, that these bodies must not only undergo no change due solely to the nature of space, but must, further, be unchanged by their changing relation to other bodies. And here we have a requisite which can no longer be fulfilled *à priori*: which, indeed, we know to be, in strictness, untrue. For the forces acting on a body depend upon its spatial relations to other bodies, and changing forces are liable to produce changing configuration. Hence, it would seem, actual measurement must be purely empirical, and must depend on the degree of rigidity to be obtained, during the process of measurement, in the bodies with which we are conversant.

This conclusion, I believe, is valid of all actual measurement. But the possibility of such empirical and approximate rigidity, I must insist, depends on the *à priori* law that *mere* motion, apart from the action of other matter, cannot effect a change

[1] See Chap. IV. § 197 ff.

of shape. For without this law, the effect of other matter would not be discoverable; the laws of motion would be absurd, and Physics would be impossible. Consider the second law, for example: How could we measure the change of motion, if motion itself produced a change in our measures? Or consider the law of gravitation: How could we establish the inverse square, unless we were able, independently of Dynamics, to measure distances? The whole science of Dynamics, in short, is fundamentally dependent on Geometry, and but for the independent possibility of measuring spatial magnitudes, none of the magnitudes of Dynamics could be measured. Time, force, and mass are alike measured by spatial correlates: these correlates are given, for time, by the first law, for force and mass, by the second and third. It is true, then, that an empirical element appears unavoidably in all actual measurement, inasmuch as we can only know empirically that a given piece of matter preserves its shape throughout the necessary change of dynamical relations to other matter involved in motion; but it is further true that, for Geometry—which regards matter simply as supplying the necessary breach in the homogeneity of space, and the necessary term for spatial relations, not as the bearer of forces which change the configuration of other material systems—for Geometry, which deals with this abstract and merely kinematical matter, rigidity is *à priori*, in so far as the only changes with which it is cognizant—changes of mere position, namely—are incapable of affecting the shapes of the imaginary and abstract bodies with which it deals. To use a scholastic distinction, we may say that matter is the *causa essendi* of space, but Geometry is the *causa cognoscendi* of Physics. Without a Geometry independent of Physics, Physics itself, which necessarily assumes the results of Geometry, could never arise; but when Geometry is used in Physics, it loses some of its *à priori* certainty, and acquires the empirical and approximate character which belongs to all accounts of actual phenomena.

**72.** (3) This argument leads us to Land's distinction of physical and geometrical rigidity. The distinction may be expressed—and I think it is better expressed—by distinguishing between the conceptions of matter proper to Dynamics and to Geometry respectively. In Dynamics, we are concerned with matter as subject to and as causing motion, as affected by and as exerting *force*. We are therefore concerned with the changes of spatial configuration to which material systems are liable: the description and explanation of these changes is the proper subject-matter of all Dynamics. But in order that such a science may exist, it is obviously necessary that spatial configuration should be already measurable. If this were not the case, motion, acceleration and force would remain perfectly indeterminate. Geometry, therefore, must already exist before Dynamics becomes possible: to make Geometry dependent for its possibility on the laws of motion or any of their consequences, is a gross ὕστερον πρότερον. Nevertheless, as we have seen, some sort of matter is essential to Geometry. But this geometrical matter is a more abstract and wholly different matter from that of Dynamics. In order to study space by itself, we reduce the properties of matter to a bare minimum: we avoid entirely the category of causation, so essential to Dynamics, and retain nothing, in our matter, but its spatial adjectives[1]. The kind of rigidity affirmed of this abstract matter—a kind which suffices for the theory of our science, though not for its application to the objects of daily life—is purely geometrical, and asserts no more than this: That since our matter is devoid, *ex hypothesi*, of causal properties, there remains nothing, in mere empty space, which is capable of changing the configuration of any geometrical system. A change of absolute position, it asserts, is nothing; therefore the only real change involved in motion is a change of relation to other matter; but such other matter, for the purposes of our science, is regarded as destitute of causal powers; hence no change can occur, in the configuration of our system, by the mere effect of motion through empty space. The necessity of such a principle may be shown by a simple *reductio ad absurdum*, as follows. A motion of translation of the universe as a whole, with constant direction and velocity, is dynamically negligeable; indeed it is, philosophically, no motion at all, for it involves no change in the condition or mutual relations of the things in the universe. But if our geometrical rigidity were denied, the change in the parameter of space might cause all bodies to

[1] Cf. the opinion of Bolyai, quoted by Erdmann, Axiome, p. 26; cf. also ib. p. 60.

change their shapes owing to the mere change of absolute position, which is obviously absurd.

To make quite plain the function of rigid bodies in Geometry, let us suppose a liquid geometer in a liquid world. We cannot suppose the liquid perfectly homogeneous and undifferentiated, in the first place because such a liquid would be indistinguishable from empty space, in the second place because our geometer's body—unless he be a disembodied spirit—will itself constitute a differentiation for him. We may therefore assume

"dim beams,
Which amid the streams
Weave a network of coloured light,"

and we may suppose this network to form the occasion for our geometer's reflections. Then he will be able to imagine a network in which the lines are straight, or circular, or parabolic, or any other shape, and he will be able to infer that such a network, if it can be woven in one part of the fluid, can be woven in another. This will form sufficient basis for his deductions. The superposition he is concerned with—since not actual equality, but only the formal conditions of equality, are the subject-matter of Geometry—is purely ideal, and is unaffected by the impossibility of congealing any actual network. But in order to apply his Geometry to the exigencies of life, he would need some standard of comparison between actual networks, and here, it is true, he would need either a rigid body, or a knowledge of the conditions under which similar networks arose. Moreover these conditions, being necessarily empirical, could hardly be known apart from previous measurement. Hence for applied, though not for pure Geometry, one rigid body at least seems essential.

**73.** The utility, for Dynamics, of our abstract geometrical matter, is sufficiently evident. For having, by its means, a power of determining the configurations of material systems in whatever part of space, and knowing that changes of configuration are not due to mere change of place, we are able to attribute these changes to the action of other matter, and thus to establish the notion of force, which would be impossible if change of shape might be due to empty space.

Thus, to conclude: Geometry requires, if it is to be *practically* possible, some body or bodies which are either rigid (in the dynamical sense), or known to undergo some definite changes of shape according to some definite law. (These changes, we may suppose, are known by the laws of Physics, which have been experimentally established, and which throughout assume the truth of Geometry.) One or more such bodies are necessary to applied Geometry—but only in the sense in which rulers and compasses are necessary. They are necessary as, in making the Ordnance Survey, an elaborate apparatus was necessary for measuring the base line on Salisbury Plain. But for the *theory* of Geometry, geometrical rigidity suffices, and geometrical rigidity means only that a shape, which is possible in one part of space, is possible in any other. The empirical element in practice, arising from the purely empirical nature of physical rigidity, is comparable to the empirical inaccuracies arising from the failure to find straight lines or circles in the world—which no one but Mill has regarded as rendering Geometry itself empirical or inaccurate. But to make Geometry await the perfection of Physics, is to make Physics, which depends throughout on Geometry, forever impossible. As well might we leave the formation of numbers until we had counted the houses in Piccadilly.

## Erdmann.

**74**. In connection with Riemann and Helmholtz, it is natural to consider Erdmann's philosophical work on their theories[1]. This is certainly the most important book on the subject which has appeared from the philosophical side, and in spite of the fact that, like the whole theory of Riemann and Helmholtz, it is inapplicable to projective Geometry, it still deserves a very full discussion.

Erdmann agrees throughout with the conclusions of Riemann and Helmholtz, except on a few points of minor importance; and his views, as this agreement would lead one to expect, are ultra-empirical. Indeed his logic seems—though I say this with

[1] Die Axiome der Geometrie: Eine philosophische Untersuchung der Riemann-Helmholtz'schen Raumtheorie, Leipzig, 1877.

hesitation—to be incompatible with any system but that of Mill: there is apparently no distinction, to him, between the general and the universal, and consequently no concept not embodied in a series of instances. Such a theory of logic, to my mind, vitiates most of his work, as it vitiated Riemann's philosophy[1]. This general criticism will find abundant illustration in the course of our account of Erdmann's views.

**75.** After a general introduction, and a short history of the development of Metageometry, Erdmann proceeds, in his second chapter, to discuss what are the axioms of Euclidean Geometry. The arithmetical axioms, as they are called, he leaves aside, as applying to magnitude in general; what we want here, he says, is a definition of space, for which the geometrical axioms are alone relevant. But a definition of space, he says—following Riemann—demands a genus of which space shall be a species, and this, since our space is psychologically unique, can only be furnished by analytical mathematics (p. 36). Now the space-forms dealt with by Geometry are magnitudes, and conceptions of magnitude are everywhere applied in Geometry. But before Riemann, only particular determinations of space could be exhibited as magnitudes, and thus the desired definition was impossible to obtain. Now, however, we can subsume space as a whole under a general conception of magnitude, and thus obtain, besides the space-intuition and the space-conception, a third form, namely, the conception of space as a magnitude (*Grössenbegriff vom Raum*, pp. 38–39). The definition of this will give us the complete, but not redundant, system of axioms, which could not be obtained by transforming the general intuition of space into the space-conception, for want of a plurality of instances (p. 40).

**76.** Before considering the subsequent method of definition, let us reflect on the theories involved in the above account of the conception of space as a magnitude. In the first place, it is assumed that conceptions cannot be formed unless we have a series of separate objects from which to abstract a common property—in other words, that the universal is always the general. In the second place, it is assumed that all

[1] On the influence of Mill, cf. Stallo, Concepts of Modern Physics, p. 216.

definition is classification under a genus. In the third place, the conception of magnitude, if I am not mistaken, is fundamentally misunderstood when it is supposed applicable to space as a whole. But in the fourth place, even if such a conception existed, it could give none of the essential properties of space. Let us consider these four points successively.

**77.** As regards the first point, it is to be observed that people certainly had some conception of space before Riemann invented the notion of a manifold, and that this conception was certainly something other than the common qualities of all the points, lines or figures in space. In the second place, Erdmann's view would make it impossible to conceive God, unless one were a polytheist, or the universe—unless, like Leibnitz, one imagined a series of possible worlds, set over against God, and none of them, therefore, a true Universe—or, to take an instance more likely to appeal to an empiricist, the necessarily unique centre of mass of the material universe. Any universal, in short, which is a bond or unity between things, and not merely a common property among independent objects, becomes impossible on Erdmann's view. We cannot, therefore, unless we adopt Mill's philosophy intact, regard the conception of space as demanding a series of instances from which to abstract. But even if we did so regard it, Riemann's manifolds would leave us without resources. For Euclidean space still appears as unique, at the end of his series of determinations. We have instances of manifolds, but not instances of Euclidean space. Thus if Erdmann's theory of conceptions were correct, he would still be left searching in vain for the conception of Euclidean space.

**78.** The second point, the view that all definition is classification, is closely allied to the first, and the two together plunge us into the depths of scholastic formal logic. The same instances of things which could not, on Erdmann's view, be conceived, may now be adduced as things which cannot be defined. Whatever was said above applies here also, and the point need not, therefore, be further discussed[1].

[1] This view seems to be derived, through Riemann, from Herbart. See Psych. als Wiss. ed. Hart. Vol. v. p. 262.

**79.** As regards the third point, the impossibility of applying conceptions of magnitude to space as a whole, a longer argument will be necessary, for we are concerned, here, with the whole question of the logical nature of judgments of magnitude. As we had before too much comparison for our needs, so we have now too little. I will endeavour to explain this point, which is of great importance, and underlies, I think, most of the philosophical fallacies of Riemann's school.

A judgment of magnitude is always a judgment of comparison, and what is more, the comparison is never concerned with quality, but only with quantity. Quality, in the judgment of magnitude, is supposed identical, in the object whose magnitude is stated, and in the unit with which it is compared. But quality, except in pure number, and in pure quantity as dealt with by the Calculus, is always present, and is partly absorbed into quantity, partly untouched by the judgment of magnitude. As Bosanquet says (Logic, Vol. I. p. 124); "Quantitative comparison is not *prima facie* coordinate with qualitative, but rather stands in its place as the *effect of comparison on quality*, which so far as comparable *becomes quantity*, and so far as incomparable furnishes the distinction of parts essential to the quantitative whole" (italics in the original). Thus, if we are to regard space as a magnitude, we must be able to adduce all those series of instances of which Erdmann speaks, and which, for the conception of space, seemed irrelevant. But it remains to be proved that the comparison, which we *can* institute between various spaces, is capable of expression in a quantitative form. Rather it would seem that the difference of quality is such as to preclude quantitative comparison between different spaces, and therefore also to preclude all judgments of magnitude about space as a whole. Here an exception might seem to be demanded by non-Euclidean spaces, whose space-constants give a definite magnitude, inherent in space as a whole, and therefore, one might think, characterizing space as a magnitude. But this is a mistake. For the space-constant, in such spaces, is the ultimate unit, the fixed term in all quantitative comparison; it is itself, therefore, destitute of quantity, since there is no independently given magnitude with which to compare it. A non-Euclidean world, in which the space-constant and all lines and figures were suddenly multiplied in a constant ratio, would be wholly unchanged; the lines, as measured against the space-constant, would have the same magnitude as before, and the space-constant itself, having no outside standard of comparison, would be destitute of quantity, and therefore not subject to change of quantity. Such an enlargement of a non-Euclidean world, in other words, is unmeaning; and this proves how inapplicable is the notion of quantity to space as a whole.

It might be objected that this only proves the absence of quantitative difference between different spaces of positive space-constant, or between those of negative space-constant: the quantitative difference persists, it might be said, between those of positive curvature in general and those of negative curvature in general, or between both together and Euclidean space. This I entirely deny. There is no qualitatively similar unit, in the three kinds of space, by which quantitative comparison could be effected. The straight lines of one space cannot be put into the other: the two straight lines, in one space, whose product is the reciprocal of the measure of curvature, have no corresponding curves in the other space, and the measures of curvature cannot, therefore, be quantitatively compared with each other. That the one may be regarded as positive, the other negative, I admit, but their values are indeterminate, and the units in the two cases are qualitatively different. A debt of £300 may be represented as the asset of – £300, and the height of the Eiffel Tower is + 300 metres; but it does not follow that the two are quantitatively comparable. So with space-constants: the space-constant is itself the unit for magnitudes in its own space, and differs qualitatively from the space-constant of another kind of space.

Again, to proceed to a more philosophical argument, two different spaces cannot co-exist in the same world: we may be unable to decide between the alternatives of the disjunction, but they remain, none the less, absolutely incompatible alternatives. Hence we cannot get that coexistence of two spaces which is essential to comparison. The fact seems to be that Erdmann, in his admiration for Riemann and Helmholtz, has fallen in with their mathematical bias, and assumed, as mathematicians naturally tend to assume, that quantity is everywhere and always applicable and adequate, and can deal with more than the mere comparison of things whose qualities are already known as similar[1].

**80.** This suggests the fourth and last of the above points, that the *qualities* of space, even if space could be successfully regarded as a magnitude, would have to be entirely omitted in such a manner of regarding it, and that, therefore, none of its important or essential properties would emerge from such treatment. For to regard space as a magnitude involves, as we saw, a comparison with something qualitatively similar, and an abstraction from the similar qualities. To some extent and by the help of certain doubtful arguments, such a comparison is instituted by Riemann and Erdmann; but when they have instituted it, they forget all about the common qualities on which its possibility depends. But these are precisely the fundamental properties of space, and those from which, as I shall endeavour to prove in Chapter III., the axioms common to Euclid and Metageometry follow *à priori*. Such are the dangers of the quantitative bias.

**81.** After this protest against the initial assumptions in Erdmann's deduction of space, let us return to consider the manner in which this deduction is carried out. Here there will be less ground for criticism, as the deduction, given its presuppositions, is, I think, as good as such a deduction can be. To define space as a magnitude, he says, let us start with two of its most obvious properties, continuity and the three dimensions. Tones and colours afford other instances of a manifold with these two properties, but differ from space in that their dimensions are not homogeneous and interchangeable. To designate this difference, Erdmann introduces a useful pair of terms: in the general case, he calls a manifold $n$-determined (n-*bestimmt*); in the case where, as in space, the dimensions are homogeneous, he calls the manifold $n$-extended (n-*ausgedehnt*). Manifolds of the latter sort he calls extents (*Ausgedehntheiten*).

[1] The same irreducibility of space to mere magnitude is proved by Kant's hands and spherical triangles, in which a difference persists in spite of complete quantitative equality.

That the difference between the two kinds is one of quality, not of quantity, he seems not to perceive; he also overlooks the fact that, in the second kind, from its very definition, the axiom of Congruence must hold, on account of the qualitative similarity of different parts. In spite of this fact, he defines space as an extent, and then regards Congruence as empirical, and as possibly false in the infinitesimal. This is the more strange, as he actually proves (p. 50) that measurement is impossible, in an extent, unless the parts are independent of their place, and can be carried about unaltered as measures. In spite of this, he proceeds immediately to discuss whether the measure of curvature is constant or variable, without investigating how, in the latter case, Geometry could exist. We cannot know, he says, from geometrical superposition, that geometrical bodies are independent of place, for if their dimensions altered in motion according to any fixed law, two bodies which could be superposed in one place could be superposed in any other. That such a hypothesis involves absolute position, and denies the qualitative similarity of the parts of space, which he declares (p. 171) to be the principle of his theory of Geometry, is nowhere perceived. But what is more, his notion that magnitude is something absolute, independent of comparison, has prevented him from seeing that such a hypothesis is unmeaning. He says himself that, even on this hypothesis, a geometrical body can be defined as one whose points retain constant distances from each other, for, since we have no absolute measure, measurement could not reveal to us the change of absolute magnitude (p. 60). But is not this a *reductio ad absurdum?* For magnitude is nothing apart from comparison, and the comparison here can only be effected by superposition; if, then, as on the above hypothesis, superposition always gives the same result, by whatever motion it is effected, there is no sense in speaking of magnitudes as no longer equal when separated: absolute magnitude is an absurdity, and the magnitude resulting from comparison does not differ from that which would result if the dimensions of bodies were unchanged in motion. Therefore, since magnitude is only intelligible as the result of comparison, the dimensions of bodies *are* unchanged in motion, and the suggested hypothesis is unmeaning. On this subject I shall have more to say in Chapter III.[1]

**82.** This hypothesis, however, is not introduced for its own sake, but only to usher in the Helmholtzian *deus ex machina*, Mechanics. For Mechanics proves—so Erdmannn confidently continues—that rigidity must hold, not merely as to ratios, in the above restricted geometrical sense, but as to absolute magnitudes (p. 62). Hence we get at last true Congruence, empirical as Mechanics is empirical, and impossible to prove apart from Mechanics. I have already criticized Helmholtz's view of the dependence of Geometry on Mechanics, and need not here speak of it at length. It is a pity that Erdmann has in no way specified the procedure by which Mechanics decides the geometrical alternatives—indeed he seems to rely on the *ipse dixit* of Helmholtz. How, if Geometry would be totally unable to discover a change in dimensions of the kind suggested, the Laws of Motion, which throughout depend on Geometry, should be able to discover it if it existed, I am wholly at a loss to understand. Uniform motion in a straight line, for example, presupposes geometrical measurement; if this measurement is mistaken, what Mechanics imagines to be uniform motion is not really such, but Mechanics can never discover the discrepancy. If the Laws of Motion had been regarded as *à priori*, Geometry might possibly have been reinforced by them; but so long as they are empirical, they presuppose geometrical measurement, and cannot therefore condition or affect it.

Erdmann's conclusion, in the second chapter, is that Congruence is probable, but cannot be verified in the infinitesimal; that its truth involves the actual existence of rigid bodies (though, by the way, we know these to be, strictly speaking, non-existent), that rigid bodies are freely moveable, and do not alter their size in rotation (Helmholtz's Monodromy); that the axiom of three dimensions is certain, since small errors are impossible; and that the remaining axioms of Euclid—those of the straight line and of parallels—are approximately, if not accurately, true of our actual space (pp. 78, 83). He does not

[1] See §§ 146-7.

discuss how Congruence, on the above view, is compatible with the atomic theory, or even with the observed deformations of approximately rigid bodies; nor how, if space, as he assumes, is homogeneous, rigid bodies can fail to be freely moveable through space. The axioms are all lumped together as empirical, and it appears, in the following chapters, that Erdmann regards their empirical nature as sufficiently proved by their applicability to empirical material (cf. pp. 159, 165)—a strange criterion, which would prove the same conclusion, with equal facility, of Arithmetic and of the laws of thought.

**83.** The third chapter, on the philosophical consequences of Metageometry, need not be discussed at length, since it deals rather with space than with Geometry. At the same time, it will be worth while to treat briefly of Erdmann's criterion of apriority. On this subject it is very difficult to discover his meaning, since it seems to vary with the topic he is discussing. Thus at one time (p. 147) he rejects most emphatically the Kantian connection of the *à priori* and the subjective[1], and yet at another time (p. 96) he regards every presentation of external things as partly *à priori*, partly empirical, merely because such a presentation is due to an interaction between ourselves and things, and is therefore partly due to subjective activity, partly due to outside objects. Hence, he says, the distinction is not between different presentations, but between different aspects of one and the same presentation. This seems to return wholly to the Kantian psychological criterion of subjectivity, with the added disadvantage that it makes the distinction, like that of analytic and synthetic, epistemologically worthless. And yet he never hesitates to pronounce every piece of knowledge in turn empirical. The fact seems to be, that where he wants a more logical criterion, he adopts a modification of Helmholtz's criterion for sensations. If space be an *à priori* form, he says, no experience could possibly change it (p. 108); but this Metageometry has proved not to be the case, since we can intuit the perceptions which non-Euclidean space would give us (p. 115).

[1] "Jeder Versuch, Kant's Lehre von der Apriorität als des subjectiven, von aller Erfahrung absolut unabhängigen Erkenntnissfactors, trotzdem zu halten, ist deshalb von vornherein aussichtslos."

I have criticised this argument in discussing Helmholtz; at present we are concerned with Erdmann's criterion of apriority. The subjectivity-criterion—though he certainly uses it in discussing the apriority of space, and solemnly decides, by its means, that space is both *à priori* and empirical, since a change either in us or in the outer world could change it (p. 97)—would seem, like several of his other tests, to be a lapse on his part: the criterion which he means to use is Helmholtz's. This criterion, I think, with a slight change of wording, might be accepted; it seems to me a necessary, but not a sufficient condition. The *à priori*, we may say, is not only that which no experience can change, but that without which experience would become impossible. It is the omission to discuss the conditions which render geometrical (and mechanical) experience possible, to my mind, which vitiates the empirical conclusions of Helmholtz and Erdmann. Why certain conditions should be necessary for experience—whether on account of the constitution of the mind, or for some other reason—is a further question, which introduces the relation of the *à priori* to the subjective. But in discussing the question as to what knowledge is *à priori*, as opposed to the question concerning the further consequences of apriority, it is well to keep to the purely logical criterion, and so preserve our independence of psychological controversies. The fact, if it be a fact, that the world might be such as to defy our attempts to know it, will not, with the above criterion, invalidate the conclusion that certain elements in knowledge are *à priori*; for whether fulfilled or not, they remain necessary conditions for the existence of any knowledge at all.

**84**. With this caution as to the meaning of apriority, we shall find, I think, that the conclusions of Erdmann's final chapter, on the principles of a theory of Geometry, are largely invalidated by the diversity and inadequacy of his tests of the *à priori*. He begins by asserting, in conformity with the quantitative bias noticed above, that the question as to the nature of geometrical axioms is completely analogous to the corresponding question of the foundations of pure mathematics (p. 138). This is, I think, a radical error: for the function of the axioms seems to be, to establish that qualitative basis on which, as we saw, all qualitative comparison must rest. But in pure mathematics, this qualitative basis is irrelevant, for we deal there with pure quantity, *i.e.* with the merely quantitative result of quantitative comparison, wherever it is possible, independently of the qualities underlying the comparison. Geometry, as Grassmann insists[1], ought not to be classed with pure mathematics, for it deals with a matter which is given to the intellect, not created by it. The axioms give the means by which this matter is made amenable to quantity, and cannot, therefore, be themselves deduced from purely quantitative considerations.

Leaving this point aside, however, let us return to Erdmann. He distinguishes, within space, a form and a matter: the form is to contain the properties common to all extents, the matter the properties which distinguish space from other extents. This distinction, he says, is purely logical, and does not correspond with Kant's: matter and form, for Erdmann, are alike empirical. The axioms and definitions of Geometry, he says, deal exclusively with the matter of space. It seems a pity, having made this distinction, to put it to so little use: after a few pages, it is dropped, and no epistemological consequences are drawn from it. The reason is, I think, that Erdmann has not perceived how much can be deduced from his definition of an extent, as a manifold in which the dimensions are homogeneous and interchangeable. For this property suffices to prove the complete homogeneity of an extent, and hence—from the absence of qualitative differences among elements—the relativity of position and the axiom of Congruence. This deduction will be made at length in the sequel[2]; at present, I have only to observe that every extent, on this view, possesses all the properties (except the three dimensions) common to Euclidean and non-Euclidean spaces. The axioms which express these properties, therefore, apply to the form of space, and follow from homogeneity alone, which Erdmann allows (p. 171) as the principle of any theory of space. The above distinction of form and matter, therefore, corresponds, when its full consequences are deduced, to the distinction between the axioms which follow from the

[1] Ausdehnungslehre von 1844, 2nd edition, pp. xxii. xxiii.

[2] See § 129 ff.

homogeneity of space and those which do not. Since, then, homogeneity is equivalent to the relativity of position, and the relativity of position is of the very essence of a form of externality, it would seem that his distinction of form and matter can also be made coextensive with the distinction of the *à priori* and empirical in Geometry. On this subject, I shall have more to say in Chapter III.

In the remainder of the chapter, Erdmann insists that the straight line, etc., though not abstracted from experience, which nowhere presents straight lines, must yet, as applicable to admittedly empirical sciences, be empirical (p. 159)—a criterion which he appears to employ only when all other grounds for an empirical opinion fail, and one which, obviously, can never refuse to do its work, since all elements of knowledge are susceptible of employment on some empirical material. He also defines the straight line (p. 155) as a line of constant curvature zero, as though curvature could be measured independently of the straight line. Even the arithmetical axioms are declared empirical (p. 165), since in a world where things were all hopelessly different from one another, these axioms could not be applied. After this reminder of Mill, we are not surprised, a few pages later (p. 172), at a vague appeal to "English logicians" as having proved Geometry to be an inductive science. Nevertheless, Erdmann declares, almost on the last page of his book (p. 173), that Geometry is distinguished from all other sciences by the homogeneity of its material: a principle of which no single application occurs throughout his book, and which, as we shall see in Chapter III., flatly contradicts the philosophical theories advocated throughout his preceding pages.

On the whole, then, it cannot be said that Erdmann has done much to strengthen the philosophical position of Riemann and Helmholtz. I have criticized him at length, because his book has the appearance of great thoroughness, and because it is undoubtedly the best defence extant of the position which it takes up. We shall now have the opposite task to perform, in defending Metageometry, on its mathematical side, from the attacks of Lotze and others, and in vindicating for it that measure of philosophical importance—far inferior, indeed, to the hopes of Erdmann—which it seems really to possess.

## Lotze.

**85.** Lotze's argument as regards Geometry[1]—which follows a metaphysical argument as to the ontological nature of space, and assumes the results of this argument—consists of two parts: the first discusses the various meanings logically assignable (pp. 233–247) to the proposition that other spaces than Euclid's are possible, and the second criticizes, in detail, the procedure of Metageometry. The first of these questions is very important, and demands considerable care as to the logical import of a judgment of possibility. Although Lotze's discussion is excellent in many respects, I cannot persuade myself that he has hit on the only true sense in which non-Euclidean spaces are possible. I shall endeavour to make good this statement in the following pages.

**86.** Lotze opens with a somewhat startling statement, which, though philosophically worthy to be true, does not appear to be historically borne out. Euclidean Geometry has been chiefly shaken, he says, by the Kantian notion of the exclusive subjectivity of space—if space is only our private form of intuition, to which there exists no analogue in the objective world, then other beings may have other spaces, without supposing any difference in the world which they arrange in these spaces (p. 233). This certainly seems a legitimate deduction from the subjectivity of space, which, so far from establishing the universal validity of Euclid, establishes his validity only after an empirical investigation of the nature of space as intuited by Tom, Dick or Harry. But as a matter of fact, those who have done most to further non-Euclidean Geometry—with the exception of Riemann, who was a disciple of Herbart—have usually inherited from Newton a naïve realism as regards absolute space. I might instance the passage quoted from Bolyai in Chapter I., or Clifford, who seems to have thought that we actually see the images of things on the retina[2], or again Helmholtz's belief in the dependence of Geometry on the behaviour of rigid bodies. This belief led to the view that

[1] Metaphysik, Book II. Chap. II. My references are to the original.

[2] See Lectures and Essays, Vol. I. p. 261.

Geometry, like Physics, is an experimental science, in which objective truth can be attained, it is true, but only by empirical methods. However, Lotze's ground for uncertainty about Euclid is a philosophically tenable ground, and it will be instructive to observe the various possibilities which arise from it.

If space is only a subjective form—so Lotze opens his argument—other beings may have a different form. If this corresponds to a different world, the difference, he says, is uninteresting: for our world alone is relevant to any metaphysical discussion. But if this different space corresponds to the same world which we know under the Euclidean form, then, in his opinion, we get a question of genuine philosophic interest. And here he distinguishes two cases: *either* the relations between things, which are presented to these hypothetical beings under the form of some different space, are relations which do not appear to us, or at any rate do not appear spatial; *or* they are the same relations which appear to us as figures in Euclidean space (p. 235). The first possibility would be illustrated, he says, by beings to whom the tone or colour-manifolds appeared extended; but we cannot, in his opinion, imagine a manifold, such as is required for this case, to have its dimensions homogeneous and comparable *inter se*, and therefore the contents of the various presentations constituting such a manifold could not be combined into a single content containing them all. But the possibility of such a combination is of the essence of anything worth calling a space: therefore the first of the above possibilities is unmotived and uninteresting. Lotze's conclusion on this point, I think, is undeniable, but I doubt whether his argument is very cogent. However, as this possibility has no connection with that contemplated by non-Euclideans, it is not worth while to discuss it further.

The second possibility also, Lotze thinks, is not that of Metageometry, but in truth it comes nearer to it than any of the other possibilities discussed. If a non-Euclidean were at the same time a believer in the subjectivity of space, he would have to be an adherent of this view. Let us see more precisely what the view is. In Book II., Chapter I., Lotze has accepted the argument of the Transcendental Aesthetic, but rejected that of the mathematical antinomies: he has decided that space is, as Kant believed, subjective, but possesses nevertheless, what Kant denied it, an objective counterpart. The relation of presented space to its objective counterpart, as conceived by Lotze, is rather hard to understand. It seems scarcely to resemble the relation of sensation to its object—*e.g.* of light to ether-vibrations—for if it did, space would not be in any peculiar sense subjective. It seems rather to resemble the relation of a perceived bodily motion to the state of mind of the person willing the motion. However this may be, the objective counterpart of space is supposed to consist of certain immediate interactions of monads, who experience the interactions as modifications of their internal states. Such interactions, it is plain, do not form the subject-matter of Geometry, which deals only with our resulting perceptions of spatial figures. Now if Lotze's construction of space be correct, there seems certainly no reason why these resulting perceptions should not, for one and the same interaction between monads, be very different in beings differently constituted from ourselves. But if they were different, says Lotze, they would have to be utterly different—as different, for example, as the interval between two notes is from a straight line. The possibility is, therefore, in his opinion, one about which we can know nothing, and one which must remain always a mere empty idea. This seems to me to go too far: for whatever the objective counterpart may be, any argument which gives us information about it must, when reversed, give us information about any possible form of intuition in which this counterpart is presented. The argument which Lotze has used in his former chapter, for example, deducing, from the relativity of position, the merely relational nature of the objective counterpart, allows us, conversely, to infer, from this relational nature, the complete relativity of position in any possible space-intuition—unless, indeed, it bore a wholly deceitful relation to those interactions of monads which form its objective counterpart. But the complete relativity of position, as I shall endeavour to establish in Chapter III., suffices to prove that our Geometry must be Euclidean, elliptic, spherical or pseudo-spherical. We have, therefore, it would seem, very considerable knowledge, on Lotze's theory of space, of the manner in which what appears to us as space *must* appear to any beings with our laws of thought. We cannot know, it is true, what *psychological* theory of space-perception would apply to such beings: they might have a sense different from any of ours, and they might have no sense in any way resembling ours, but yet their Geometry would have points of resemblance to ours, as that of the blind coincides with that of the seeing. If space has any objective counterpart whatever, in short, and if any inference is possible, as Lotze holds it to be, from space to its counterpart, then a converse argument is also possible, though it may give some only of the qualities of Euclidean space, since some only of these qualities may be found to have a necessary analogue in the counterpart.

**87.** Admitting, then, in Lotze's sense, the subjectivity of space, the above possibility does not seem so empty as he imagines. He discusses it briefly, however, in order to pass on to what he regards as the real meaning of Metageometry. In this he is guilty of a mathematical mistake, which causes much irrelevant reasoning. For he believes that Metageometry constructs its spaces out of straight lines and angles in all respects similar to Euclid's, whence he derives an easy victory in proving that these elements can lead only to the one space. In this he has been misled by the phraseology of non-Euclideans, as well as by Euclid's separation of definitions and axioms. For the fact is, of course, that straight lines are only fully defined when we add to the formal definition the axioms of the straight line and of parallels. Within Euclidean space, Euclid's definition suffices to distinguish the straight line from all other curves; the two axioms referred to are then absorbed into the definition of space. But apart from the restriction to Euclidean space, the definition has to be supplemented by the two axioms, in order to define completely the Euclidean straight line. Thus Lotze has misconceived the bearing of non-Euclidean constructions, and has simply missed the point in arguing as he does. The possibility contemplated by a non-Euclidean, if it fell under any of Lotze's cases, would fall under the second case discussed above.

**88.** But the bearing of Metageometry is really, I think, different from anything imagined by Lotze; and as few writers seem clear on this point, I will enter somewhat fully into what I conceive to be its purpose.

In the first place, there are some writers—notably Clifford—who, being naïve realists as regards space, hold that our evidence is wholly insufficient, as yet, to decide as to its nature in the infinite or in the infinitesimal (cf. Essays, Vol. I. p. 320): these writers are not concerned with any possibility of beings different from ourselves, but simply with the everyday space we know, which they investigate in the spirit of a chemist discussing whether hydrogen is a metal, or an astronomer discussing the nebular hypothesis.

But these are a minority: most, more cautious, admit that our space, so far as observation extends, is Euclidean, and if not accurately Euclidean, must be only slightly spherical or pseudo-spherical. Here again, it is the space of daily life which is under discussion, and here further the discussion is, I think, independent of any philosophical assumption as to the nature of our space-intuition. For even if this be purely subjective, the translation of an intuition into a conception can only be accomplished approximately, within the errors of observation incident to self-analysis; and until the intuition of space has become a conception, we get no scientific Geometry. The apodeictic certainty of the axiom of parallels shrinks to an unmotived subjective conviction, and vanishes altogether in those who entertain non-Euclidean doubts. To reinforce the Euclidean faith, reason must now be brought to the aid of intuition; but reason, unfortunately, abandons us, and we are left to the mercy of approximate observations of stellar triangles —a meagre support, indeed, for the cherished religion of our childhood.

**89**. But the possibility of an inaccuracy so slight, that our finest instruments and our most distant parallaxes show no trace of it, would trouble men's minds no more than the analogous chance of inaccuracy in the law of gravitation, were it not for the philosophical import of even the slenderest possibility in this sphere. And it is the philosophical bearing of Metageometry alone, I think, which constitutes its real importance. Even if, as we will suppose for the moment, observation had established, beyond the possibility of doubt, that our space might be safely regarded as Euclidean, still Metageometry would have shown a philosophical possibility, and on this ground alone it could claim, I think, very nearly all the attention which it at present deserves.

But what is this possibility? A thing is possible, according to Bradley (Logic, p. 187), when it would follow from a certain number of conditions, some of which are known to be realized. Now the conditions to which a form of externality must conform, in order to be affirmed, are: first, of course, that it should be experienced, or legitimately inferred from something experienced; but secondly, that it should conform to certain logical conditions, detailed in Chapter III., which may be summed up in the relativity of position. Now what Metageometry has done, in any case, is to suggest the proof that the second of these conditions is fulfilled by non-Euclidean spaces. Euclid is affirmed, therefore, on the ground of immediate experience alone, and his truth, as unmediated by logical necessity, is merely assertorical, or, if we prefer it, empirical. This is the most important sense, it seems to me, in which non-Euclidean spaces are possible. They are, in short, a step in a philosophical argument, rather than in the investigation of fact: they throw light on the nature of the grounds for Euclid, rather than on the actual conformation of space[1]. This import of Metageometry is denied by Lotze, on the ground that non-Euclidean logic is faulty, a ground which he endeavours, by much detail and through many pages, to make good—with what success, we will now proceed to examine.

**90.** Lotze's attack on Metageometry—although it remains, so far as I know, the best hostile criticism extant, and although its arguments have become part of the regular stock-in-trade of Euclidean philosophers—contains, if I am not mistaken, several misunderstandings due to insufficient mathematical knowledge of the subject. As these misunderstandings have been widely spread among philosophers, and cannot be easily removed except by a critic who has gone into non-Euclidean Geometry with some care, it seems desirable to discuss Lotze's strictures point by point.

[1] On the meaning of geometrical possibility, cf. Veronese, Grundzüge der Geometrie (German translation), pp. xi.–xiii.

**91.** The mathematical criticism begins (§ 131) with a somewhat question-begging definition of parallel straight lines. Two straight lines $a\alpha$, $b\beta$, according to this definition, are

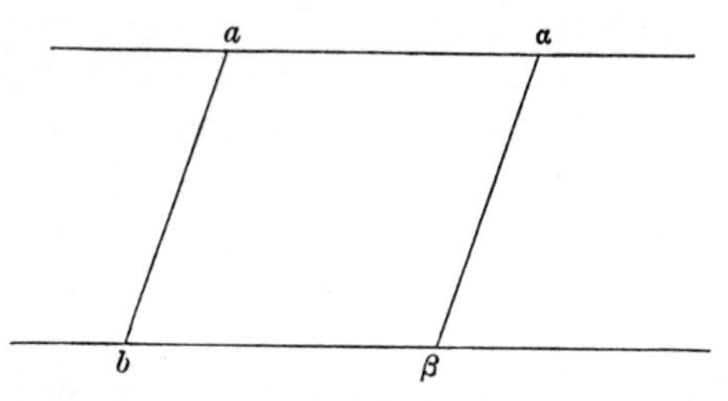


parallel when—$a$ and $b$ being arbitrary points on the two lines—if $a\alpha = b\beta$, then $ab = \alpha\beta$, where $\alpha$, $\beta$ are two other points on the two straight lines respectively. This definition—which contains Euclid's axiom and definition combined in a very convenient and enticing form—is of course thoroughly suitable to Euclidean Geometry, and leads immediately to all the Euclidean propositions about parallels. But it is perhaps more honest to follow Euclid's course; when an axiom is thus buried in a definition, it is apt to seem, since definitions are supposed to be arbitrary, as though the difficulty had been overcome, while in reality, the possibility of parallels, as above defined, involves the very point in question, namely, the disputed axiom of parallels. For what this axiom asserts is simply the existence of lines conforming to Lotze's definition. The deduction of the principal propositions on parallels, with which Lotze follows up his definition, is of course a very simple proceeding—a proceeding, however, in which the first step begs the question.

**92.** The next argument for the apriority of Euclidean Geometry has, oddly enough, an exactly opposite bearing, although it is a great favourite with opponents of Metageometry. Measurements of stellar triangles, and all similar attempts at an empirical determination of the space-constant are, according to Lotze, beside the mark; for any observed departure from two right angles, or any finite annual parallax for distant stars, would be attributed to some new kind of refraction, or, as in the case of aberration, to some other physical cause, and never to the geometrical nature of space. This is a strong argument for the empirical validity of Euclid, but as an argument for the apodeictic certainty of the orthodox system, it has an opposite tendency. For observations of the kind contemplated would have to be due to departures from Euclidean straightness, hitherto unknown, on the part of stellar light-rays. Such departure could, in certain cases, be accounted for by a finite space-constant, but it could also, probably, be accounted for by a change in Optics, for example, by attributing refractive properties to the ether. Such properties could only exist if ether were of varying density, if (say) it were denser in the neighbourhood of any of the heavenly bodies. But such an assumption would, I believe, destroy the utility of ether for Physics; a slight alteration in our Geometry, so slight as not appreciably to affect distances within the Solar System, would probably be in the end, therefore, should such errors ever be discovered, a simpler explanation than any that Physics could offer. But this is not the point of my contention. The point is that, if the physical explanation, as Lotze holds, be possible in the above case, the converse must also hold: it must be possible to explain the present phenomena by supposing ether refractive and space non-Euclidean. From this conclusion there is no escape. If every conceivable behaviour of light-rays can be explained, within Euclid, by physical causes, it must also be possible, by a suitable choice of hypothetical physical causes, to explain the actual phenomena as belonging to a non-Euclidean space. Such a hypothesis would be rightly rejected by Science, for the present, on account of its unnecessary complexity. Nevertheless it would remain, for philosophy, a possibility to be reckoned with, and the choice could only be decided upon empirical grounds of simplicity. It may well be doubted whether, in the world we know, the phenomena could be attributed to a distinctly non-Euclidean space, but this conclusion follows inevitably from the contention that no phenomena could force us to assume such a space. Lotze's argument, therefore, if pushed home, disproves his own view, and puts Euclidean space, as an empirical explanation of phenomena, on a level with luminiferous ether[1].

[1] Compare Calinon, "Sur l'Indétermination géométrique de l'Univers," Revue Philosophique, 1893, Vol. xxxvi. pp. 595–607.

**93.** Lotze now proceeds (§ 132) to a detailed criticism of Helmholtz, whom he regards as a typical exponent of Metageometry. It is possible that, at the time when he wrote, Helmholtz really did occupy this position; but it is unfortunate that, in the minds of philosophers, he should still continue to do so, after the very material advances brought about by the projective treatment of the subject. It is also unfortunate that his somewhat careless attempts to popularise mathematical results have so often been disposed of, without due attention to his more technical and solid contributions. Thus his romances about Flatland and Sphereland—at best only fairy-tale analogies of doubtful value—have been attacked as if they formed an essential feature of Metageometry.

But to proceed to particulars: Lotze readily allows that the Flatlanders would set up Plane Geometry, as we know it, but refuses to admit that the Spherelanders could, without inferring the third dimension, set up a two-dimensional spherical Geometry which should be free from contradictions. I will endeavour to give a free rendering of Lotze's argument on this point.

Suppose, he says, a north and south pole, $N$ and $S$, arbitrarily fixed, and an equator $EW$. Suppose a being, $B$, capable of impressions only from things on the surface of the sphere, to move in a meridian $NBS$. Let $B$ start from some point $a$, and finally, after describing a great circle, return to the same point $a$. If $a$ is known only by the quality of the impression it makes on $B$, $B$ may imagine he has not reached the same point $a$, but another similar point $a'$, bearing a relation to $a$ similar to that of the octave in singing: he might even not arrange his impressions spatially at all. In order that this may occur, we require the further assumption, that every difference in the above-mentioned feelings (as he describes the meridian) may be presented as a spatial distance between two places. Even now, $B$ may think he is describing a Euclidean straight line, containing similar points at certain intervals. Allowing, however, that he realizes the identity of $a$ with his initial position,

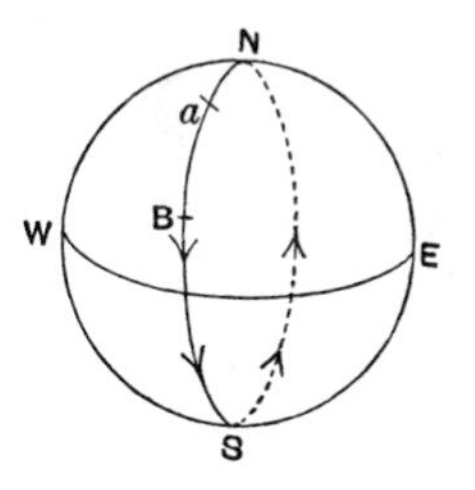

he will now seem, by motion in a straight line, to have returned to the point from which he started, for his motion cannot, without the third dimension, seem to him other than rectilinear.

Up to this point, there seems little ground for objection, except, perhaps, to the idea of a straight line with periodical similar points—if *B* were as philosophical as, in these discussions, we usually suppose him to be, he would probably object to this interpretation of his experiences, on the ground that it regards empty space as something independent of the objects in it. It is worth pointing out, also, that *B* would not need to describe the whole circle, in order suddenly to find himself home again with his old friends. Accurate measurements of small triangles would suffice to determine his space-constant, and show him the length of a great circle (or straight line, as he would call it). We must admit, also, that so hypothetical a being as *B* might form no space-intuition at all, but as he is introduced solely for the purposes of the analogy, it is convenient to allow him all possible qualifications for his post. But these points do not touch the kernel of the argument, which lies in the statement that such a straight line, returning into itself after a finite time, would appear to *B* as an "unendurable contradiction," and thus force him, for logical though not for sensational purposes, into the assumption of a third dimension. This assertion seems to me quite unwarranted: the whole of Metageometry is a solid array in disproof of it. Helmholtz's argument is, it must be remembered, only an analogy, and the contradiction would exist *only* for a Euclidean. A complete *three*-dimensional Geometry has, we have seen in Chapter I., been developed on the assumption that straight lines are of finite length. A *constant* value for the measure of curvature, as our discussion of Riemann showed, involves neither reference to the fourth dimension, nor any kind of internal contradiction. This fact disproves Lotze's contention, which arises solely from inability to divest his imagination of Euclidean ideas.

Lotze next attacks Helmholtz for the assertion that *B* would know nothing of parallel lines—parallel *straight* lines, as the context shows, he meant to say[1]. Lotze, however, takes him

[1] Vorträge und Reden, Vol. II. p. 9: "Parallele Linien würden die

as meaning, apparently, mere curves of constant distance from a given straight line, which are part of the regular stock-in-trade of Metageometry. Parallels of latitude, in the geographical sense, would not—with the exception of the equator—appear to *B* as straight lines, but as circles. *Great* circles he *would* call straight, and this fact seems to have misled Lotze into thinking *all* circles were to be treated as straight lines. Parallels of latitude, therefore, though *B* might call them parallels, would not invalidate Helmholtz's contention, which applies only to straight lines.

The argument that such small circles would be parallel, which we have just disposed of, is only the preface to another proof that *B* would need a third dimension. Let us call two of these parallels of latitude $l_n$ and $l_s$, and let them be equidistant from the equator, one in the northern, one in the southern hemisphere. Consecutive tangent planes, along these parallels, converge, in the one case northwards, in the other southwards. Either *B* could become aware of their difference, says Lotze, or he could not. In the former case, which he regards as the more probable, he easily proves that *B* would infer a third dimension. But this alternative is, I think, wholly inadmissible. Tangent planes, like Euclidean planes in general, would have no meaning to *B*; unless, indeed, he were a metageometrician, which, with all his metaphysical and mathematical subtlety, the argument supposes him not to be—and to such a supposition Lotze, surely, is the last person who has a right to object. Lotze's attempted proof that this is the right alternative rests, if I understand him aright, on a sheer error in ordinary spherical Geometry. *B* would observe, he says, that the meridians made smaller angles with his path towards the nearer than towards the further pole—as a matter of fact, they would be simply perpendicular to his path in both directions. What Lotze means is, perhaps, that all the meridians would meet sooner in one direction than in the other, and this, of course, is true.

Bewohner der Kugel gar nicht kennen. Sie würden behaupten, dass jede beliebige zwei *geradeste* Linien, gehörig verlängert, sich schliesslich nicht nur in einem, sondern in zwei Punkten schneiden müssten." (The italics are mine.) The omission of *straight* in such phrases is a frequent laxity of mathematicians.

But the poles, in which the meridians meet, would appear to *B* as the centres of the respective parallels, while the parallels themselves would appear to be circles. Now I am at a loss to see what difficulty would arise, to *B*, in supposing two different circles to have different centres[1]. We must, therefore, take the first alternative, that *B* would have no sort of knowledge as to the direction in which the tangent planes converged. Here Lotze attempts, if I have not misunderstood him, to prove a *reductio ad absurdum*: *B* would think, he says, that he was describing two paths wholly the same in direction, and then he *might* regard both paths as circles in a plane. It may be observed that direction, when applied to a circle as a whole, is meaningless; indeed direction, in all Metageometry, can only mean, even when applied to straight lines, direction towards a point. To speak of two lines, which do not meet, as having the same direction, is a surreptitious introduction of the axiom of parallels. Apart from this, I cannot conceive any objection, on *B*'s part, to such a view—one should say *must*, not *might*. The whole argumentation, therefore, unless its obscurity has led me astray, must be pronounced fruitless and inconclusive.

**94.** After this preliminary discussion of Sphereland, Lotze proceeds to the question of a fourth dimension, and thence to spherical and pseudo-spherical space. As before, he appears to know only the more careless and popular utterances of Helmholtz and Riemann, and to have taken no trouble to understand even the foundations of mathematical Metageometry. By this neglect, much of what he says is rendered wholly worthless. To begin with, he regards, as the purpose of Helmholtz's fairy tale, the suggestion of a possible fourth dimension, whereas the real purpose was quite the opposite—to make intelligible a purely three-dimensional non-Euclidean space. Helmholtz introduced Flatland only because its relation to Sphereland is analogous to the relation of ours to spherical space[2]. But

[1] It has been suggested to me that Lotze regards the meridians as projected on to a plane, as in a map. If this be so, there is an obviously illegitimate introduction of the third dimension.

[2] This is proved by Helmholtz's remark at the end of a detailed attempt to make spherical and pseudo-spherical spaces imaginable (l.c. p. 28): "Anders ist es mit den drei Dimensionen des Raumes. Da alle unsere Mittel sinnlicher Anschauung sich nur auf einen Raum von drei Dimensionen erstrecken, und

Lotze says: The Flatlanders would find no difficulty in a third dimension, since it would in no way contradict their own Geometry, while the people in Sphereland, from the contradictions in their two-dimensional system, would already have been led to it. The latter contention I have already tried to answer; the former has an odd sound, in view of the attempt, a few pages later, to prove *à priori* that all forms of intuition, in any way analogous to space, *must* have three dimensions. One cannot help suspecting that the Flatlanders, with two instead of three dimensions, would make a similar attempt. But to return to Lotze's argument: Neither analogy can be used, he says, to prove that we ought perhaps to set up a fourth dimension, since, for us, no contradictions or otherwise inexplicable phenomena exist. The only people, so far as I know, who have used this analogy, are Dr Abbot and a few Spiritualists—the former in joke, the latter to explain certain phenomena more simply explained, perhaps, by Maskelyne and Cooke. But although Lotze's conclusion in this matter is sound, and one with which Helmholtz might have agreed, his arguments, to my mind, are irrelevant and unconvincing. There is this difference, he says, between us and the Spherelanders: the latter were logically forced to a new dimension, and found it possible; we are not forced to it, and find it, in our space, impossible. I have contended that, on the contrary, nothing would force the Spherelanders to assume a third dimension, while they would find it impossible exactly as we find a fourth impossible—not logically, that is to say, but only as a presentable construction in given space.

After a somewhat elephantine piece of humour, about socialistic whales in a four-dimensional sea of Fourrier's *eau sucrée*, Lotze proceeds to a proof, by logic, that every form of intuition, which embraces the whole system of ordered relations of a coexisting manifold, *must* have three dimensions. One might object, on *à priori* grounds, to any such attempt: what belongs to pure intuition could hardly, one would have

die vierte Dimension nicht bloss eine Abänderung von Vorhandenem, sondern etwas vollkommen Neues wäre, so befinden wir uns schon wegen unserer körperlichen Organisation in der absoluten Unmöglichkeit, uns eine Anschauungsweise einer vierten Dimension vorzustellen."

thought, be determined by *à priori* reasoning[1]. I will not, however, develop this argument here, but endeavour to point out, as far as its obscurity will allow, the particular fallacy of the proof in question.

Lotze's argument is as follows. In this discussion, though our terminology is necessarily taken from space, we are really concerned with a much more general conception. We assume, in order to preserve the homogeneity of dimensions, that the difference (distance) between any two elements (points) of our manifold—to borrow Riemann's word—is of the same kind as, and commensurable with, the difference between any other two elements. Let us take a series of elements at successive distances $x$ such that the distance between any two is the sum of the distances between intermediate elements. Such a series corresponds to a straight line, which is taken as the $x$-axis. Then a series $OY$ is called perpendicular to the $x$-axis $OX$,

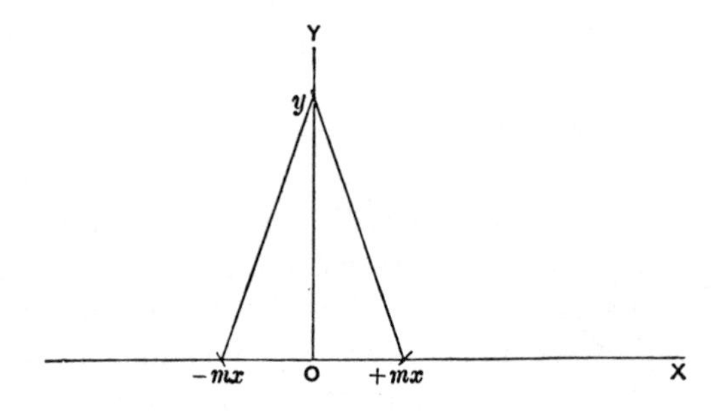


when the distances of any element $y$, on $OY$, from $+mx$ and $-mx$ are equal. By our hypothesis, these distances are comparable with, and qualitatively similar to, $x$ and $y$. So long as $OY$ is defined only by relation to $OX$, it is conceptually unique. But now let us suppose the same relation as that between $OX$ and $OY$, to be possible between $OY$ and a new series $OZ$; we then get a third series $OZ$, perpendicular to $OY$, and again conceptually unique, so long as it is defined by relation to $OY$ alone. We might proceed, in the same way, to a fourth line $OU$ perpendicular to $OZ$. But it is necessary, for our purposes, that $OZ$ should be perpendicular to $OX$ as well as $OY$. Without this condition, $OZ$ might extend into

[1] Cf. Grassmann, Ausdehnungslehre von 1844, 2nd Edition, p. xxiii.

another world, and have no corresponding relation to $OX$—this is a possibility only excluded by our unavoidable spatial images. At this point comes the crux of the argument. *That* $OZ$, says Lotze, which, besides being perpendicular to $OY$, is also perpendicular to $OX$, must be among the series of $OY$'s, for these were defined only by perpendicularity to $OX$. *Hence*, he concludes, there can only be even a third dimension if $OZ$ coincides with one, and—as soon as $OX$ is considered fixed—with *only* one, of the many members of the $OY$ series.

In this argument it is difficult—to me at any rate—to see any force at all. The only way I can account for it is, to suppose that Lotze has neglected the possibility of any but single infinities. On this interpretation, the argument might be stated thus: There is an infinite series of continuously varying $OY$'s; to the common property of these, we add another property, which will divide their total number by infinity. The remaining $OZ$, therefore, must be uniquely determined. The same form of argument, however, would prove that two surfaces can only cut one another in a single point, and numberless other absurdities. The fact is, that infinities may be of different orders. For example, the number of points in a line may be taken as a single infinity, and so may the number of lines in a plane through any point; hence, by multiplication, the number of points in a plane is a double infinity, $\infty^2$, and if we divide this number by a single infinity, we get still an infinite number left. Thus Lotze's argument assumes what he has to prove, that the number of lines perpendicular to a given line, through any point, is a single infinity, which is equivalent to the axiom of three dimensions. The whole passage is so obscure, that its meaning may have escaped me. It is obvious *à priori*, however, as I pointed out in the beginning, that any proof of the axiom must be fallacious somewhere, and the above interpretation of the argument is the only one I have been able to find.

**95.** The rest of the Chapter is devoted to an attack on spherical and pseudo-spherical space, on the ground that they interfere with the homogeneity of the three dimensions, and with the similarity of all parts of space. This is simply false. Such spaces, like the surface of a sphere, *are* exactly alike throughout. Lotze shows, here and elsewhere, that he has not taken the pains to find out what Metageometry really is. I hold myself, and have tried to prove in this Essay, that Congruence is an *à priori* axiom, without which Geometry would be impossible; but the wish to uphold this axiom is, as Lotze ought to have known, the precise motive which led Metageometry to limit itself to spaces of constant measure of curvature. We see here the importance of distinguishing between Helmholtz the philosopher and Helmholtz the mathematician. Though the philosopher wished to dispense with Congruence, the mathematician, as we saw in Chapter I., retained and strongly emphasized it. A little later Lotze shows, again, how he has been misled by the unfortunate analogy of Sphereland. A spherical *surface*, he says, he can understand; but how are we to pass from this to a spherical space? Either this surface is the whole of our space, as in Sphereland, or it generates space by a gradually growing radius. Such concentric spheres, as Lotze triumphantly points out, of course generate Euclidean space. His disjunction, however, is utterly and entirely false, and could never have been suggested by any one with even a superficial knowledge of Metageometry. This point is less laboured than the former, which, in all its nakedness, is thus re-stated in the last sentence of the Chapter: "I cannot persuade myself that one could, without the elements of homogeneous space, even form or define the presentation of heterogeneous spaces, or of such as had variable measures of curvature." As though such spaces were ever set up by non-Euclidean mathematics!

In conclusion, Lotze expresses a hope that Philosophy, on this point, will not allow itself to be imposed upon by Mathematics. I must, instead, rejoice that Mathematics has not been imposed upon by Philosophy, but has developed freely an important and self-consistent system, which deserves, for its subtle analysis into logical and factual elements, the gratitude of all who seek for a philosophy of space.

**96.** The objections to non-Euclidean Geometry which have just been discussed fall under four heads:

I. Non-Euclidean spaces are not homogeneous; Metageometry therefore unduly reifies space.

II. They involve a reference to a fourth dimension.

III. They cannot be set up without an implicit reference to Euclidean space, or to the Euclidean straight line, on which they are therefore dependent.

IV. They are self-contradictory in one or more ways.

The reader who has followed me in regarding these four objections as fallacious, will have no difficulty in disposing of any other critic of Metageometry, as these are the only mathematical arguments, so far as I know, ever urged against non-Euclideans[1]. The logical validity of Metageometry, and the mathematical possibility of three-dimensional non-Euclidean spaces, will therefore be regarded, throughout the remainder of the work, as sufficiently established.

**97.** Two other objections may, indeed, be urged against Metageometry, but these are rather of a philosophical than of a strictly mathematical import. The first of these, which has been made the base of operations by Delbœuf, applies equally to all non-Euclidean spaces. The second, which has not, so far as I know, been much employed, but yet seems to me deserving of notice, bears directly against spaces of positive curvature alone; but if it could discredit these, it might throw doubt on the method by which all alike are obtained. The two objections are:

I. Space must be such as to allow of similarity, *i.e.* of the increase or diminution, in a constant ratio, of all the lines in a figure, without change of angles; whereas in non-Euclid, lines, like angles, have absolute magnitude.

II. Space must be infinite, whereas spherical and elliptic spaces are finite.

I will discuss the first objection in connection with Delbœuf's articles referred to above. The second, which has not, to my knowledge, been widely used in criticism, will be better deferred to Chapter III.

[1] See especially Stallo, Concepts of Modern Physics, International Science Series, Vol. XLII. Chaps. XIII. and XIV.; Renouvier, "Philosophie de la règle et du compas," Année Philosophique, II.; Delbœuf, "L'ancienne et les nouvelles géométries," Revue Philosophique, Vols. XXXVI.–XXXIX.

### Delbœuf.

**98.** M. Delbœuf's four articles in the Revue Philosophique contain much matter that has already been dealt with in the criticism of Lotze, and much that is irrelevant for our present purpose. The only point, which I wish to discuss here, is the question of absolute magnitude, as it is called—the question, that is, whether the possibility of similar but unequal geometrical figures can be known *à priori*[1].

In discussing this question, it is important, to begin with, to distinguish clearly the sense in which absolute magnitude *is* required in non-Euclidean Geometry, from another sense, in which it would be absurd to regard any magnitude as absolute. Judgments of magnitude can only result from comparison, and if Metageometry required magnitudes which could be determined without comparison, it would certainly deserve condemnation. But this is not required. All we require is, that it shall be impossible, while the rest of space is unaffected, to alter the magnitude of any figure, as compared with other figures, while leaving the relative internal magnitudes of its parts unchanged. This construction, which is possible in Euclid, is impossible in Metageometry. We have to discuss whether such an impossibility renders non-Euclidean spaces logically faulty.

M. Delbœuf's position on this axiom—which he calls the postulate of homogeneity[2]—is, that all Geometry must presuppose it, and that Metageometry, consequently, though logically sound, is logically subsequent to Euclid, and can only make its constructions within a Euclidean "homogeneous" space (Rev. Phil. Vol. XXXVII., pp. 380–1). He would appear to think, nevertheless, that homogeneity (in his sense) is learnt from experience, though on this point he is not very explicit. (See Vol. XXXVIII., p. 129.) No *à priori* proof, at any rate, is offered

[1] M. Delbœuf deserves credit for having based Euclid, already in 1860, in his "Prolégomènes Philosophiques de la Géométrie," on this axiom—certainly a better basis, at first sight, than the axiom of parallels.

[2] This meaning of homogeneity must not be confounded with the sense in which I have used the word. In Delbœuf's sense, it means that figures may be similar though of different sizes; in my sense it means that figures may be similar though in different places. This property of space is called by Delbœuf isogeneity.

in his articles. As a result of experience, every one would admit, similarity is known to be possible within the limits of observation; but the fact that this possibility extends to Ordnance maps, which deal with a spherical surface, should make us chary of inferring, from such a datum, the certainty of Euclid for large spaces. Moreover if homogeneity be empirical, Metageometry, which dispenses with it, is not necessarily in *logical* dependence upon Euclid, since homogeneity and isogeneity are *logically* separable. I shall assume, therefore, as the only contention which can be interesting to our argument, that homogeneity is regarded as *à priori*, and as logically essential to Geometry.

**99.** Now we saw, in discussing Erdmann's views of the judgment of quantity, that in non-Euclidean space, as in Euclidean, a change of all spatial magnitudes, in the same ratio, would be no change at all; the ratios of all magnitudes to the space-constant would be unchanged, and the space-constant, as the ultimate standard of comparison, cannot, in any intelligible sense, be said to have any particular magnitude. The absolute magnitudes of Metageometry, therefore, are absolute only as against any other *particular* magnitude, not as against other magnitudes in general. If this were not the case, the comparative nature of the judgment of magnitude would be contradicted, and metrical Metageometry would become absurd. But as it is, the difference from Euclid consists only in this: that in Metageometry we have, while in Euclid we have not, a standard of comparison involved in the nature of our space as a whole, which we call the space-constant. We have to discuss whether the assertion of such a standard involves an undue reification of space.

I do not believe that this is the case. For an undue reification of space would only arise, if we were no longer able to regard position as wholly relative, and as geometrically definable only by departure from other positions. But the relativity of position, as we have abundantly seen, is preserved by all spaces of constant curvature—in all of these, positions can only be defined, geometrically, by relations to fresh positions[1]. This series of definitions may lead to an infinite regress, but it may

[1] For a full proof of this proposition, see Chap. III.

also, as in spherical space, form a vicious circle, and return again to the position from which it started. No reification of space, no independent existence of mere relations, seems involved in such a procedure. The whole of Metageometry, in short, is a proof that the relativity of position is compatible with absolute magnitude, in the only sense required by non-Euclidean spaces. We must conclude, therefore, that there is nothing incompatible, in a denial of homogeneity (in Delbœuf's sense), either with the relational nature of space, or with the comparative nature of magnitude. This last *à priori* objection to Metageometry, therefore, cannot be maintained, and the issue must be decided on empirical grounds alone.

**100.** The foundations of Geometry have been the subject of much recent speculation in France, and this seems to demand some notice. But in spite of the splendid work which the French have done on the allied question of number and continuous quantity, I cannot persuade myself that they have succeeded in greatly advancing the subject of geometrical philosophy. The chief writers have been, from the mathematical side, *Calinon* and *Poincaré*, from the philosophical, *Renouvier* and *Delbœuf*; as a mediator between mathematics and philosophy, *Lechalas*.

*Calinon*, in an interesting article on the geometrical indeterminateness of the universe, maintains that any Geometry may be applied to the actual world by a suitable hypothesis as to the course of light-rays. For the earth only is known to us otherwise than by Optics, and the earth is an infinitesimal part of the universe. This line of argument has been already discussed in connection with Lotze, but Calinon adds a new suggestion, that the space-constant may perhaps vary with the time. This would involve a causal connection between space and other things, which seems hardly conceivable, and which, if regarded as possible, must surely destroy Geometry, since Geometry depends throughout on the irrelevance of Causation[1]. Moreover, in all operations of measurement, some time is spent; unless we knew that space was unchanging throughout the operation, it is hard to see how our results could be trustworthy, and how, consequently, a change in the parameter could be

[1] See Chap. III., especially § 133.

discovered. The same difficulties would arise, in fact, as those which result from supposing space not homogeneous.

*Poincaré* maintains that the question, whether Euclid or Metageometry should be accepted, is one of convenience and convention, not of truth; axioms are definitions in disguise, and the choice between definitions is arbitrary. This view has been discussed in Chapter I., in connection with Cayley's theory of distance, on which it depends.

*Lechalas* is a philosophical disciple of Calinon. He is a rationalist of the pre-Kantian type, but a believer in the validity of Metageometry. He holds that Geometry can dispense with all purely spatial postulates, and work with axioms of magnitude alone[1], which, in his opinion, are purely analytic. The principle of contradiction, to him, is the sole and only test of truth; we make long chains of reasoning from our premisses to see if contradictions will emerge. It might be objected that this view, though it saves general Geometry from being logically empirical, leaves it only empirically logical; this must, in fact, be the fate of every piece of *à priori* knowledge, if M. Lechalas's were the only test of truth. However, he concludes that general Geometry is apodeictic, while the space of our actual world, like all other phenomena, is contingent.

*Delbœuf* criticizes non-Euclidean space from an ultra-realist standpoint: he holds that *real* space is neither homogeneous nor isogeneous, but that *conceived* space, as abstracted from real space, has both these properties. He offers no justification for his real space, which seems to be maintained in the spirit of naïve realism, nor does he show how he has acquired his intimate knowledge of its constitution[2]. His arguments against Metageometry, in so far as they are not repetitions of Lotze, have been discussed above.

*Renouvier*, finally, is a pure Kantian, of the most orthodox type. His views as to the importance, for Geometry, of the distinction between synthetic and analytic judgments, have

[1] For a criticism of this view, see the above discussions on Riemann and Erdmann.

[2] Cf. Couturat, "De l'Infini Mathématique," Paris, Félix Alcan, 1896, p. 544.

been discussed, in connection with Kant, at the beginning of the present Chapter[1].

**101.** Before beginning the constructive argument of the next Chapter, let us endeavour briefly to sum up the theories which have been polemically advocated throughout the criticisms we have just concluded. We agreed to accept, with Kant, necessity for any possible experience as the test of the *à priori*, but

[1] The following is a list of the most important recent French philosophical writings on Geometry, so far as I am acquainted with them.

Andrade: "Les bases expérimentales de la géométrie euclidienne"; Rev. Phil. 1890, II., and 1891, I.

Bonnel: "Les hypothèses dans la géométrie"; Gauthier-Villars, 1897.

L'Abbé de Broglie: "La géométrie non-euclidienne," two articles; Annales de Phil. Chrét. 1890.

Calinon: "Les espaces géométriques"; Rev. Phil. 1889, I., and 1891, II.
"Sur l'indétermination géométrique de l'univers"; ib. 1893, II.

Couturat: "L'Année Philosophique de F. Pillon," Rev. de Mét. et de Morale, Jan. 1893.
"Note sur la géométrie non-euclidienne et la relativité de l'espace"; ib., May, 1893.
"Études sur l'espace et le temps," ib. Sep. 1896.

Delbœuf: "L'ancienne et les nouvelles géométries," four articles; Rev. Phil. 1893—5.

Lechalas: "La géométrie générale"; Crit. Phil. 1889.
"La géométrie générale et les jugements synthétiques à priori" and "Les bases expérimentales de la géométrie"; Rev. Phil. 1890, II.
"M. Delbœuf et Le problème des mondes semblables"; ib. 1894, I.
"Note sur la géométrie non-euclidienne et le principe de similitude"; Rev. de Mét. et de Morale, March, 1893.
"La courbure et la distance en géométrie générale"; ib., March, 1896.
"La géométrie générale et l'intuition"; Annales de Phil. Chrét., 1890.
"Étude sur l'espace et le temps"; Paris, Alcan, 1896.

Liard: "Des définitions géométriques et des définitions empiriques," 2nd ed.; Paris, Alcan, 1888.

Mansion: "Premiers principes de la métagéométrie"; two articles in Rev. Néo-Scholastique, 1896. Separately published, Gauthier-Villars, 1896.

Milhaud: "La géométrie non-euclidienne et la théorie de la connaissance"; Rev. Phil. 1888, I.

Poincaré: "Non-Euclidian Geometry"; Nature, Vol. XLV., 1891—2.
"L'espace et la géométrie"; Rev. de Mét. et de Morale, Nov. 1895.
"Réponse à quelques critiques," ib. Jan. 1897.

Renouvier: "Philosophie de la règle et du compas"; Crit. Phil., 1889, and L'Année Phil., II$^{me}$ année, 1891.

Sorel: "Sur la géométrie non-euclidienne"; Rev. Phil., 1891, I.

Tannery: "Théorie de la connaissance mathématique"; Rev. Phil., 1894, II.

we refused, for the present, to discuss the connection of the *à priori* with the subjective, regarding the purely logical test as sufficient for our immediate purpose. We also refused to attach importance to the distinction of analytic and synthetic, since it seemed to apply, not to different judgments, but only to different aspects of any judgment.

We then discussed Riemann's attempt to identify the empirical element in Geometry with the element not deducible from ideas of magnitude, and we decided that this identification was due to a confusion as to the nature of magnitude. For judgments of magnitude, we said, require always some qualitative basis, which is not quantitatively expressible.

In criticizing Helmholtz, we decided that Mechanics logically presupposes Geometry, though space presupposes matter; but that the matter which space presupposes, and to which Geometry indirectly refers, is a more abstract matter than that of Mechanics, a matter destitute of force and of causal attributes, and possessed only of the purely spatial attributes required for the possibility of spatial figures. But we conceded that Geometry, when applied to mixed mathematics or to daily life, demands more than this, demands, in fact, some means of discovering, in the more concrete matter of Mechanics, either a rigid body, or a body whose departure from rigidity follows some empirically discoverable law. *Actual* measurement, therefore, we agreed to regard as empirical.

Our conclusions, as regards the empiricism of Riemann and Helmholtz, were reinforced by a criticism of Erdmann. We then had an opposite task to perform, in defending Metageometry against Lotze. Here we saw that there are two senses in which Metageometry is possible. The first concerns our actual space, and asserts that it may have a very small space-constant; the second concerns philosophical theories of space, and asserts a purely logical possibility, which leaves the decision to experience. We saw also that Lotze's mathematical strictures arose from insufficient knowledge of the subject, and could all be refuted by a better acquaintance with Metageometry.

Finally, we discussed the question of absolute magnitude, and found in it no logical obstacle to non-Euclidean spaces. Our conclusion, then, in so far as we are as yet entitled to a conclusion, is that all spaces with a space-constant are *à priori* justifiable, and that the decision between them must be the work of experience. Spaces without a space-constant, on the other hand, spaces, that is, which are not homogeneous throughout, we found logically unsound and impossible to know, and therefore to be condemned *à priori.* The constructive proof of this thesis will form the argument of the following chapter.

# CHAPTER III.

## Section A.

### THE AXIOMS OF PROJECTIVE GEOMETRY.

**102.** PROJECTIVE Geometry proper, as we saw in Chapter I., does not employ the conception of magnitude, and does not, therefore, require those axioms which, in the systems of the second or metrical period, were required solely to render possible the application of magnitude to space. But we saw, also, that Cayley's reduction of metrical to projective properties was purely technical and philosophically irrelevant. Now it is in metrical properties alone—apart from the exception to the axiom of the straight line, which itself, however, presupposes metrical properties[1]—that non-Euclidean and Euclidean spaces differ. The properties dealt with by projective Geometry, therefore, in so far as these are obtained without the use of imaginaries, are properties common to all spaces. Finally, the differences which appear between the Geometries of different spaces of the same curvature—*e.g.* between the Geometries of the plane and the cylinder—are differences in projective properties[2]. Thus the necessity which arises, in metrical Geometry, for further qualifications besides those of constant curvature, disappears when our general space is defined by purely projective properties.

**103.** We have good ground for expecting, therefore, that the axioms of projective Geometry will be the simplest and most complete expression of the indispensable requisites of

[1] See infra, Axiom of Distance, in Sec. B. of this Chapter.

[2] Thus on a cylinder, two geodesics, *e.g.* a generator and a helix, may have any number of intersections—a very important difference from the plane.

any geometrical reasoning: and this expectation, I hope, will not be disappointed. Projective Geometry, in so far as it deals only with the properties common to all spaces, will be found, if I am not mistaken, to be wholly *à priori*, to take nothing from experience, and to have, like Arithmetic, a creature of the pure intellect for its object. If this be so, it is that branch of pure mathematics which Grassmann, in his *Ausdehnungslehre* of 1844, felt to be possible, and endeavoured, in a brilliant failure, to construct without any appeal to the space of intuition.

**104.** But unfortunately, the task of discovering the axioms of projective Geometry is far from easy. They have, as yet, found no Riemann or Helmholtz to formulate them philosophically. Many geometers have constructed systems, which they intended to be, and which, with sufficient care in interpretation, really are, free from metrical presuppositions. But these presuppositions are so rooted in all the very elements of Geometry, that the task of eliminating them demands a reconstruction of the whole geometrical edifice. Thus Euclid, for example, deals, from the start, with spatial equality—he employs the circle, which is necessarily defined by means of equality, and he bases all his later propositions on the congruence of triangles as discussed in Book I.[1] Before we can use any elementary proposition of Euclid, therefore, even if this expresses a projective property, we have to prove that the property in question can be deduced by projective methods. This has not, in general, been done by projective geometers, who have too often assumed, for example, that the quadrilateral construction—by which, as we saw in Chap. I., they introduce projective coordinates—or anharmonic ratio, which is *primâ facie* metrical, could be satisfactorily established on their principles. Both these assumptions, however, can be justified, and we may admit, therefore, that the claims of projective Geometry to logical independence of measurement or congruence are valid. Let us see, then, how it proceeds.

**105.** In the first place, it is important to realize that

[1] Cf. Cremona, Projective Geometry (Clarendon Press, 2nd ed. 1893) p. 50: "Most of the propositions in Euclid's Elements are metrical, and it is not easy to find among them an example of a purely descriptive theorem."

when coordinates are used, in projective Geometry, they are not coordinates in the ordinary metrical sense, *i.e.* the numerical measures of certain spatial magnitudes. On the contrary, they are a set of numbers, arbitrarily but systematically assigned to different points, like the numbers of houses in a street, and serving only, from a philosophical standpoint, as convenient designations for points which the investigation wishes to distinguish. But for the brevity of the alphabet, in fact, they might, as in Euclid, be replaced by letters. How they are introduced, and what they mean, has been discussed in Chapter I. Here we have only to repeat a caution, whose neglect has led to much misunderstanding.

**106.** The distinction between various points, then, is not a result, but a condition, of the projective coordinate system. The coordinate system is a wholly extraneous, and merely convenient, set of marks, which in no way touches the essence of projective Geometry. What we must begin with, in this domain, is the possibility of distinguishing various points from one another. This may be designated, with Veronese, as the first axiom of Geometry[1]. How we are to define a point, and how we distinguish it from other points, is for the moment irrelevant; for here we only wish to discover the nature of projective Geometry, and the kind of properties which it uses and demonstrates. How, and with what justification, it uses and demonstrates them, we will discuss later.

**107.** Now it is obvious that a mere collection of points, distinguished one from another, cannot found a Geometry: we must have some idea of the manner in which the points are interrelated, in order to have an adequate subject-matter for discussion. But since all ideas of quantity are excluded, the relations of points cannot be relations of distance in the ordinary sense, nor even, in the sense of ordinary Geometry, anharmonic ratios, for anharmonic ratios are usually defined as the ratios of four distances, or of four sines, and are thus quantitative. But since all quantitative comparison presupposes an identity of quality, we may expect to find, in projective Geometry, the qualitative substrata of the metrical superstructure.

And this, we shall see, is actually the case. We have not

[1] Op. cit. p. 226.

distance, but we *have* the straight line; we have not quantitative anharmonic ratio, but we *have* the property, in any four points on a line, of being the intersections with the rays of a given pencil. And from this basis, we can build up a qualitative science of abstract externality, which is projective Geometry. How this happens, I shall now proceed to show.

**108.** All geometrical reasoning is, in the last resort, circular: if we start by assuming points, they can only be defined by the lines or planes which relate them; and if we start by assuming lines or planes, they can only be defined by the points through which they pass. This is an inevitable circle, whose ground of necessity will appear as we proceed. It is, therefore, somewhat arbitrary to start either with points or with lines, as the eminently projective principle of duality mathematically illustrates; nevertheless we will elect, with most geometers, to start with points[1]. We suppose, therefore, as our datum, a set of discrete points, for the moment without regard to their interconnections. But since connections are essential to any reasoning about them as a system, we introduce, to begin with, the axiom of the straight line. Any two of our points, we say, lie on a line which those two points completely define. This line, being determined by the two points, may be regarded as a relation of the two points, or an adjective of the system formed by both together. This is the only purely qualitative adjective—as will be proved later—of a system of two points. Now projective Geometry can only take account of qualitative adjectives, and can distinguish between different points only by their relations to other points, since all points, *per se*, are qualitatively similar. Hence it comes that, for projective Geometry, when two points only are given, they are qualitatively indistinguishable from any two other points on the same straight line, since any two such other points have the same qualitative relation. Reciprocally, since one straight line is a figure determined by any two of its points, and all points are qualitatively similar, it follows that all straight lines are qualitatively similar. We may regard a point, therefore, as determined by two straight lines which meet in it, and the

[1] Some ground for this choice will appear when we come to metrical Geometry.

point, on this view, becomes the only qualitative relation between the two straight lines. Hence, if the point only be regarded as given, the two straight lines are qualitatively indistinguishable from any other pair through the point.

**109.** The extension of these two reciprocal principles is the essence of all projective transformations, and indeed of all projective Geometry. The fundamental operations, by which figures are projectively transformed, are called projection and section. The various forms of projection and section are defined in Cremona's "Projective Geometry," Chapter I., from which I quote the following account.

"*To project from a fixed point S* (the *centre of projection*) a figure (*ABCD...abcd...*) composed of points and straight lines, is to construct the straight lines or *projecting rays SA*, *SB*, *SC*, *SD*,...and the planes (*projecting planes*) *Sa*, *Sb*, *Sc*, *Sd*,.... We thus obtain a new figure composed of straight lines and planes which all pass through the centre *S*.

"*To cut by a fixed plane* $\sigma$ (*transversal plane*) a figure ($\alpha\beta\gamma\delta$ ...*abcd*...) made up of planes and straight lines, is to construct the straight lines or *traces* $\sigma\alpha$, $\sigma\beta$, $\sigma\gamma$... and the points or *traces* $\sigma a$, $\sigma b$, $\sigma c$ ...[1]. By this means we obtain a new figure composed of straight lines and points lying in the plane $\sigma$.

"*To project from a fixed straight line s* (the *axis*) a figure *ABCD* composed of points, is to construct the planes *sA*, *sB*, *sC*.... The figure thus obtained is composed of planes which all pass through the axis *s*.

"*To cut by a fixed straight line s* (a *transversal*) a figure $\alpha\beta\gamma\delta$... composed of planes, is to construct the points $s\alpha$, $s\beta$, $s\gamma$.... In this way a new figure is obtained, composed of points all lying on the fixed transversal *s*.

"If a figure is composed of straight lines *a*, *b*, *c*... which all pass through a fixed point or *centre S*, it can be *projected* from a straight line or *axis s* passing through *S*; the result is a figure composed of planes *sa*, *sb*, *sc*....

"If a figure is composed of straight lines *a*, *b*, *c*... all lying in a fixed plane, it may be cut by a straight line (transversal)

[1] The straight line $\sigma\alpha$ denotes the straight line common to the planes $\sigma$ and $\alpha$, the point $\sigma a$ denotes the point common to the plane $\sigma$ and the straight line $a$, and similarly for the rest of the notation.

*s* lying in the same plane; the figure which results is formed by the points *sa*, *sb*, *sc*...."

**110.** The successive application, to any figure, of two reciprocal operations of projection and section, is regarded as producing a figure projectively indistinguishable from the first, provided only that the dimensions of the original figure were the same as those of the resulting figure, that, for example, if the second operation be section by a plane, the original figure shall have been a plane figure. The figures obtained from a given figure, by projection or section alone, are related to that figure by the principle of duality, of which we shall have to speak later on.

I shall endeavour to show, in what follows, first, in what sense figures obtained from each other by projective transformation are qualitatively alike; secondly, what axioms, or adjectives of space, are involved in the principle of projective transformation; and thirdly, that these adjectives must belong to any form of externality with more than one dimension, and are, therefore, *à priori* properties of any possible space.

For the sake of simplicity, I shall in general confine myself to two dimensions. In so doing, I shall introduce no important difference of principle, and shall greatly simplify the mathematics involved.

**111.** The two mathematically fundamental things in projective Geometry are anharmonic ratio, and the quadrilateral construction. Everything else follows mathematically from these two. Now what is meant, in projective Geometry, by anharmonic ratio?

If we start from anharmonic ratio as ordinarily defined, we are met by the difficulty of its quantitative nature[1]. But among the properties deduced from this definition, many, if not most, are purely qualitative. The most fundamental of these is that, if through any four points in a straight line we draw four straight lines which meet in a point, and if we then draw a new straight line meeting these four, the four new

[1] Cremona (op. cit. Chap. IX. p. 50) defines anharmonic ratio as a metrical property which is unaltered by projection. This, however, destroys the logical independence of projective Geometry, which can only be maintained by a purely descriptive definition.

points of intersection have the same anharmonic ratio as the four points we started with. Thus, in the figure, $abcd$, $a'b'c'd'$, $a''b''c''d''$, all have the same anharmonic ratio. The reciprocal

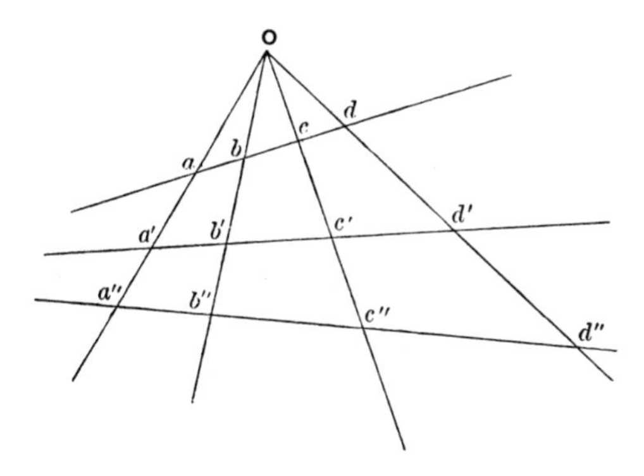


relation holds for the anharmonic ratio of four straight lines. Here we have, plainly, the required basis for a qualitative definition. The definition must be as follows:

Two sets of four points each are defined as having the same anharmonic ratio, when (1) each set of four lies in one straight line, and (2) corresponding points of different sets lie two by two on four straight lines through a single point, or when both sets have this relation to any third set[1]. And reciprocally: Two sets of four straight lines are defined as having the same anharmonic ratio when (1) each set of four passes through a single point, and (2) corresponding lines of different sets pass, two by two, through four points in one straight line, or when both sets have this relation to any third set.

Two sets of points or of lines, which have the same anharmonic ratio, are treated by projective Geometry as equivalent: this qualitative equivalence replaces the quantitative equality of metrical Geometry, and is obviously included, by its definition, in the above account of projective transformations in general.

**112.** We have next to consider the quadrilateral con-

[1] There is no corresponding property of *three* points on a line, because they can be projectively transformed into any other three points on the same line. See § 120.

struction[1]. This has a double purpose: first, to define the important special case known as a harmonic range; and secondly, to afford an unambiguous and exhaustive method of assigning different numbers to different points. This last method has, again, a double purpose: first, the purpose of giving a convenient symbolism for describing and distinguishing different points, and of thus affording a means for the introduction of analysis; and secondly, of so assigning these numbers that, if they had the ordinary metrical significance, as distances from some point on the numbered straight line, they would yield $-1$ as the anharmonic ratio of a harmonic range, and that, if four points have the same anharmonic ratio as four others, so have the corresponding numbers. This last purpose is due to purely technical motives: it avoids the confusion with our preconceptions which would result from any other value for a harmonic range; it allows us, when metrical interpretations of projective results are desired, to make these interpretations without tedious numerical transformations, and it enables us to perform projective transformations by algebraical methods. At the same time, from the strictly projective point of view, as observed above, the numbers introduced have a purely conventional meaning; and until we pass to metrical Geometry, no reason can be shown for assigning the value $-1$ to a harmonic range. With this preliminary, let us see in what the quadrilateral construction consists.

**113.** A harmonic range, in elementary Geometry, is one whose anharmonic ratio is $-1$, or one in which the three segments formed by the four points are in harmonic progression, or again, one in which the ratio of the two internal segments is equal to the ratio of the two external segments. If $a$, $b$, $c$, $d$ be the four points, it is easily seen that these definitions are equivalent to one another: they give respectively:

$$\frac{ab}{bc} \Big/ \frac{ad}{dc} = -1, \quad \frac{1}{ab} - \frac{1}{ac} = \frac{1}{ac} - \frac{1}{ad}, \text{ and } \frac{ab}{bc} = \frac{ad}{cd}.$$

[1] Due to v. Staudt's "Geometrie der Lage."

But as they are all quantitative, they cannot be used for our present purpose. Nor are any definitions which involve bisection of lines or angles available. We must have a definition which proceeds entirely by the help of straight lines and points, without measurement of distances or angles. Now from the above definitions of a harmonic range, we see that *a, b, c, d* have the same anharmonic ratio as *c, b, a, d*. This gives us the property we require for our definition. For it shows that, in a harmonic range, we can find a projective transformation which will interchange *a* and *c*. This is a necessary and sufficient condition for a harmonic range, and the quadrilateral construction is the general method for giving effect to it.

Given any three points *A, B, D* in one straight line, the quadrilateral construction finds the point *C* harmonic to *A* with respect to *B, D* by the following method: Take any point *O* outside the straight line *ABD*, and join it to *B* and *D*. Through *A* draw any straight line cutting *OD, OB* in *P* and *Q*.

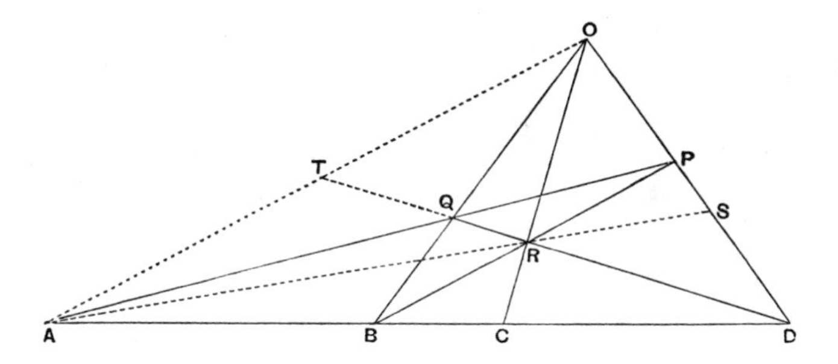


Join *DQ, BP*, and let them intersect in *R*. Join *OR*, and let *OR* meet *ABD* in *C*. Then *C* is the point required.

To prove this, let *DRQ* meet *OA* in *T*, and draw *AR*, meeting *OD* in *S*. Then a projective transformation of *A, B, C, D* from *R* on to *OD* gives the points *S, P, O, D*, which, projected from *A* on to *DQ*, give *R, Q, T, D*. But these again, projected from *O* on to *ABD*, give *C, B, A, D*. Hence *A, B, C, D* can be projectively transformed into *C, B, A, D*, and therefore form a harmonic range. From this point, the proof that the construction is unique and general follows simply[1].

[1] See Cremona, op. cit. Chapter VIII.

The introduction of numbers, by this construction, offers no difficulties of principle—except, indeed, those which always attend the application of number to continua—and may be studied satisfactorily in Klein's Nicht-Euklid (I. p. 337 ff.). The principle of it is, to assign the numbers 0, 1, $\infty$ to $A, B, D$ and therefore the number 2 to $C$, in order that the differences $AB$, $AC$, $AD$ may be in harmonic progression. By taking $B, C, D$ as a new triad corresponding to $A, B, D$, we find a point harmonic to $B$ with respect to $C, D$ and assign to it the number 3, and so on. In this way, we can obtain any number of points, and we are sure of having no number and no point twice over, so that our coordinates have the essential property of a unique correspondence with the points they denote, and *vice versa.*

**114.** The point of importance in the above construction, however, and the reason why I have reproduced it in detail, is that it proceeds entirely by means of the general principles of transformation enunciated above. From this stage onwards, everything is effected by means of the two fundamental ideas we have just discussed, and everything, therefore, depends on our general principle of projective equivalence. This principle, as regards two dimensions, may be stated more simply than in the passage quoted from Cremona. It starts, in two dimensions, from the following definitions:

To project the points $A, B, C, D\ldots$ from a centre $O$, is to construct the straight lines $OA$, $OB$, $OC$, $OD\ldots$.

To cut a number of straight lines $a, b, c, d\ldots$ by a transversal $s$, is to construct the points $sa$, $sb$, $sc$, $sd\ldots$[1].

The successive application of these two operations, provided the original figure consisted of points on one straight line or of straight lines through one point, gives a figure projectively indistinguishable from the former figure; and hence, by extension, if any points in one straight line in the original figure lie in one straight line in the derived figure, and reciprocally for straight lines through points, the two operations have given projectively similar figures. This general principle may be regarded as consisting of two parts, according to the order of the operations: if we begin with projection and end with

[1] The corresponding definitions, for the two-dimensional manifold of lines through a point, follow by the principle of duality.

section, we transform a figure of points into another figure of points; by the converse order, we transform a figure of lines into another figure of lines.

**115.** Before we can be clear as to the meaning of our principle, we must have some notion as to our definition of points and straight lines. But this definition, in projective Geometry, cannot be given without some discussion of the principle of duality, the mathematical form of the philosophical circle involved in geometrical definitions.

Confining ourselves for the moment to two dimensions, the principle asserts, roughly speaking, that any theorem, dealing with lines through a point and points on a line, remains true if these two terms, wherever they occur, are interchanged. Thus: two points lie on one straight line which they completely determine; and two straight lines meet in one point, which they completely determine. The four points of intersection of a transversal with four lines through a point have an anharmonic ratio independent of the particular transversal; and the four lines joining four points on one straight line to a fifth point have an anharmonic ratio independent of that fifth point. So also our general principle of projective transformation has two sides: one in which points move along fixed lines, and one in which lines turn about fixed points.

This duality suggests that any definition of points must be effected by means of the straight line, and any definition of the straight line must be effected by means of points. When we take the third dimension into account, it is true, the duality is no longer so simple; we have now to take account also of the plane, but this only introduces a circle of three terms, which is scarcely preferable to a circle of two terms. We now say: Three points, or a line and a point, determine a plane: but conversely, three planes, or a line and plane, determine a point. We may regard the straight line as a relation between two of its points, but we may also regard the point as a relation between two straight lines through it. We may regard the plane as a relation between three points, or between a point and a line, but we may also regard the point as a relation between three planes, or between a line and a plane, which meet in it.

**116.** How are we to get outside this circle? The fact is that, in pure Geometry, we cannot get outside it. For space, as we shall see more fully hereafter, is nothing but relations; if, therefore, we take any spatial figure, and seek for the terms between which it is a relation, we are compelled, in Geometry, to seek these terms within space, since we have nowhere else to seek them, but we are doomed, since anything purely spatial is a mere relation, to find our terms melting away as we grasp them.

Thus the relativity of space, while it is the essence of the principle of duality, at the same time renders impossible the expression of that principle, or of any other principle of pure Geometry, in a manner which shall be free from contradictions. Nevertheless, if we are to advance at all with our analysis of geometrical reasoning and with our definitions of lines and points, we must, for a while, ignore this contradiction; we must argue as though it did not exist, so as to free our science from any contradictions which are not inevitable.

**117.** In accordance with this procedure, then, let us define our points as the terms of spatial relations, regarding whatever is not a point as a relation between points. What, on this view, must our points be taken to be? Obviously, if extension is mere relativity, they must be taken to contain no extension; but if they are to supply the terms for spatial relations, *e.g.* for straight lines, these relations must exhibit them as the terms of the figures they relate. In other words, since what can really be taken, without contradiction, as the term of a spatial relation, is unextended, we must take, as the term to be used in Geometry, where we cannot go outside space, the least spatial thing which Geometry can deal with, the thing which, though *in* space, *contains* no space; and this thing we define as the point[1].

Neglecting, then, the fundamental contradiction in this definition, the rest of our definitions follow without difficulty.

[1] It is important to observe that this definition of the Point introduces metrical ideas. Without metrical ideas, we saw, nothing appears to give the Point precedence of the straight line, or indeed to distinguish it conceptually from the straight line. A reference to quantity is therefore inevitable in defining the Point, if the definition is to be geometrical. A non-metrical definition would have to be also non-geometrical. See Chap. IV. §§ 196–199.

The straight line is the relation between two points, and the plane is the relation between three. These definitions will be argued and defended at length in section B of this Chapter[1], where we can discuss at the same time the alternative metrical definitions; for our present purpose, it is sufficient to observe that projective Geometry, from the first, regards the straight line as determined by two points, and the plane as determined by three, from which it follows, if we take points as possible terms for spatial relations, that the straight line and the plane may be regarded as relations between two and three points respectively. If we agree on these definitions, we can proceed to discuss the fundamental principle of projective Geometry, and to analyse the axioms implicated in its truth.

**118.** Projective Geometry, we have seen, does not deal with quantity, and therefore recognizes no difference where the difference is purely quantitative. Now quantitative comparison depends on a recognized identity of quality; the recognition of qualitative identity, therefore, is logically prior to quantity, and presupposed by every judgment of quantity. Hence all figures, whose differences can be exhaustively described by quantity, *i.e.* by pure measurement, must have an identity of quality, and this must be recognizable without appeal to quantity. It follows that, by defining the word quality in geometrical matters, we shall discover what sets of figures are projectively indiscernible. If our definition is correct, it ought to yield the general projective principle with which we set out.

**119.** We agreed to regard points as the terms of spatial relations, and we agreed that different points could be distinguished. But we postponed the discussion of the conditions under which this distinction could be effected. This discussion will yield us the definition of quality and the proof of our general projective principle.

Points, to begin with, have been defined as nothing but the terms for spatial relations. They have, therefore, no intrinsic properties; but are distinguished solely by means of their relations. Now the relation between two points, we said,

[1] §§ 163–175.

is the straight line on which they lie. This gives that identity of quality for all pairs of points on the same straight line, which is required both by our projective principle and by metrical Geometry. (For only where there is identity of quality can quantity be properly applied.) If only two points are given, they cannot, without the use of quantity, be distinguished from any two other points on the same straight line; for the qualitative relation between any two such points is the same as for the original pair, and only by a difference of relation can points be distinguished from one another.

But conversely, one straight line is nothing but the relation between two of its points, and all points are qualitatively alike. Hence there can be nothing to distinguish one straight line from another except the points through which it passes, and these are distinguished from other points only by the fact that it passes through them. Thus we get the reciprocal transformation: if we are given only one point, any pair of straight lines through that point is qualitatively indistinguishable from any other. This again is, on the one hand, the basis of the second part of our general projective principle, and on the other hand the condition of applying quantity, in the measurement of angles, to the departure of two intersecting straight lines.

**120.** We can now see the reason for what may have hitherto seemed a somewhat arbitrary fact, namely, the necessity of *four* collinear points for anharmonic ratio. Recurring to the quadrilateral construction and the consequent introduction of number, we see that anharmonic ratio is an intrinsic projective relation of four collinear points or concurrent straight lines, such that given three terms and the relation, the fourth term can be uniquely determined by projective methods. Now consider first a pair of points. Since all straight lines are projectively equivalent, the relation between one pair of points is precisely equivalent to that between another pair. Given one point only, therefore, no projective relation, to any second point, can be assigned, which shall in any way limit our choice of the second point. Given two points, however, there is such a relation—the third point may be given collinear with the first two. This limits its position to one straight line, but since two points determine nothing but one straight line, the third point cannot be further limited. Thus we see why no intrinsic projective relation can be found between three points, which shall enable us, from two, uniquely to determine the third. With three given collinear points, however, we have more given than a mere straight line, and the quadrilateral construction enables us uniquely to determine any number of fresh collinear points. This shows why anharmonic ratio must be a relation between four points, rather than between three.

**121.** We can now prove, I think, that two figures, which are projectively related, are qualitatively similar. Let us begin with a collection of points on a straight line. So long as these are considered without reference to other points or figures, they are all qualitatively similar. They can be distinguished by immediate intuition, but when we endeavour, without quantity, to distinguish them conceptually, we find the task impossible, since the only qualitative relation of any two of them, the straight line, is the same for any other two. But now let us choose, at hap-hazard, some point outside the straight line. The points of our line now acquire new adjectives, namely their relations to the new point, *i.e.* the straight lines joining them to this new point. But these straight lines, reciprocally, alone define our external point, and all straight lines are qualitatively similar. If we take some other external point, therefore, and join it to the same points of our original straight line, we obtain a figure in which, so long as quantity is excluded, there is no conceptual difference from the former figure. Immediate intuition can distinguish the two figures, but qualitative discrimination cannot do so. Thus we obtain a projective transformation of four lines into four other lines, as giving a figure qualitatively indistinguishable from the original figure. A similar argument applies to the other projective transformations. Thus the only reason, within projective Geometry, for not regarding projective figures as actually identical, is the intuitive perception of difference of position. This is fundamental, and must be accepted as a *datum*. It is presupposed in the distinction of various points, and forms the very life of Geometry. It is, in fact, the essence of the notion of a form of externality, which notion forms the subject-matter of projective Geometry.

**122.** We may now sum up the results of our analysis of projective Geometry, and state the axioms on which its reasoning is based. We shall then have to prove that these axioms are necessary to any form of externality, with which we shall pass, from mere analysis, to a transcendental argument.

The axioms which have been assumed in the above analysis, and which, it would seem, suffice to found projective Geometry, may be roughly stated as follows:

I. We can distinguish different parts of space, but all parts are qualitatively similar, and are distinguished only by the immediate fact that they lie outside one another.

II. Space is continuous and infinitely divisible; the result of infinite division, the zero of extension, is called a *point*[1].

III. Any two points determine a unique figure, called a straight line, any three in general determine a unique figure, the plane. Any four determine a corresponding figure of three dimensions, and for aught that appears to the contrary, the same may be true of any number of points. But this process comes to an end, sooner or later, with some number of points which determine the whole of space. For if this were not the case, no number of relations of a point to a collection of given points could ever determine its relation to fresh points, and Geometry would become impossible[2].

This statement of the axioms is not intended to have any exclusive precision: other statements equally valid could easily be made. For all these axioms, as we shall see hereafter, are philosophically interdependent, and may, therefore, be enunciated in many ways. The above statement, however, includes, if I am not mistaken, everything essential to projective Geometry, and everything required to prove the principle of projective transformation. Before discussing the apriority of these axioms, let us once more briefly recapitulate the ends which they are intended to attain.

**123.** From the exclusively mathematical standpoint, as we

[1] On this axiom, however, compare § 131.

[2] For the proof of this proposition, see Chap. III. Sec. B, Axiom of Dimensions.

have seen, projective Geometry discusses only what figures can be obtained from each other by projective transformations, *i.e.* by the operations of projection and section. These operations, in all their forms, presuppose the point, straight line, and plane[1], whose necessity for projective Geometry, from the purely mathematical point of view, is thus self-evident from the start. But philosophically, projective Geometry has, as we saw, a wider aim. This wider aim, which gives, to the investigation of projectively equivalent figures, its chief importance, consists in the determination of qualitative spatial similarity, in the determination, that is, of all the figures which, when any one figure is given, can be distinguished from the given figure, so long as quantity is excluded, only by the mere fact that they are external to it.

**124**. Now when we consider what is involved in such absolute qualitative equivalence, we find at once, as its most obvious prerequisite, the perfect homogeneity of space. For it is assumed that a figure can be completely defined by its internal relations, and that the external relations, which constitute its position, though they suffice to distinguish it from other figures, in no way affect its internal properties, which are regarded as qualitatively identical with those of figures with quite different external relations. If this were not the case, anything analogous to projective transformation would be impossible. For such transformation always alters the position, *i.e.* the external relations, of a figure, and could not, therefore, if figures were dependent on their relations to other figures or to empty space, be studied without reference to other figures, or to the absolute position of the original figure. We require for our principle, in short, what may be called the mutual passivity and reciprocal independence of two parts or figures of space.

This passivity and this independence involve the homogeneity of space, or its equivalent, the relativity of position.

[1] The straight line and plane, in all discussions of general Geometry, are not necessarily Euclidean. They are simply figures determined, in general, by two and by three points respectively; whether they conform to the axiom of parallels and to Euclid's form of the axiom of the straight line, is not to be considered in the general definition.

For if the internal properties of a figure are the same, whatever its external relations may be, it follows that all parts of space are qualitatively similar, since a change of external relation is a change in the part of space occupied. It follows, also, that all position is relative and extrinsic, *i.e.*, that the position of a point, or the part of space occupied by a figure, is not, and has no effect upon, any intrinsic property of the point or figure, but is exclusively a relation to other points or figures in space, and remains without effect except where such relations are considered.

**125.** The homogeneity of space and the relativity of position, therefore, are presupposed in the qualitative spatial comparison with which projective Geometry deals. The latter, as we saw, is also the basis of the principle of duality. But these properties, as I shall now endeavour to prove, belong of necessity to any form of externality, and are thus *à priori* properties of all possible spaces. To prove this, however, we must first define the notion of a form of externality in general.

Let us observe, to begin with, that the distinction between Euclidean and non-Euclidean Geometries, so important in metrical investigations, disappears in projective Geometry proper. This suggests that projective Geometry, though originally invented as the science of Euclidean space, and subsequently of non-Euclidean spaces also, deals really with a wider conception, a conception which includes both, and neglects the attributes in which they differ. This conception I shall speak of as a form of externality.

**126.** In Grassmann's profound philosophical introduction to his *Ausdehnungslehre* of 1844, he suggested that Geometry, though improperly regarded as pure, was really a branch of applied mathematics, since it dealt with a subject-matter not created, like number, by the intellect, but given to it, and therefore not wholly subject to its laws alone. But it must be possible —so he contended—to construct a branch of pure mathematics, a science, that is, in which our object should be wholly a creature of the intellect, which should yet deal, as Geometry does, with extension—extension as conceived, however, not as empirically perceived in sensation or intuition.

From this point of view, the controversy between Kantians

and anti-Kantians becomes wholly irrelevant, since the distinction between pure and mixed mathematics does not lie in the distinction between the subjective and the objective, but between the purely intellectual on the one hand, and everything else on the other. Now Kant had contended, with great emphasis, that space was not an intellectual construction, but a subjective intuition. Geometry, therefore, with Grassmann's distinction, belongs to mixed mathematics as much on Kant's view as on that of his opponents. And Grassmann's distinction, I contend, is the more important for Epistemology, and the one to be adopted in distinguishing the *à priori* from the empirical. For what is merely intuitional can change, without upsetting the laws of thought, without making knowledge formally impossible: but what is purely intellectual cannot change, unless the laws of thought should change, and all our knowledge simultaneously collapse. I shall therefore follow Grassmann's distinction in constructing an *à priori* and purely conceptual form of externality.

**127.** The pure doctrine of extension, as constructed by Grassmann, need not be discussed—it included much empirical material, and was philosophically a failure. But his principles, I think, will enable us to prove that projective Geometry, abstractly interpreted, is the science which he foresaw, and deals with a matter which can be constructed by the pure intellect alone. If this be so, however, it must be observed that projective Geometry, for the moment, is rendered purely hypothetical[1]. All necessary truth, as Bradley has shown, is hypothetical[2], and asserts, *primâ facie*, only the ground on which rests the necessary connection of premisses and conclusion. If we construct a mere conception of externality, and thus abandon our actually given space, the result of our construction, until we return to something actually given, remains without existential import—if there *be* experienced externality, it asserts, then there must be a form of externality with such and such properties. That there must be experienced externality, Kant's first argument about space proves, I think, to

[1] That projective Geometry must have existential import, I shall attempt to prove in Chapter IV.

[2] Logic, Book I. Chapter II.

those who admit experience of a world of diverse but interrelated things. But this is a question which belongs to the next Chapter.

What we have to do here is, not to discuss whether there is a form of externality, but whether, if there be such a form, it must possess the properties embodied in the axioms of projective Geometry. Now first of all, what do we mean by such a form?

**128.** In any world in which perception presents us with various things, with discriminated and differentiated contents, there must be, in perception, at least one "principle of differentiation[1]," an element, that is, by which the things presented are distinguished as various This element, taken in isolation, and abstracted from the content which it differentiates, we may call a form of externality. That it must, when taken in isolation, appear as a form, and not as a mere diversity of material content, is, I think, fairly obvious. For a diversity of material content cannot be studied apart from that material content; what we wish to study here, on the contrary, is the bare possibility of such diversity, which forms the residuum, as I shall try to prove hereafter[2], when we abstract from any sense-perception all that is distinctive of its particular matter. This possibility, then, this principle of bare diversity, is our form of externality. How far it is necessary to assume such a form, as distinct from interrelated things, I shall consider later on[3]. For the present, since space, as dealt with by Geometry, is certainly a form of this kind, we have only to ask: What properties must such a form, when studied in abstraction, necessarily possess?

**129.** In the first place, externality is an essentially relative conception—nothing can be external to itself. To be external to something is to be another with some relation to that thing. Hence, when we abstract a form of externality from all material content, and study it in isolation, position will appear, of

[1] Cf. Bradley's Logic, p. 63. It will be seen that the sense in which I have spoken of space as a principle of differentiation is not the sense of a "principle of individuation" which Bradley objects to.

[2] Chap. IV. §§ 186–191.

[3] Chap. IV. § 201 ff.

necessity, as purely relative—a position can have no intrinsic quality, for our form consists of pure externality, and externality contains no shadow or trace of an intrinsic quality. Thus we obtain our fundamental postulate, the relativity of position, or, as we may put it, the complete absence, on the part of our form, of any vestige of thinghood.

The same argument may also be stated as follows: If we abstract the conception of externality, and endeavour to deal with it *per se*, it is evident that we must obtain an object alike destitute of elements and of totality. For we have abstracted from the diverse matter which filled our form, while any element, or any whole, would retain some of the qualities of a matter. Either an element or a whole, in fact, would have to be a thing not external to itself, and would thus contain something not pure externality. Hence arise infinite divisibility, with the self-contradictory notion of the point, in the search for elements, and unbounded extension, with the contradiction of an infinite regress or a vicious circle, in the search for a completed whole. Thus again, our form contains neither elements nor totality, but only endless relations—the terms of these relations being excluded by our abstraction from the matter which fills our form.

**130.** In like manner we can deduce the homogeneity of our form. The diversity of content, which was possible only within the form of externality, has been abstracted from, leaving nothing but the bare possibility of diversity, the bare principle of differentiation, itself uniform and undifferentiated. For if diversity presupposes such a form, the form cannot, unless it were contained in a fresh form, be itself diverse or differentiated.

Or we may deduce the same property from the relativity of position. For any quality in one position, by which it was marked out from another, would be necessarily more or less intrinsic, and would contradict the pure relativity. Hence all positions are qualitatively alike, *i.e.* the form is homogeneous throughout.

**131.** From what has been said of homogeneity and relativity, follows one of the strangest properties of a form of externality. This property is, that the relation of externality between any two things is infinitely divisible, and may be regarded, consequently, as made up of an infinite number of the would-be elements of our form, or again as the sum of two relations of externality[1]. To speak of dividing or adding relations may well sound absurd—indeed it reveals the impropriety of the word relation in this connexion. It is difficult, however, to find an expression which shall be less improper. The fact seems to be, that externality is not so much a relation as bare relativity, or the bare possibility of a relation. On this subject, I shall enlarge in Chapter IV.[2] At this point it is only important to realize, what the subsequent argument will assume, that the relation—if we may so call it—of externality between two or more things must, since our form is homogeneous, be capable of continuous alteration, and must, since our infinitely divisible form is constituted by such relations, be capable of infinite division. But the result of infinite division is defined as the element of our form. (Our form has no elements, but we have to imagine elements in order to reason about it, as will be shown more fully in Chapter IV.) Hence it follows, that every relation of externality may be regarded, for scientific purposes, as an infinite congeries of elements, though philosophically, the relations alone are valid, and the elements are a self-contradictory result of hypostatizing the form of externality. This way of regarding relations of externality is important in understanding the meaning of such ideas as three or four collinear points.

As this point is difficult and important, I will repeat, in somewhat greater detail, the explanation of the manner in which straight lines and planes come to be regarded as congeries of points. From the strictly projective standpoint, though all other figures *are* merely a collection of any required number of points, lines or planes, given by some projective construction, straight lines and planes themselves are given integrally, and are not to be considered as divisible or composed of parts. To

[1] It is important to observe, however, that this way of regarding spatial relations is metrical; from the projective standpoint, the relation between two points is the whole unbounded straight line on which they lie, and need not be regarded as divisible into parts or as built up of points.

[2] §§ 207, 208. Cf. Hegel, Naturphilosophie, § 254.

say that a point lies on a straight line means, for projective Geometry proper, that the straight line is a relation between this and some other point. Here the points concerned, if our statement is to be freed from contradictions, must be regarded, if I may use such an expression, as *real* points—*i.e.* as unextended material centres[1]. Straight lines and planes are then relations between these material atoms. They are relations, however, which may undergo a metrical alteration while remaining projectively unchanged. When the projective relation between the two points $A$, $B$ is the same as that between the two points $A$, $C$, while the metrical relation (distance) is different, the three points $A$, $B$, $C$ are said to be collinear. Now the metrical manner of regarding spatial figures demands that they should be hypostatized, and no longer regarded as mere relations. For when we regard a quantity as extensive, *i.e.* as divisible into parts, we necessarily regard it as more than a mere relation or adjective, since no mere relation or adjective can be divided. For quantitative treatment, therefore, spatial relations must be hypostatized[2]. When this is done, we obtain, as we saw above, a homogeneous and infinitely divisible form of externality. We find now that distance, for example, may be continuously altered without changing the straight line on which it is measured. We thus obtain, on the straight line in question, a continuous series of points, which, since it is continuous, we regard as constituting our straight line. It is thus solely from the hypostatizing of relations, which metrical Geometry requires, that the view of straight lines and planes as *composed* of points arises, and it is from this hypostatizing that the difficulties of metrical Geometry spring.

**132**. The next step, in defining a form of externality, is obtained from the idea of *dimensions*. Positions, we have seen, are defined solely by their relations to other positions. But in order that such definition may be possible, a finite number of relations must suffice, since infinite numbers are philosophically inadmissible. A position must be definable, therefore, if knowledge of our form is to be possible at all, by some finite integral

[1] See Chap. IV. §§ 196–199.

[2] See a forthcoming article on "The relations of number and quantity" by the present writer in *Mind*, July, 1897.

number of relations to other positions. Every relation thus necessary for definition we call a dimension. Hence we obtain the proposition: *Any form of externality must have a finite integral number of dimensions.*

**133.** The above argument, it may be urged, has overlooked a possibility. It has used a transcendental argument, so an opponent may contend, without sufficiently proving that knowledge about externality must be possible without reference to the matters external to each other. The definition of a position may be impossible, so long as we neglect the matter which fills the form, but may become possible when this matter is taken into account. Such an objection can, I think, be successfully met, by a reference to the passivity and homogeneity of our form. For any dependence of the definition of a position on the particular matter filling that position, would involve some kind of interaction between the matter and its position, some effect of the diverse content on the homogeneous form. But since the form is totally destitute of thinghood, perfectly impassive, and perfectly void of differences between its parts, any such effect is inconceivable. An effect on a position would have to alter it in some way, but how could it be altered? It has no qualities except those which make it the position it is, as opposed to other positions; it cannot change, therefore, without becoming a different position. But such a change contradicts the law of identity. Hence it is not the position which has changed, but the content which has moved in the form. Thus it must be possible, if knowledge of our form can be obtained at all, to obtain this knowledge in logical independence of the particular matter which fills it. The above argument, therefore, granted the possibility of knowledge in the department in question, shows the necessity of a finite integral number of dimensions.

**134.** Let us repeat our original argument in the light of this elucidation. A position is completely defined when, and only when, enough relations are known to enable us to determine its relation to any fresh known position. Only by relations within the form of externality, as we have just seen, and never by relations which involve a reference to the particular matter filling the form, can such a definition be effected. But the possibility of such a definition follows from the Law of Excluded Middle, when this law is interpreted to mean, as Bosanquet makes it mean, that "Reality...is a system of reciprocally determinate parts[1]." For this implies that, given the relations of a part $A$ to other parts $B, C\ldots$, a sufficient wealth of such relations throws light on the relations of $B$ to $C$, etc. If this were not the case, the parts $A$, $B$, $C\ldots$could not be said to form such a system; for in such a system, to define $A$ is to define, at the same time, all the other members, and to give an adjective to $A$, is to give an adjective to $B$ and $C$. But the relations between positions are, when we restore the matter from which the positions were abstracted, relations between the things occupying those positions, and these relations, we have seen, can be studied without reference to the particular nature, in other respects, of the related things. It follows that, when we apply the general principle of systematic unity to these relations in particular, we find these relations to be dependent on each other, since they are not dependent, for their definition, on anything else. This gives the axiom of dimensions, in the above general form, as the result, on our abstract geometrical level, of the relativity of position and the law of excluded middle.

**135**. Before proceeding further, it is necessary to discuss the important special case where a form of externality has only one dimension. Of the two such forms, given in experience, one, namely time, presents an instance of this special case. But it may be shown, I think, that the function, in constituting the possibility of experience, which we demand of such forms, could not be accomplished by a one-dimensional form alone. For in a one-dimensional form, the various contents may be arranged in a series, and cannot, without interpenetration, change the order of contents in the series. But interpenetration is impossible, since a form of externality is the mere expression of diversity among things, from which it follows that things cannot occupy the same position in a form, unless there is another form by which to differentiate them. For without externality, there is no diversity[2]. Thus two bodies

[1] Logic, Vol. II. Chap. VII. p. 211.

[2] Real, as opposed to logical, diversity is throughout intended. Diverse

may occupy the same space, but only at different times: two things may exist simultaneously, but only at different places. A form of one dimension, therefore, could not, by itself, allow that change of the relations of externality, by which alone a varied world of interrelated things can be brought into consciousness. In a one-dimensional space, for example, only a single object, which must appear as a point, or two objects at most, one in front and one behind, could ever be perceived. Thus two or more dimensions seem an essential condition of anything worth calling an experience of interrelated things.

**136**. It may be objected, to this argument, that its validity depends upon the assumption that the change of a relation of externality must be continuous. Both to make and to meet this objection, in a manner which shall not imply time, seems almost impossible. For we cannot speak of change, whether continuous or discrete, without imagining time. Let us, therefore, allow time to be known, and discuss whether the temporal change, in any other form of externality, is necessarily continuous[1]. We must reply, I think, that continuity is necessary. The change of relation, in our non-temporal form, may be safely described as motion, and the law of Causality—since we have already assumed time—may be applied to this motion. It then follows that discrete motion would involve a finite effect from an infinitesimal cause, for a cause acting only for a moment of time would be infinitesimal. It involves, also, a validity in the point of time, whereas what is valid in any form of externality is not, as we have already seen, the infinitesimal and self-contradictory element resulting from infinite division, but the finite relation which mathematics analyzes into vanishing elements. Hence change must be continuous, and the possibility of serial arrangement holds good.

In a one-dimensional form other than time, the same argument must hold. For something analogous to Causality would be necessary to experience, and the relativity of the form would still necessarily hold. Hence, since only these two

aspects may coexist in a thing at one time and place, but two diverse real things cannot so coexist.

[1] On the insufficiency of time alone, see Chapter IV. § 191.

properties of time have been assumed, the above contention would remain valid of any second form whose relations were correlated with those of the first, as the analogue of Causality would require them to be.

**137.** The next step in the argument, which assumes two or more dimensions, is concerned with the general analogues of straight lines and planes, *i.e.* with figures—which may be regarded either as relations between positions or as series of positions—uniquely determined by two or by three positions. If this step can be successfully taken, our deduction of the above projective axioms will be complete, and descriptive Geometry will be established as the abstract *à priori* doctrine of forms of externality.

To prove this contention, consider of what nature the relations can be by which positions are defined. We have seen already that our form is purely relational and infinitely divisible, and that positions (points) are the self-contradictory outcome of the search for something other than relations. What we really mean, therefore, by the relations defining a position, is, when we undo our previous abstraction, the relations of externality by which some thing is related to other things. But how, when we remain in the abstract form, must such relations appear?

**138.** We have to prove that two positions must have a relation independent of any reference to other positions. To prove this, let us recur to what was said, in connection with dimensions, as to the passivity and homogeneity of our form. Since positions are defined only by relations, there must be relations, within the form, between positions. But if there are such relations, there must be a relation which is intrinsic to two positions. For to suppose the contrary, is to attribute an interaction or causal connection, of some kind, between those two positions and other positions—a supposition which the perfect homogeneity of our form renders absurd, since all positions are qualitatively similar, and cannot be changed without losing their identity. We may put this argument thus: since positions are only defined by their relations, such definition could never begin, unless it began with a relation between only two positions. For suppose three positions $A$,

*B*, *C* were necessary, and gave rise to the relation *abc* between the three. Then there would remain no means of defining the different pairs *BC*, *CA*, *AB*, since the only relation defining them would be one common to all three pairs. Nothing would be gained, in this case, by reference to fresh points, for it follows, from the homogeneity and passivity of the form, that these fresh points could not affect the internal relations of our triad, which relations, if they can give definiteness at all, must give it without the aid of external reference. Two positions must, therefore, if definition is to be possible, have some relation which they by themselves suffice to define. Precisely the same argument applies to three positions, or to four; the argument loses its scope only when we have exhausted the dimensions of the form considered. Thus, in three dimensions, five positions have no fresh relation, not deducible from those already known, for by the definition of dimensions, all the relations involved can be deduced from those of the fourth point to the first three, together with those of the fifth to the first three.

We may give the argument a more concrete, and perhaps a more convincing shape, by considering the matter arranged in our form. If two things are mutually external, they must since they belong to the same world, have some relation of externality; there is, therefore, a relation of externality between two things. But since our form is homogeneous, the same relation of externality may subsist in other parts of the form, *i.e.* while the two things considered alter their relations of externality to other things. The relation of externality between two things is, therefore, independent of other things. Hence, when we return to the abstract language of the form, two positions have a relation determined by those two positions alone, and independent of other positions.

Precisely the same argument applies to the relations of three positions, and in each case the relation must appear in the form as not a mere inference from the positions it relates. For relations, as we have seen, actually constitute a form of externality, and are not mere inferences from terms, which are nowhere to be found in the form[1].

[1] Geometrically, the axiom of the plane is, not that three points determine a figure at all, which follows from the axiom of the straight line, but that the

To sum up: Since position is relative, two positions must have *some* relation to each other; and since our form of

straight line joining two casual points of the plane lies wholly in the plane. This axiom requires a projective method of constructing the plane, *i.e.* of finding all the triads of points which determine the same projective figure as the given triad. The required construction will be obtained if we can find any projective figure determined by three points, and any projective method of reaching other points which determine the same figure.

Let $O$, $P$, $Q$ be the three points whose projective relation is required. Then we have given us the three straight lines $PQ$, $QO$, $OP$. Metrically, the

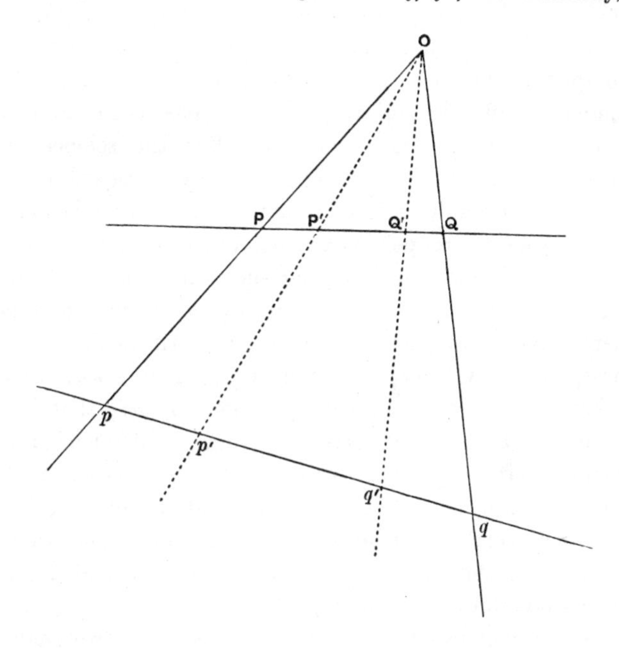


relation between these points is made up of the area, and the magnitude of the sides and angles, of the triangle $OPQ$, just as the relation between two points is distance. But projectively, the figure is unchanged when $P$ and $Q$ travel along $OP$ and $OQ$, or when $OP$ and $OQ$ turn about $O$ in such a way as still to meet $PQ$. This is a result of the general principle of projective equivalence enunciated above (§§ 108, 109). Hence the projective relation between $O$, $P$, $Q$ is the same as that between $O$, $p$, $q$ or $O$, $P'$, $Q'$; that is, $p$, $q$ and $P'$, $Q'$ lie in the plane $OPQ$. In this way, any number of points on the plane may be obtained, and by repeating the construction with fresh triads, every point of the plane can be reached. We have to prove that, when the plane is so constructed, the straight line joining any two points of the plane lies wholly in the plane.

It is evident, from the manner of construction, that any point of $PQ$, $OP$, $OQ$, $OP'$ or $OQ'$ lies in the plane. If we can prove that any point of $pq$ lies in externality is homogeneous, this relation can be kept unchanged while the two positions change their relations to other positions. Hence their relation is intrinsic, and independent of other positions. Since the form is a mere complex of relations, the relation in question must, if the form is sensuous or intuitive, be itself sensuous or intuitive, and not a mere inference. In this case, a unique relation must be a unique figure—in spatial terms, the straight line joining the two points.

**139**. With this, our deduction of projective Geometry from the *à priori* conceptual properties of a form of externality is completed. That such a form, when regarded as an independent thing, is self-contradictory, has been abundantly evident throughout the discussion. But the science of the form has been founded on the opposite way of regarding it: we have held it throughout to be a mere complex of relations, and have deduced its properties exclusively from this view of it. The many difficulties, in applying such an *à priori* deduction to intuitive space, and in explaining, as logical necessities, properties which appear as sensuous or intuitional data, must be postponed to Chapter IV. For the present, I wish to point out that projective Geometry is wholly *à priori*; that it deals with an object whose properties are logically deduced from its definition, not empirically discovered from data; that its definition, again, is founded on the possibility of experiencing diversity in relation, or multiplicity in unity; and that our whole science, therefore, is logically implied in, and deducible from, the possibility of such experience.

**140**. In metrical Geometry, on the contrary, we shall find a very different result. Although the geometrical conditions which render spatial measurement possible, will be found identical, except for slight differences in the form of statement, with the *à priori* axioms discussed above, yet the actual

the plane, we shall have proved all that is required, since $pq$ may be transformed, by successive repetitions of the same construction, into any straight line joining two points of the plane. But we have seen that the same plane is determined by $O$, $p$, $q$ and by $O$, $P$, $Q$. The straight lines $PQ$, $pq$ have, therefore, the same relation to the plane. But $PQ$ lies wholly in the plane; therefore $pq$ also lies wholly in the plane. Hence our axiom is proved.

measurement—which deals with actually given space, not the mere intellectual construction we have been just discussing—gives results which can only be known empirically and approximately, and can be deduced by no necessity of thought. The Euclidean and non-Euclidean spaces give the various results which are *à priori* possible; the axioms peculiar to Euclid—which are properly not axioms, but empirical results of measurement—determine, within the errors of observation, which of these *à priori* possibilities is realized in our actual space. Thus measurement deals throughout with an empirically given matter, not with a creature of the intellect, and its *à priori* elements are only the conditions presupposed in the possibility of measurement. What these conditions are, we shall see in the second section of this chapter.

## Section B.

### THE AXIOMS OF METRICAL GEOMETRY.

**141.** We have now reviewed the axioms of projective Geometry, and have seen that they are *à priori* deductions from the fact that we can experience externality, *i.e.* a co-existent multiplicity of different but interrelated things. But projective Geometry, in spite of its claims, is not the whole science of space, as is sufficiently proved by the fact that it cannot discriminate between Euclidean and non-Euclidean spaces[1]. For this purpose, spatial measurement is required: metrical Geometry, with its quantitative tests, can alone effect the discrimination. For all application of Geometry to physics, also, measurement is required; the law of gravitation, for example, requires the determination of actual distances. For many purposes, in short, projective Geometry is wholly insufficient: thus it is unable to distinguish between different kinds of conics, though their distinction is of fundamental importance in many departments of knowledge.

[1] A detailed proof has been given above, Chap. I. 3rd period. It is to be observed that any reference to infinitely distant elements involves metrical ideas.

Metrical Geometry is, then, a necessary part of the science of space, and a part not included in descriptive Geometry. Its *à priori* element, nevertheless, so far as this is spatial and not arithmetical, is the same as the postulate of projective Geometry, namely, the homogeneity of space, or its equivalent, the relativity of position. We can see, in fact, that the *à priori* element in both is likely to be the same. For the *à priori* in metrical Geometry will be whatever is presupposed in the possibility of spatial measurement, *i.e.* of quantitative spatial comparison. But such comparison presupposes simply a known identity of quality, the determination of which is precisely the problem of projective Geometry. Hence the conditions for the possibility of measurement, in so far as they are not arithmetical, will be precisely the same as those for projective Geometry.

**142.** Metrical Geometry, therefore, though distinct from projective Geometry, is not independent of it, but presupposes it, and arises from its combination with the extraneous idea of *quantity*. Nevertheless the mathematical form of the axioms, in metrical Geometry, is slightly different from their form in projective Geometry. The homogeneity of space is replaced by its equivalent, the axiom of Free Mobility. The axiom of the straight line is replaced by the axiom of distance: Two points determine a unique quantity, distance, which is unaltered in any motion of the two points as a single figure. This axiom, indeed, will be found to involve the axiom of the straight line—such a quantity could not exist unless the two points determined a unique curve—but its mathematical form is changed. Another important change is the collapse of the principle of duality: quantity can be applied to the straight line, because it is divisible into similar parts, but cannot be applied to the indivisible point. We thus obtain a reason, which was wanting in descriptive Geometry, for preferring points, as spatial elements, to straight lines or planes[1]. Finally, an entirely new idea is introduced with quantity, namely, the idea of *Motion*. Not that we study motion, or that any of our results have reference to motion, but that they cannot, though in projective

[1] Cf. Section A, §§ 115—117.

Geometry they could, be obtained without at least an ideal motion of our figures through space.

Let us now examine in detail the prerequisites of spatial measurement. We shall find three axioms, without which such measurement would be impossible, but with which it is adequate to decide, empirically and approximately, the Euclidean or non-Euclidean nature of our actual space. We shall find, further, that these three axioms can be deduced from the conception of a form of externality, and owe nothing to the evidence of intuition. They are, therefore, like their equivalents the axioms of projective Geometry, *à priori*, and deducible from the conditions of spatial experience. This experience, accordingly, can never disprove them, since its very existence presupposes them.

## I. *The Axiom of Free Mobility.*

**143**. Metrical Geometry, to begin with, may be defined as the science which deals with the comparison and relations of spatial magnitudes. The conception of magnitude, therefore, is necessary from the start. Some of Euclid's axioms, accordingly, have been classed as arithmetical, and have been supposed to have nothing particular to do with space. Such are the axioms that equals added to or subtracted from equals give equals, and that things which are equal to the same thing are equal to one another. These axioms, it is said, are purely arithmetical, and do not, like the others, ascribe an adjective to space. As regards their use in arithmetic, this is of course true. But if an arithmetical axiom is to be applied to spatial magnitudes, it must have some spatial import[1], and thus even this class is not, in Geometry, *merely* arithmetical. Fortunately, the geometrical element is the same in all the axioms of this class—we can see at once, in fact, that it can amount to no more than a definition of spatial magnitude[2]. Again, since the space with which Geometry deals is infinitely divisible, a definition of spatial magnitude

[1] Contrast Erdmann, op. cit. p. 138.

[2] Cf. Erdmann, op. cit. p. 164.

reduces itself to a definition of spatial equality, for, as soon as we have this last, we can compare two spatial magnitudes by dividing each into a number of equal units, and counting the number of such units in each[1]. The ratio of the number of units is, of course, the ratio of the two magnitudes.

**144.** We require, then, at the very outset, some criterion of spatial equality: without such a criterion metrical Geometry would become wholly impossible. It might appear, at first sight, as though this need not be an axiom, but might be a mere definition. In part this is true, but not wholly. The part which is merely a definition is given in Euclid's eighth axiom: "Magnitudes which exactly coincide are equal." But this gives a sufficient criterion only when the magnitudes to be compared already occupy the same position. When, as will normally be the case, the two spatial magnitudes are external to one another —as, indeed, must be the case, if they are distinct, and not whole and part—the two magnitudes can only be made to coincide by a motion of one or both of them. In order, therefore, that our definition of spatial magnitude may give unambiguous results, coincidence when superposed, if it can ever occur, must occur always, whatever path be pursued in bringing it about. Hence, if mere motion could alter shapes, our criterion of equality would break down. It follows that the application of the conception of magnitude to figures in space involves the following axiom[2]: *Spatial magnitudes can be moved from place to place without distortion;* or, as it may be put, *Shapes do not in any way depend upon absolute position in space.*

The above axiom is the axiom of Free Mobility[3]. I propose to prove (1) that the denial of this axiom would involve logical and philosophical absurdities, so that it must be classed as

[1] Strictly speaking, this method is only applicable where the two magnitudes are commensurable. But if we take infinite divisibility rigidly, the units can theoretically be taken so small as to obtain any required degree of approximation. The difficulty is the universal one of applying to continua the essentially discrete conception of number.

[2] Cf. Erdmann, op. cit. p. 50.

[3] Also called the axiom of congruence. I have taken congruence to be the *definition* of spatial equality by superposition, and shall therefore generally speak of the *axiom* as Free Mobility.

wholly *à priori*; (2) that metrical Geometry, if it refused this axiom, would be unable, without a logical absurdity, to establish the notion of spatial magnitude at all. The conclusion will be, that the axiom cannot be proved or disproved by experience, but is an *à priori* condition of metrical Geometry. As I shall thus be maintaining a position which has been much controverted, especially by Helmholtz and Erdmann, I shall have to enter into the arguments at some length.

**145**. A. *Philosophical Argument.* The denial of the axiom involves absolute position, and an action of mere space, *per se*, on things. For the axiom does not assert that real bodies, as a matter of empirical fact, never change their shape in any way during their passage from place to place; on the contrary, we know that such changes do occur, sometimes in a very noticeable degree, and always to some extent. But such changes are attributed, not to the change of place as such, but to physical causes: changes of temperature, pressure, etc. What our axiom has to deal with is not actual material bodies, but geometrical figures[1], and it asserts that a figure which is possible in any one position in space is possible in every other. Its meaning will become clearer by reference to a case where it does not hold, say the space formed by the surface of an egg. Here, a triangle drawn near the equator cannot be moved without distortion to the point, as it would no longer fit the greater curvature of the new position; a triangle drawn near the point cannot be fitted on to the flatter end, and so on. Thus the method of superposition, such as Euclid employs in Book I. Prop. IV., becomes impossible; figures cannot be freely moved about, indeed, given any figure, we can determine a certain series of possible positions for it on the egg, outside which it becomes impossible. What I assert is, then, that there is a philosophic absurdity in supposing space in general to be of this nature. On the egg we have marked points, such as the two ends; the space formed by its surface is not homogeneous, and if things are moved about in it, it must of itself exercise a distorting effect upon them, quite independently of physical causes; if it did not exercise such an effect, the things

[1] For the sense in which these figures are to be regarded as material, see criticism of Helmholtz, Chapter II. §§ 69 ff.

could not be moved. Thus such a space would not be homogeneous, but would have marked points, by reference to which bodies would have absolute position, quite independently of any other bodies. Space would no longer be passive, but would exercise a definite effect upon things, and we should have to accommodate ourselves to the notion of marked points in empty space; these points being marked, not by the bodies which occupied them, but by their effects on any bodies which might from time to time occupy them. This want of homogeneity and passivity is, however, absurd; space must, since it is a form of externality, allow only of relative, not of absolute, position, and must be completely homogeneous throughout. To suppose it otherwise, is to give it a thinghood which no form of externality can possibly possess. We must, then, on purely philosophical grounds, admit that a geometrical figure which is possible anywhere is possible everywhere, which is the axiom of Free Mobility.

**146.** B. *Geometrical Argument.* Let us see next what sort of Geometry we could construct without this axiom. The ultimate standard of comparison of spatial magnitudes must, as we saw in introducing the axiom, be equality when superposed; but need we, from this equality, infer equality when separated? It has been urged by Erdmann that, for the more immediate purposes of Geometry, this would be unnecessary[1]. We might construct a new Geometry, he thinks, in which sizes varied with motion on any definite law. Such a view, as I shall show below, involves a logical error as to the nature of magnitude. But before pointing this out, let us discuss the geometrical consequences of assuming its truth. Suppose the length of an infinitesimal arc in some standard position were $ds$; then in any other position $p$ its length would be $ds \,.\, f(p)$, where the form of the function $f(p)$ must be supposed known. But how are we to determine the position $p$? For this purpose, we require $p$'s coordinates, *i.e.*, some measurement of distance from the origin. But the distance from the origin could only be measured if we assumed our law $f(p)$ to measure it by. For suppose the origin to be $O$, and $Op$ to be a straight line whose length is required. If we have a measuring rod with which we travel

[1] Op. cit. p. 60.

along the line and measure successive infinitesimal arcs, the measuring rod will change its size as we move, so that an arc which appears by the measure to be $ds$ will really be $f(s) . ds$, where $s$ is the previously traversed distance. If, on the other hand, we move our line $Op$ slowly through the origin, and measure each piece as it passes through, our measure, it is true, will not alter, but now we have no means of discovering the law by which any element has changed its length in coming to the origin. Hence, until we assume our function $f(p)$, we have no means of determining $p$, for we have just seen that distances from the origin can only be estimated by means of the law $f(p)$. It follows that experience can neither prove nor disprove the constancy of shapes throughout motion, since, if shapes were not constant, we should have to *assume* a law of their variation before measurement became possible, and therefore measurement could not itself reveal that variation to us[1].

Nevertheless, such an arbitrarily assumed law *does*, at first sight, give a mathematically possible Geometry. The fundamental proposition, that two magnitudes which can be superposed in any one position can be superposed in any other, still holds. For two infinitesimal arcs, whose lengths in the standard position are $ds_1$ and $ds_2$, would, in any other position $p$, have lengths $f(p) . ds_1$ and $f(p) . ds_2$, so that their ratio would be unaltered. From this constancy of ratio, as we know through Riemann and Helmholtz, the above proposition follows. Hence all that Geometry requires, it would seem, as a basis for measurement, is an axiom that the alteration of shapes during motion follows a definite known law, such as that assumed above.

**147.** There is, however, in such a view, as I remarked above, a logical error as to the nature of magnitude. This error has been already pointed out in dealing with Erdmann[2], and need only be briefly repeated here. A judgment of magnitude is essentially a judgment of comparison: in unmeasured quantity, comparison as to the mere more or less, but in measured mag-

[1] The view of Helmholtz and Erdmann, that mechanical experience suffices here, though geometrical experience fails us, has been discussed above, Chapter II. §§ 73, 82.

[2] Chapter II. § 81.

nitude, comparison as to the precise how many times. To speak of differences of magnitude, therefore, in a case where comparison cannot reveal them, is logically absurd. Now in the case contemplated above, two magnitudes, which appear equal in one position, appear equal also when compared in another position. There is no sense, therefore, in supposing the two magnitudes unequal when separated, nor in supposing, consequently, that they have changed their magnitudes in motion. This senselessness of our hypothesis is the logical ground of the mathematical indeterminateness as to the law of variation. Since, then, there is no means of comparing two spatial figures, as regards magnitude, except superposition, the only logically possible axiom, if spatial magnitude is to be self-consistent, is the axiom of Free Mobility in the form first given above.

**148**. Although this axiom is *à priori*, its application to the measurement of actual bodies, as we found in discussing Helmholtz's views, always involves an empirical element[1]. Our axiom, then, only supplies the *à priori* condition for carrying out an operation which, in the concrete, is empirical—just as arithmetic supplies the *à priori* condition for a census. As this topic has been discussed at length in Chapter II., I shall say no more about it here.

**149**. There remain, however, a few objections and difficulties to be discussed. First, how do we obtain equality in solids, and in Kant's cases of right and left hands, or of right and left-handed screws, where actual superposition is impossible? Secondly, how can we take congruence as the only possible basis of spatial measurement, when we have before us the case of time, where no such thing as congruence is conceivable? Thirdly, it might be urged that we can immediately estimate spatial equality by the eye, with more or less accuracy, and thus have a measure independent of congruence. Fourthly, how is metrical Geometry possible on non-congruent surfaces, if congruence be the basis of spatial measurement? I will discuss these objections successively.

**150**. (1) How do we measure the equality of solids? These could only be brought into actual congruence if we had

[1] Chapter II. § 72.

a fourth dimension to operate in[1], and from what I have said before of the absolute necessity of this test, it might seem as though we should be left here in utter ignorance. Euclid is silent on the subject, and in all works on Geometry it is assumed as self-evident that two cubes of equal side are equal. This assumption suggests that we are not so badly off as we should have been without congruence, as a test of equality in one or two dimensions; for now we can at least be sure that two cubes have all their sides and all their faces equal. Two such cubes differ, then, in no sensible spatial quality save position, for volume, in this case at any rate, is not a sensible quality. They are, therefore, as far as such qualities are concerned, indiscernible. If their places were interchanged, we might know the change by their colour, or by some other non-geometrical property; but so far as any property of which Geometry can take cognisance is concerned, everything would seem as before. To suppose a difference of volume, then, would be to ascribe an effect to mere position, which we saw to be inadmissible while discussing Free Mobility. Except as regards position, they are geometrically indiscernible, and we may call to our aid the Identity of Indiscernibles to establish their agreement in the one remaining geometrical property of volume. This may seem rather a strange principle to use in Mathematics, and for Geometry their equality is, perhaps, best regarded as a definition; but if we demand a philosophical ground for this definition, it is, I believe, only to be found in the Identity of Indiscernibles. We can, without error, make our *definition* of three-dimensional equality rest on two-dimensional congruence. For since direct comparison as to volume is impossible, we are at liberty to *define* two volumes as equal, when all their various lines, surfaces, angles and solid angles are congruent, since there remains, in such a case, no *measurable* difference between the figures composing the two volumes. Of course, as soon as we have established this one case of equality of volumes, the rest of the theory follows; as appears from the ordinary method of integrating volumes, by dividing them into small cubes.

Thus congruence *helps* to establish three-dimensional equality,

[1] Contrast Delboeuf, L'ancienne et les nouvelles géométries, II. Rev. Phil. 1894, Vol. XXXVII. p. 354.

though it cannot directly *prove* such equality; and the same philosophical principle, of the homogeneity of space, by which congruence was proved, comes to our rescue here. But how about right-handed and left-handed screws? Here we can no longer apply the Identity of Indiscernibles, for the two are very well discernible. But as with solids, so here, Free Mobility can help us much. It can enable us, by ordinary measurement, to show that the internal relations of both screws are the same, and that the difference lies only in their relation to other things in space. Knowing these internal relations, we can calculate, by the Geometry which Free Mobility has rendered possible, all the geometrical properties of these screws—radius, pitch, etc.—and can show them to be severally equal in both. But this is all we require. Mediate comparison is possible, though immediate comparison is not. Both can, for instance, be compared with the cylinder on which both would fit, and thus their equality can be proved. A precisely similar proof holds, of course, for the other cases, right and left hands, spherical triangles, etc. On the whole, these cases confirm my argument; for they show, as Kant intended them to show[1], the essential relativity of space.

**151**. (2) As regards time, no congruence is here conceivable, for to effect congruence requires always—as we saw in the case of solids—one more dimension than belongs to the magnitudes compared. No day can be brought into temporal coincidence with any other day, to show that the two exactly cover each other; we are therefore reduced to the arbitrary assumption that some motion or set of motions, given us in experience, is uniform. Fortunately, we have a large set of motions which all roughly agree; the swing of the pendulum, the rotation and revolution of the earth and the planets, etc. These do not exactly agree, but they lead us to the laws of motion, by which we are able, on our arbitrary hypothesis, to estimate their small departures from uniformity; just as the assumption of Free Mobility enabled us to measure the departures of actual

[1] Prolegomena, § 13. See Vaihinger's Commentar, II. pp. 518—532 esp. pp. 521—2. The above was Kant's whole purpose in 1768, but only part of his purpose in the Prolegomena, where the intuitive nature of space was also to be proved.

bodies from rigidity. But here, as there, another possibility is mathematically open to us, and can only be excluded by its philosophic absurdity; we might have assumed that the above set of approximately agreeing motions all had velocities which varied approximately as some arbitrarily assumed function of the time, $f(t)$ say, measured from some arbitrary origin. Such an assumption would still keep them as nearly synchronous as before, and would give an equally possible, though more complex, system of Mechanics; instead of the first law of motion, we should have the following: A particle perseveres in its state of rest, or of rectilinear motion with velocity varying as $f(t)$, except in so far as it is compelled to alter that state by the action of external forces. Such a hypothesis *is* mathematically possible, but, like the similar one for space, it is excluded logically by the comparative nature of the judgment of quantity, and philosophically by the fact that it involves absolute time, as a determining agent in change, whereas time can never, philosophically, be anything but a passive form, abstracted from change. I have introduced this parallel from time, not as directly bearing on the argument, but as a simpler case which may serve to illustrate my reasoning in the more complex case of space. For since time, in mathematics, is one-dimensional, the mathematical difficulties are simpler than in Geometry; and although nothing accurately corresponds to congruence, there is a very similar mixture of mathematical and philosophical necessity, giving, finally, a thoroughly definite axiom as the basis of time-measurement, corresponding to congruence as the basis of space-measurement[1].

**152.** (3) The case of time-measurement suggests the third of the above objections to the absolute necessity of the axiom of Free Mobility. Psycho-physics has shown that we have an approximate power, by means of what may be called the sense of duration, of immediately estimating equal short times. This establishes a rough measure independent of any assumed uniform motion, and in space also, it may be said, we have a similar power of immediate comparison. We can see, by im-

[1] On the subject of time measurement, cf. Bosanquet's Logic, Vol. i. pp. 178—183. Since time, in the above account, is measured by motion, its measurement presupposes that of spatial magnitudes.

mediate inspection, that the sub-divisions on a foot rule are not grossly inaccurate; and so, it may be said, we both have a measure independent of congruence, and also could discover, by experience, any gross departure from Free Mobility. Against this view, however, there is at the outset a very fundamental psychological objection. It has been urged that all our comparison of spatial magnitudes proceeds by ideal superposition. Thus James says (Psychology, Vol. II. p. 152): "Even where we only feel one sub-division to be vaguely larger or less, the mind must pass rapidly between it and the other sub-division, and receive the immediate sensible shock of the more," and "so far as the sub-divisions of a sense-space are to be *measured* exactly against each other, objective forms occupying one subdivison must be directly or indirectly superposed upon the other[1]."

Even if we waive this fundamental objection, however, others remain. To begin with, such judgments of equality are only very rough approximations, and cannot be applied to lines of more than a certain length, if only for the reason that such lines cannot well be seen together. Thus this method can only give us any security in our own immediate neighbourhood, and could in no wise warrant such operations as would be required for the construction of maps &c., much less the measurement of astronomical distances. They might just enable us to say that some lines were longer than others, but they would leave Geometry in a position no better than that of the Hedonical Calculus, in which we depend on a purely subjective measure. So inaccurate, in fact, is such a method acknowledged to be, that the foot-rule is as much a need of daily life as of science. Besides, no one would trust such immediate judgments, but for the fact that the stricter test of congruence to some extent confirms them; if we could not apply this test, we should have no ground for trusting them even as much as we do. Thus we should have, here, no real escape from our absolute dependence upon the axiom of Free Mobility.

**153.** (4) One last elucidatory remark is necessary before our proof of this axiom can be considered complete. We spoke above of the Geometry on an egg, where Free Mobility does not hold. What, I may be asked, is there about a thoroughly non-

[1] Cf. Stumpf. Ursprung der Raumvorstellung, p. 68.

congruent Geometry, more impossible than this Geometry on the egg? The answer is obvious. The Geometry of non-congruent surfaces is *only* possible by the use of infinitesimals, and in the infinitesimal all surfaces become plane. The fundamental formula, that for the length of an infinitesimal arc, is only obtained on the assumption that such an arc may be treated as a straight line, and that Euclidean Plane Geometry may be applied in the immediate neighbourhood of any point. If we had not our Euclidean measure, which could be moved without distortion, we should have no method of comparing small arcs in different places, and the Geometry of non-congruent surfaces would break down. Thus the axiom of Free Mobility, as regards three-dimensional space, is necessarily implied and presupposed in the Geometry of non-congruent surfaces; the possibility of the latter, therefore, is a dependent and derivative possibility, and can form no argument against the *à priori* necessity of congruence as the test of equality.

**154.** It is to be observed that the axiom of Free Mobility, as I have enunciated it, includes also the axiom to which Helmholtz gives the name of Monodromy. This asserts that a body does not alter its dimensions in consequence of a complete revolution through four right angles, but occupies at the end the same position as at the beginning. The supposed mathematical necessity of making a separate axiom of this property of space has been disproved by Sophus Lie (v. Chap. I. § 45); philosophically, it is plainly a particular case of Free Mobility[1], and indeed a particularly obvious case, for a translation really does make some change in a body, namely, a change in position, but a rotation through four right angles may be supposed to have been performed any number of times without appearing in the result, and the absurdity of ascribing to space the power of making bodies grow in the process is palpable; everything that was said above on congruence in general applies with even greater evidence to this special case.

**155.** The axiom of Free Mobility involves, if it is to be true, the homogeneity of space, or the complete relativity of

[1] As is Helmholtz's other axiom, that the possibility of superposition is independent of the course pursued in bringing it about.

position. For if any shape, which is possible in one part of space, be always possible in another, it follows that all parts of space are qualitatively similar, and cannot, therefore, be distinguished by any intrinsic property. Hence positions in space, if our axiom be true, must be wholly defined by external relations, *i.e. Position is not an intrinsic, but a purely relative, property of things in space.* If there could be such a thing as absolute position, in short, metrical Geometry would be impossible. This relativity of position is the fundamental postulate of all Geometry, to which each of the necessary metrical axioms leads, and from which, conversely, each of these axioms can be deduced.

**156.** This converse deduction, as regards Free Mobility, is not very difficult, and follows from the argument of Section A[1], which I will briefly recapitulate. In the first place, externality is an essentially relative conception—nothing can be external to itself. To be external to something is to be an other with some relation to that thing. Hence, when we abstract a form of externality from all material content, and study it in isolation, position will appear of necessity as purely relative—it can have no intrinsic quality, for our form consists of pure externality, and externality contains no shadow or trace of an intrinsic quality. Hence we derive our fundamental postulate, the relativity of position. From this follows the homogeneity of our form, for any quality in one position, which marked out that position from another, would be necessarily more or less intrinsic, and would contradict the pure relativity. Finally Free Mobility follows from homogeneity, for our form would not be homogeneous unless it allowed, in every part, shapes or systems of relations, which it allowed in any other part. Free Mobility, therefore, is a necessary property of every possible form of externality.

**157.** In summing up the argument we have just concluded, we may exhibit it, in consequence of the two preceding paragraphs, in the form of a completed circle. Starting from the conditions of spatial measurement, we found that the comparison, required for measurement, could only be effected by superposition. But we found, further, that the result of such

[1] Cf. §§ 129, 130.

comparison will only be unambiguous, if spatial magnitudes and shapes are unaltered by motion in space, if, in other words, shapes do not depend upon absolute position in space. But this axiom can only be true if space is homogeneous and position merely relative. Conversely, if position is assumed to be merely relative, a change of magnitude in motion—involving as it does, the assertion of absolute position—is impossible, and our test of spatial equality is therefore adequate. But position in any form of externality must be purely relative, since externality cannot be an intrinsic property of anything. Our axiom, therefore, is *à priori* in a double sense. It is presupposed in all spatial measurement, and it is a necessary property of any form of externality. A similar double apriority, we shall see, appears in our other necessary axioms.

## II. *The Axiom of Dimensions*[1].

**158**. We have seen, in discussing the axiom of Free Mobility, that all position is relative, that is, a position exists only by virtue of relations[2]. It follows that, if positions can be defined at all, they must be uniquely and exhaustively defined by some finite number of such relations. If Geometry is to be possible, it must happen that, after enough relations have been given to determine a point uniquely, its relations to any fresh known point are deducible from the relations already given. Hence we obtain, as an *à priori* condition of Geometry, logically indispensable to its existence, the axiom that *Space must have a finite integral number of Dimensions.* For every relation required in the definition of a point constitutes a dimension, and a fraction of a relation is meaningless. The number of relations required must be finite, since an infinite number of dimensions would be practically impossible to determine. If we remember our axiom of Free Mobility,

[1] This deduction is practically the same as that in Sec. A, but I have stated it here with more special reference to space and to metrical Geometry.

[2] The question: "Relations to what?" is a question involving many difficulties. It will be touched on later in this chapter, and answered, as far as possible, in the fourth chapter. For the present, in spite of the glaring circle involved, I shall take the relations as relations to other positions.

and remember also that space is a continuum, we may state our axiom, for metrical Geometry, in the form given by Helmholtz (v. Chap. I. § 25): "In a space of $n$ dimensions, the position of every point is uniquely determined by the measurement of $n$ continuous independent variables (coordinates).[1]"

**159.** So much, then, is *à priori* necessary to metrical Geometry. The restriction of the dimensions to three seems, on the contrary, to be wholly the work of experience[2]. This restriction cannot be logically necessary, for as soon as we have formulated any analytical system, it appears wholly arbitrary. Why, we are driven to ask, cannot we add a fourth coordinate to our $x$, $y$, $z$, or give a geometrical meaning to $x^4$? In this more special form, we are tempted to regard the axiom of dimensions, like the number of inhabitants of a town, as a purely statistical fact, with no greater necessity than such facts have.

Geometry affords intrinsic evidence of the truth of my division of the axiom of dimensions into an *à priori* and empirical portion. For while the extension of the number of dimensions to four, or to $n$, alters nothing in plane and solid Geometry, but only adds a new branch which interferes in no way with the old, *some* definite number of dimensions is assumed in all Geometries, nor is it possible to conceive of a Geometry which should be free from this assumption[3].

**160.** Let us, since the point seems of some interest, repeat our proof of the apriority of this axiom from a slightly different point of view. We will begin, this time, from the most abstract conception of space, such as we find in Riemann's dissertation, or in Erdmann's extents. We have here, an ordered manifold, infinitely divisible and allowing of Free Mobility[4]. Free Mobility involves, as we saw, the power of passing continuously from any one point to any other, by any course which may seem pleasant to us; it involves, also, that, in such a

[1] Wiss. Abh. Vol. II. p. 614.

[2] Cp. Grassmann, Ausdehnungslehre von 1844, 2nd ed. p. XXIII.

[3] Delboeuf, it is true, speaks of Geometries with $m/n$ dimensions, but gives no reference (Rev. Phil. T. xxxvi. p. 450).

[4] In criticizing Erdmann, it will be remembered, we saw that Free Mobility is a necessary property of his extents, though he does not regard it as such.

course, no changes occur except changes of mere position, *i.e.*, positions do not differ from one another in any qualitative way. (This absence of qualitative difference is the distinguishing mark of space as opposed to other manifolds, such as the colour- and tone-systems: in these, every element has a definite qualitative sensational value, whereas in space, the sensational value of a position depends wholly on its spatial relation to our own body, and is thus not intrinsic, but relative.) From the absence of qualitative differences among positions, it follows logically that positions exist only by virtue of other positions; one position differs from another just because they are two, not because of anything intrinsic in either. Position is thus defined simply and solely by relation to other positions. Any position, therefore, is completely defined when, and only when, enough such relations have been given to enable us to determine its relation to any new position, this new position being defined by the same number of relations. Now, in order that such definition may be at all possible, a finite number of relations must suffice. But every such relation constitutes a dimension. Therefore, if Geometry is to be possible, it is *à priori* necessary that space should have a finite integral number of dimensions.

**161.** The limitation of the dimensions to three is, as we have seen, empirical; nevertheless, it is not liable to the inaccuracy and uncertainty which usually belong to empirical knowledge. For the alternatives which logic leaves to sense are discrete—if the dimensions are not three, they must be two or four or some other number—so that *small* errors are out of the question[1]. Hence the final certainty of the axiom of three dimensions, though in part due to experience, is of quite a different order from that of (say) the law of Gravitation. In the latter, a small inaccuracy might exist and remain undetected; in the former, an error would have to be so considerable as to be utterly impossible to overlook. It follows that the certainty of our whole axiom, that the number of dimensions is three, is almost as great as that of the *à priori* element,

[1] Cf. Riemann, Hypothesen welche der Geometrie zu Grunde liegen, Gesammelte Werke, p. 266; also Erdmann, op. cit. p. 154.

since this element leaves to sense a definite disjunction of discrete possibilities.

### III. *The Axiom of Distance.*

**162.** We have already seen, in discussing projective Geometry, that two points must determine a unique curve, the straight line. In metrical Geometry, the corresponding axiom is, that two points must determine a unique spatial quantity, distance. I propose to prove, in what follows, (1) that if distance, as a quantity completely determined by two points, did not exist, spatial magnitude would not be measurable; (2) that distance can only be determined by two points, if there is an actual curve in space determined by those two points; (3) that the existence of such a curve can be deduced from the conception of a form of externality, and (4) that the application of quantity to such a curve necessarily leads to a certain magnitude, namely distance, uniquely determined by any two points which determine the curve. The conclusion will be, if these propositions can be successfully maintained, that the axiom of distance is *à priori* in the same double sense as the axiom of Free Mobility, *i.e.* it is presupposed in the possibility of measurement, and it is necessarily true of any possible form of externality.

**163.** (1) The possibility of spatial measurement allows us to infer the existence of a magnitude uniquely determined by any two points. The proof of this depends on the axiom of Free Mobility, or its equivalent, the homogeneity of space. We have seen that these are involved in the possibility of spatial measurement; we may employ them, therefore, in any argument as to the conditions of this possibility.

Now to begin with, two points must, if Geometry is to be possible, have *some* relation to each other, for we have seen that such relations alone constitute position or localization. But if two points have a relation to each other, this must be an intrinsic relation. For it follows, from the axiom of Free Mobility, that two points, forming a figure congruent with the given pair, can be constructed in any part of space. If this were not possible, we have seen that metrical Geometry could not exist. But both the figures may be regarded as composed of two points and their relation; if the two figures are congruent, therefore, it follows that the relation is quantitatively the same for both figures, since congruence is the test of spatial equality. Hence the two points have a quantitative relation, which is such that they can traverse all space in a combined motion without in any way altering that relation. But in such a general motion, any external relation of the two points, any relation involving other points or figures in space, must be altered[1]. Hence the relation between the two points, being unaltered, must be an intrinsic relation, a relation involving no other point or figure in space; and this intrinsic relation we call distance[2].

**164.** It might be objected, to the above argument, that it involves a *petitio principii.* For it has been assumed that the two points and their relation form a figure, to which other figures can be congruent. Now if two points have no intrinsic relation, it would seem that they cannot form such a figure. The argument, therefore, apparently assumes what it had to prove. Why, it may be asked, should not three points be required, before we obtain any relation, which Free Mobility allows us to construct afresh in other parts of space?

The answer to this, as to the corresponding question in the first section of this chapter, lies, I think, in the passivity of space, or the mutual independence of its parts. For it follows, from this independence, that any figure, or any assemblage of points, may be discussed without reference to other figures or points. This principle is the basis of infinite divisibility, of

[1] This is subject, in spherical space, to the modification pointed out below, in dealing with the exception to the axiom of the straight line. See §§ 168—171.

[2] In speaking of distance at once as a quantity and as an intrinsic relation, I am anxious to guard against an apparent inconsistency. I have spoken of the judgment of quantity, throughout, as one of comparison; how, then, can a quantity be intrinsic? The reply is that, although measurement and the judgment of quantity express the result of comparison, yet the terms compared must exist before the comparison; in this case, the terms compared in measuring distances, *i.e.* in comparing them *inter se*, are intrinsic relations between points. Thus, although the *measurement* of distance involves a reference to other distances, and its expression as a magnitude requires such a reference, yet its existence does not depend on any external reference, but exclusively on the two points whose distance it is.

the use of quantity in Geometry, and of all possibility of isolating particular figures for discussion. It follows that two points cannot be dependent, as to their relation, on any other points or figures, for if they were so dependent, we should have to suppose some action of such points or figures on the two points considered, which would contradict the mutual independence of different positions. To illustrate by an example: the relation of two given points does not depend on the other points of the straight line on which the given points lie. For only through their relation, *i.e.* through the straight line which they determine, can the other points of the straight line be known to have any peculiar connection with the given pair.

**165.** But why, it may be asked, should there be only one such relation between two points? Why not several? The answer to this lies in the fact that points are wholly constituted by relations, and have no intrinsic nature of their own[1]. A point is defined by its relations to other points, and when once the relations necessary for definition have been given, no fresh relations to the points used in definition are possible, since the point defined has no qualities from which such relations could flow. Now one relation to any one other point is as good for definition as more would be, since however many we had, they would all remain unaltered in a combined motion of both points. Hence there can only be one relation determined by any two points.

**166.** (2) We have thus established our first proposition—two points have one and only one relation uniquely determined by those two points. This relation we call their distance apart. It remains to consider the conditions of the measurement of distance, *i.e.*, how far a unique value for distance involves a curve uniquely determined by the two points.

In the first place, some curve joining the two points is involved in the above notion of a combined motion of the two points, or of two other points forming a figure congruent with the first two. For without some such curve, the two point-pairs cannot be known as congruent, nor can we have any test by which to discover when a point-pair is moving as a single

[1] See the end of the argument on Free Mobility, § 155 ff.

figure[1]. Distance must be measured, therefore, by some line which joins the two points. But need this be a line which the two points completely determine?

**167.** We are accustomed to the definition of the straight line as the *shortest* distance between two points, which implies that distance might equally well be measured by curved lines. This implication I believe to be false, for the following reasons. When we speak of the length of a curve, we can give a meaning to our words only by supposing the curve divided into infinitesimal rectilinear arcs, whose sum gives the length of an equivalent straight line; thus unless we presuppose the straight line, we have no means of comparing the lengths of different curves, and can therefore never discover the applicability of our definition. It might be thought, perhaps, that some other line, say a circle, might be used as the basis of measurement. But in order to estimate in this way the length of any curve other than a circle, we should have to divide the curve into infinitesimal circular arcs. Now two successive points do not determine a circle, so that an arc of two points would have an indeterminate length. It is true that, if we exclude infinitesimal radii for the measuring circles, the lengths of the infinitesimal arcs would be determinate, even if the circles varied, but that is only because all the small circular arcs through two consecutive points coincide with the straight line through those two points. Thus, even with the help of the arbitrary restriction to a finite radius, all that happens is that we are brought back to the straight line. If, to mend matters, we take three consecutive points of our curve, and reckon distance by the arc of the circle of curvature, the notion of distance loses its fundamental property of being a relation between *two* points. For two consecutive points of the arc could

[1] In Frischauf's "Absolute Geometrie nach Johann Bolyai," Anhang, there is a series of definitions, starting from the sphere, as the locus of congruent point-pairs when one point of the pair is fixed, and hence obtaining the circle and the straight line. From the above it follows, that the sphere so defined already involves a curve between the points of the point-pair, by which various point-pairs can be known as congruent; and it will appear, as we proceed, that this curve must be a straight line. Frischauf's definition by means of the sphere involves, therefore, a vicious circle, since the sphere presupposes the straight line, as the test of congruent point-pairs.

not then be said to have any corresponding distance apart—three points would be necessary before the notion of distance became applicable. Thus the circle is not a possible basis for measurement, and similar objections apply, of course, with increased force, to any other curve. All this argument is designed to show, in detail, the logical impossibility of measuring distance by any curve not completely defined by the two points whose distance apart is required. If in the above we had taken distance as measured by circles of *given radius*, we should have introduced into its definition a relation to other points besides the two whose distance was to be measured, which we saw to be a logical fallacy. Moreover, how are we to know that all the circles have equal radii, until we have an independent measure of distance?

**168.** A straight line, then, is not the *shortest* distance, but is simply *the* distance between two points—so far, this conclusion has stood firm. But suppose we had two or more curves through two points, and that all these curves were congruent *inter se*. We should then say, in accordance with the definition of spatial equality, that the lengths of all these curves were equal. Now it might happen that, although no one of the curves was uniquely determined by the two end-points, yet the common length of all the curves was so determined. In this case, what would hinder us from calling this common length the distance apart, although no unique figure in space corresponded to it? This is the case contemplated by spherical Geometry, where, as on a sphere, antipodes can be joined by an infinite number of geodesics, all of which are of equal length. The difficulty supposed is, therefore, not a purely imaginary one, but one which modern Geometry forces us to face. I shall consequently discuss it at some length.

**169.** To begin with, I must point out that my axiom is not quite equivalent to Euclid's. Euclid's axiom states that two straight lines cannot enclose a space, *i.e.*, cannot have more than one common point. Now if every two points, without exception, determine a unique straight line, it follows, of course, that two different straight lines can have only one point in common—so far, the two axioms are equivalent. But it may happen, as in spherical space, that two points *in general* determine a unique straight line, but fail to do so when they have to each other the special relation of being antipodes. In such a system every pair of straight lines in the same plane meet in two points, which are each other's antipodes; but two points, *in general*, still determine a unique straight line. We are still able, therefore, to obtain distances from unique straight lines, except in limiting cases; and in such cases, we can take any point intermediate between the two antipodes, join it by the *same* straight line to both antipodes, and measure its distance from those antipodes in the usual way. The sum of these distances then gives a unique value for the distance between the antipodes.

Thus even in spherical space, we are greatly assisted by the axiom of the straight line; all linear measurement is effected by it, and exceptional cases can be treated, through its help, by the usual methods for limits. Spherical space, therefore, is not so adverse as it at first appeared to be to the *à priori* necessity of the axiom. Nevertheless we have, so far, not attacked the kernel of the objection which spherical space suggested. To this attack it is now our duty to proceed.

**170.** It will be remembered that, in our *à priori* proof that two points must have one definite relation, we held it impossible for those two points to have, to the rest of space, any relation which would be unaltered by motion. Now in spherical space, in the particular case where the two points are antipodes, they *have* a relation, unaltered by motion, to the rest of space—the relation, namely, that their distance is half the circumference of the universe. In our former discussion, we assumed that any relation to outside space must be a relation of position—and a relation of position must be altered by motion. But with a finite space, in which we have absolute magnitude, another relation becomes possible, namely, a relation of magnitude. Antipodal points, accordingly, like coincident points, no longer determine a unique straight line. And it is instructive to observe that there is, in consequence, an ambiguity in the expression for distance, like the ordinary ambiguity in angular measurement. If $1/k^2$ be the space constant, and $d$ be one value for the distance between two points, $2\pi kn \pm d$, where $n$ is any integer, is an equally good value.

Distance is, in short, a periodic function like angle. Thus such a state of things rather confirms than destroys my contention, that distance depends on a curve uniquely determined by two points. For as soon as we drop this unique determination, we see ambiguities creeping into our expression for distance. Distance still has a set of *discrete* values, corresponding to the fact that, given one point, the straight line is uniquely determined for all other points but one, the antipodal point. It is tempting to go on, and say: If through *every* pair of points there were an infinite number of the curves used in measuring distance, distance would be able, for the same pair of points, to take, not only a discrete series, but an infinite *continuous* series of values.

**171.** This, however, is mere speculation. I come now to the *pièce de résistance* of my argument. The ambiguity in spherical space arose, as we saw, from a relation of *magnitude* to the rest of space—such a relation being unaltered by a motion of the two points, and therefore falling outside our introductory reasoning. But what is this relation of magnitude? Simply a relation of the *distance* between the two points to a *distance* given in the nature of the space in question. It follows that such a relation *presupposes* a measure of distance, and need not, therefore, be contemplated in any argument which deals with the *à priori* requisites for the possibility of definite distances[1].

**172.** I have now shown, I hope conclusively, that spherical space affords no objection to the apriority of my axiom. Any two points have one relation, their distance, which is independent of the rest of space, and this relation requires, as its measure, a curve uniquely determined by those two points. I might have taken the bull by the horns, and said: Two points *can* have no relation but what is given by lines which join them, and therefore, if they have a relation independent of the rest of space, there must be one line joining them which they completely determine. Thus James says[2]:

[1] Nor in any argument which, like those of projective Geometry, avoids the notion of magnitude or distance altogether. It follows that the propositions of projective Geometry apply, without reserve, to spherical space, since the exception to the axiom of the straight line arises only on metrical ground.

[2] Psychology, Vol. II. pp. 149—150.

"Just as, in the field of quantity, the relation between two numbers is another number, so in the field of space the relations are facts of the same order with the facts they relate....... When we speak of the relation of direction of two points towards each other, we mean simply the sensation of the line that joins the two points together. *The line is the relation*...... The relation of position between the top and bottom points of a vertical line is that line, and nothing else."

If I had been willing to use this doctrine at the beginning, I might have avoided all discussion. A unique relation between two points *must* in this case, involve a unique line between them. But it seemed better to avoid a doctrine not universally accepted, the more so as I was approaching the question from the logical, not the psychological, side. After disposing of the objections, however, it is interesting to find this confirmation of the above theory from so different a standpoint. Indeed, I believe James's doctrine could be proved to be a logical necessity, as well as a psychological fact. For what sort of thing can a spatial relation between two distinct points be? It must be something spatial, and it must, since points are wholly constituted by their relations, be something at least as real and tangible as the points it relates. There seems nothing which can satisfy these requirements, except a line joining them. Hence, once more, a unique relation must involve a unique line. That is, linear magnitude is logically impossible, unless space allows of curves uniquely determined by any two of their points.

**173.** (3) But farther, the existence of curves uniquely determined by two points can be deduced from the nature of any form of externality[1]. For we saw, in discussing Free Mobility, that this axiom, together with homogeneity and the relativity of position, can be so deduced, and we saw in the beginning of our discussion on distance, that the existence of a unique relation between two points could be deduced from the homogeneity of space. Since position is relative, we may say, any two points must have *some* relation to each other: since

[1] This step in the argument has been put very briefly, since it is a mere repetition of the corresponding argument in Section A, and is inserted here only for the sake of logical completeness. See § 137 ff.

our form of externality is homogeneous, this relation can be kept unchanged while the two points move in the form, *i.e.*, change their relations to other points; hence their relation to each other is an intrinsic relation, independent of their relations to other points. But since our form *is* merely a complex of relations, a relation of externality must appear in the form, with the same evidence as anything else in the form; thus if the form be intuitive or sensational, the relation must be immediately presented, and not a mere inference. Hence the intrinsic relation between two points must be a unique figure in our form, *i.e.* in spatial terms, the straight line joining the two points.

**174.** (4) Finally, we have to prove that the existence of such a curve necessarily leads, when quantity is applied to the relation between two points, to a unique magnitude, which those two points completely determine. With this, we shall be brought back to distance, from which we started, and shall complete the circle of our argument.

We saw, in section A § 119, that the figure formed by two points is projectively indistinguishable from that formed by any two other points in the same straight line; the figure, in both cases, is, from the projective standpoint, simply the straight line on which the two points lie. The difference of relation, in the two cases, is not qualitative, since projective Geometry cannot deal with it; nevertheless, there is some difference of relation. For instance, if one point be kept fixed, while the other moves, there is obviously some change of relation. This change, since all parts of the straight line are qualitatively alike, must be a change of quantity. If two points, therefore, determine a unique figure, there must exist, for the distinction between the various other points of this figure, a unique quantitative relation between the two determining points, and therefore, since these points are arbitrary, between only two points. This relation is *distance*, with which our argument began, and to which it at least returns.

**175.** To sum up: If points are defined simply by relations to other points, *i.e.*, if all position is relative, *every point must have to every other point one, and only one, relation independent of the rest of space. This relation is the distance between the* *two points.* Now a relation between two points can only be defined by a line joining them—nay further, it may be contended that a relation can only *be* a line joining them. Hence a unique relation involves a unique line, *i.e.*, a line determined by any two of its points. Only in a space which admits of such a line is linear magnitude a logically possible conception. But when once we have established the possibility, *in general*, of drawing such lines, and therefore of measuring linear magnitudes, we may find that a certain magnitude has a peculiar relation to the constitution of space. The straight line may turn out to be of finite length, and in this case its length will give a certain peculiar magnitude, the space-constant. Two antipodal points, that is, points which bisect the entire straight line, will then have a relation of magnitude which, though unaltered by motion, is rendered peculiar by a certain constant relation to the rest of space. This peculiarity presupposes a measure of linear magnitude in general, and cannot, therefore, upset the apriority of the axiom of the straight line. But it destroys, for points having the peculiar antipodal relation to each other, the argument which proved that the relation between two points could not, since it was unchanged by motion, have reference to the rest of space. Thus it is intelligible that, for such special points, the axiom breaks down, and an infinite number of straight lines are possible between them; but unless we had started with assuming the general validity of the axiom, we could never have reached a position in which antipodal points could have been known to be peculiar, or, indeed, a position which would have enabled us to give any quantitative definition whatever of particular points.

Distance and the straight line, as relations uniquely determined by two points, are thus *à priori* necessary to metrical Geometry. But further, they are properties which must belong to any form of externality. Since their necessity for Geometry was deduced from homogeneity and the relativity of position, and since these are necessary properties of any form of externality, the same argument proves both conclusions. We thus obtain, as in the case of Free Mobility, a double apriority: The axiom of Distance, and its implication, the axiom of the Straight Line, are, on the one hand, presupposed in the possibility of spatial magnitude, and cannot, therefore, be contradicted by any experience resulting from the measurement of space; while they are consequences, on the other hand, of the necessary properties of any form of externality which is to render possible experience of an external world.

**176.** In connection with the straight line, it will be convenient to discuss the conditions of a metrical coordinate system. The projective coordinate system, as we have seen, aims only at a convenient nomenclature for different points, and can be set up without introducing the notion of spatial quantity. But a metrical coordinate system does much more than this. It defines every point quantitatively, by its quantitative spatial relations to a certain coordinate figure. Only when the system of coordinates is thus metrical, *i.e.*, when every coordinate represents some spatial magnitude, which is itself a relation of the point defined to some other point or figure—can operations with coordinates lead to a metrical result. When, as in projective Geometry, the coordinates are not spatial magnitudes, no amount of transformation can give a metrical result. I wish to prove, here, that a metrical coordinate system necessarily involves the straight line, and cannot, without a logical fallacy, be set up on any other basis. The projective system of coordinates, as we saw, is entirely based on the straight line; but the metrical system is more important, since its quantities embody actual information as to spatial magnitudes, which, in projective Geometry, is not the case.

In the first place, a point's metrical coordinates constitute a complete quantitative definition of it; now a point can only be defined, as we have seen, by its relations to other points, and these relations can only be defined by means of the straight line. Consequently, any metrical system of coordinates must involve the straight line, as the basis of its definitions of points.

This *à priori* argument, however, though I believe it to be quite sound, is not likely to carry conviction to any one persuaded of the opposite. Let us, therefore, examine metrical coordinate systems in detail, and show, in each case, their dependence on the straight line.

We have already seen that the notion of distance is impossible without the straight line. We cannot, therefore, define our coordinates in any of the ordinary ways, as the distances from three planes, lines, points, spheres, or what not. Polar coordinates are impossible, since,—waiving the straightness of the radius vector—the length of the radius vector becomes unmeaning. Triangular coordinates involve not only angles, which must in the limit be rectilinear, but straight lines, or at any rate some well-defined curves. Now curves can only be metrically defined in two ways: *Either* by relation to the straight line, as, *e.g.*, by the curvature at any point, *or* by purely analytical equations, which presuppose an intelligible system of metrical coordinates. What methods remain for assigning these arbitrary values to different points? Nay, how are we to get any estimate of the difference—to avoid the more special notion of distance—between two points? The very notion of a point has become illusory. When we have a coordinate system, we may define a point by its three coordinates; in the absence of such a system, we may define the notion of point *in general* as the intersection of three surfaces or of two curves. Here we take surfaces and curves as notions which intuition makes plain, but if we wish them to give us a precise numerical definition of *particular* points, we must specify the kind of surface or curve to be used. Now this, as we have seen, is only possible when we presuppose either the straight line, or a coordinate system. It follows that every coordinate system presupposes the straight line, and is logically impossible without it.

**177.** The above three axioms, we have seen, are *à priori* necessary to metrical Geometry. No others can be necessary, since metrical systems, logically as unassailable as Euclid's, and dealing with spaces equally homogeneous and equally relational, have been constructed by the metageometers, without the help of any other axioms. The remaining axioms of Euclidean Geometry—the axiom of parallels, the axiom that the number of dimensions is three, and Euclid's form of the axiom of the straight line (two straight lines cannot enclose a space)—are not essential to the possibility of metrical Geometry, *i.e.*, are not deducible from the fact that a science of spatial magnitudes is possible. They are rather to be regarded as empirical laws, obtained, like the empirical laws of other sciences, by actual investigation of the given subject-matter—in this instance, experienced space.

**178.** In summing up the distinctive argument of this Section, we may give it a more general form, and discuss the conditions of measurement in any continuous manifold, *i.e.*, the qualities necessary to the manifold, in order that quantities in it may be determinable, not only as to the more or less, but as to the precise *how much.*

Measurement, we may say, is the application of number to continua, or, if we prefer it, the transformation of mere quantity into number of units. Using *quantity* to denote the vague more or less, and *magnitude* to denote the precise number of units, the problem of measurement may be defined as the transformation of quantity into magnitude.

Now a number, to begin with, is a whole consisting of smaller units, all of these units being qualitatively alike. In order, therefore, that a continuous quantity may be expressible as a number, it must, on the one hand, be itself a whole, and must, on the other hand, be divisible into qualitatively similar parts. In the aspect of a whole, the quantity is *intensive*; in the aspect of an aggregate of parts, it is *extensive.* A purely intensive quantity, therefore, is not numerable—a purely extensive quantity, if any such could be imagined, would not be a single quantity at all, since it would have to consist of wholly unsynthesized particulars. A measurable quantity, therefore, is a whole divisible into similar parts. But a continuous quantity, if divisible at all, must be *infinitely* divisible. For otherwise the points at which it could be divided would form natural barriers, and so destroy its continuity. But further, it is not sufficient that there should be a possibility of division into mutually external parts; while the parts, to be perceptible as parts, must be mutually external, they must also, to be knowable as *equal* parts, be capable of overcoming their mutual externality. For this, as we have seen, we require superposition, which involves Free Mobility and homogeneity—the absence of Free Mobility in time, where all other requisites of measurement are fulfilled, renders direct measurement of time impossible. Hence infinite divisibility, free mobility, and homogeneity are necessary for the possibility of measurement in *any* continuous manifold, and these, as we have seen, are equivalent to our three axioms. These axioms are necessary, therefore, not only for spatial measurement, but for all measurement. The only manifold given in experience, in which these conditions are satisfied, is space. All other exact measurement—as could be proved, I believe, for every separate case—is effected, as we saw in the case of time, by reduction to a spatial correlative. This explains the paramount importance, to exact science, of the mechanical view of nature, which reduces all phenomena to motions in time and space. For number is, of all conceptions, the easiest to operate with, and science seeks everywhere for an opportunity to apply it, but finds this opportunity only by means of spatial equivalents to phenomena[1].

**179.** We have now seen in what the *à priori* element of Geometry consists. This *à priori* element may be defined as the axioms common to Euclidean and non-Euclidean spaces, as the axioms deducible from the conception of a form of externality, or—in metrical Geometry—as the axioms required for the possibility of measurement. It remains to discuss, in a final chapter, some questions of a more general philosophic nature, in which we shall have to desert the firm ground of mathematics and enter on speculations which I put forward very tentatively, and with little faith in their ultimate validity. The chief questions for this final chapter will be two: (1) How is such *à priori* and purely logical necessity possible, as applied to an actually given subject-matter like space? (2) How can we remove the contradictions which have haunted us in this chapter, arising out of the relativity, infinite divisibility, and unbounded extension of space? These two questions are forced upon us by the present chapter, but as they open some of the fundamental problems of philosophy, it would be rash to expect a conclusive or wholly satisfactory answer. A few hints and suggestions may be hoped for, but a complete solution could only be obtained from a complete philosophy, of which the prospects are far too slender to encourage a confident frame of mind.

[1] Cf. Hannequin, Essai critique sur l'hypothèse des atomes, Paris, 1895, passim.

## CHAPTER IV.

### PHILOSOPHICAL CONSEQUENCES.

**180.** IN the present chapter, we have to discuss two questions which, though scarcely geometrical, are of fundamental importance to the theory of Geometry propounded above. The first of these questions is this: What relation can a purely logical and deductive proof, like that from the nature of a form of externality, bear to an experienced subject-matter such as space? You have merely framed a general conception, I may be told, containing space as a particular species, and you have then shown, what should have been obvious from the beginning, that this general conception contained some of the attributes of space. But what ground does this give for regarding these attributes as *à priori?* The conception Mammal has some of the attributes of a horse; but are these attributes therefore *à priori* adjectives of the horse? The answer to this obvious objection is so difficult, and involves so much general philosophy, that I have kept it for a final chapter, in order not to interrupt the argument on specially geometrical topics.

**181.** I have already indicated, in general terms, the ground for regarding as *à priori* the properties of any form of externality. This ground is transcendental, *i.e.* it is to be found in the conditions required for the possibility of experience. The form of externality, like Riemann's manifolds, is a general class-conception, including time as well as Euclidean and non-Euclidean spaces. It is not motived, however, like the manifolds, by a *quantitative* resemblance to space, but by the fact that it fulfils, if it has more than one dimension, all those functions which, in our actual world, are fulfilled by space. But a form of externality, in order to accomplish this, must be, not a mere conception, but an actually experienced intuition. Hence the conception of such a form is the general *conception*, containing under it every logically possible *intuition* which can fulfil the function actually fulfilled by space. And this function is, to render possible experience of diverse but interrelated things. Some form in sense-perception, then, whose conception is included under our form of externality, is *à priori* necessary to experience of diversity in relation, and without experience of this, we should, as modern logic shows, have no experience at all. This still leaves untouched the relation of the *à priori* to the subjective: the form of externality is necessary to experience, but is not, *on that account*, to be declared purely subjective. Of course, necessity for experience can only arise from the nature of the mind which experiences; but it does not follow that the necessary conditions could be fulfilled, unless the objective world had certain properties. The *ground* of necessity, we may safely say, arises from the mind; but it by no means follows that the *truth* of what is necessary depends only on the constitution of the mind. Where this is not the case, our conclusion, when a piece of knowledge has been declared *à priori*, can only be: Owing to the constitution of the *mind*, experience will be impossible unless the *world* accepts certain adjectives.

Such, in outline, will be the argument of the first half of this chapter, and such will be the justification for regarding as *à priori* those axioms of Geometry, which were deduced above from the conception of a form of externality. For these axioms, and these only, are necessarily true of any world in which experience is possible.

**182**[1]. The view suggested has, obviously, much in common with that of the Transcendental Aesthetic. Indeed the whole of it, I believe, can be obtained by a certain limitation and interpretation of Kant's classic arguments. But as it differs, in many important points, from the conclusions aimed at by Kant, and as the agreement may easily seem greater than it is, I will begin by a brief comparison, and endeavour, by reference

[1] Compare, with the following paragraphs, the admirable discussion in Mr Hobhouse's Theory of Knowledge (Methuen 1896), Part I. Chapter II.

to authoritative criticisms, to establish the legitimacy of my divergence from him.

**183**. In the first place, the psychological element is much larger in Kant's thesis than in mine. I shall contend, it is true, that a form of externality, if it is to do its work, must not be a mere conception or a mere inference, but must be a given element in sense-perception—not, of course, originally given in isolation, but discoverable, through analysis, by attention to the object of sense-perception[1]. But Kant contended, not only that this element is given, but also that it is subjective. Space, for him, is, on the one hand, not conceptual, but on the other hand, not sensational. It forms, for him, no part of the data of sense, but is added by a subjective intuition, which he regards as not only logically, but psychologically, prior to objects in space[2].

This part of Kant's argument is wholly irrelevant for us. Whether a form of externality be given in sense, or in a pure intuition, is for us unimportant, since we neglect the question as to the connection of the *à priori* and the subjective; while the temporal priority of space to objects in it has been generally recognized as irrelevant to Epistemology, and has often been regarded as forming no part of Kant's thesis[3]. If we call intuitional whatever is given in sense-perception, then we may contend that a form of externality must be intuitional; but whether it is a pure intuition, in Kant's sense, or not, is irrelevant to us, as is its priority to the objects in it.

That the non-sensational nature of space is no essential part of Kant's *logical* teaching, appears from an examination of his argument. He has made, in the introduction, the purely logical distinction of matter and form, but has given to this distinction, in the very moment of suggesting it, a psychological implication. This he does by the assertion that the form, in which the matter of sensations is ordered, cannot itself be sensational. From this assumption it follows, of course, that space cannot be sensational. But the assumption is

[1] I speak of sense-perception instead of sensation, so as not to prejudge the issue as to the sensational nature of space,

[2] See Vaihinger's Commentar, II. pp. 86—7, 168—171.

[3] See Caird, Critical Philosophy of Kant, Vol. I. p. 287.

totally unsupported by argument, being set forth, apparently, as a self-evident axiom; it has been severely criticized by Stumpf[1] and others[2], and has been described by Vaihinger as a fatal *petitio principii*[3]; it is irrelevant to the logical argument, when this argument is separated, as we have separated it, from all connection with psychological subjectivity; and finally, it leaves us a prey to psychological theories of space, which have seemed, of late, but little favourable to the pure Kantian doctrine.

**184.** We have a right, therefore, in an epistemological inquiry, to neglect Kant's psychological teaching—in so far, at any rate, as it distinguishes spatial intuition from sensation—and attend rather to the logical aspect alone. That part of his psychological teaching, which maintains that space is not a mere conception, is, with certain limitations, sufficiently evident as applied to actual space; but for us, it must be transformed into a much more difficult thesis, namely, that *no* form of externality, which renders experience of diversity in relation possible, can be merely conceptual. This question, to which we must return later, is no longer psychological, but belongs wholly to Epistemology.

**185.** What, then, remains the kernel, for our purposes, of Kant's first argument for the apriority of space? His argument, in the form in which he gave it, is concerned with the eccentric projection of sensations. In order that I may refer sensations, he says, to something outside myself, I must already have the subjective space-form in the mind. In this shape, as Vaihinger points out (Commentar, II. pp. 69, 165), the argument rests on a *petitio principii*, for only if sensations are necessarily non-spatial does their projection demand a subjective space-form. But, further, is the logical apriority of space concerned with the externality of things to ourselves?

Space *seems* to perform two functions: on the one hand, it reveals things, by the eccentric projection of sensations, as external to the self, while, on the other hand, it reveals simultaneously presented things as mutually external. These

[1] Ursprung der Raumvorstellung, pp. 12—30.

[2] See the references in Vaihinger's Commentar, II. p. 76 ff.

[3] Commentar, II. p. 71 ff.

two functions, though often treated as coordinate and almost equivalent[1], seem to me widely different. Before we discuss the apriority of space, we must carefully distinguish, I think, between these two functions, and decide which of them we are to argue about.

Now externality to the Self, it would seem, must necessarily raise the whole question of the nature and limits of the Ego, and what is more, it cannot be derived from spatial presentation, unless we give the Self a definite position in space. But things acquire a position in space only when they can appear in sense-perception; we are forced, therefore, if we adopt this view of the function of space, to regard the Self as a phenomenon presented to sense-perception. But this reduces externality to the Self to externality to the body. The body, however, is a presented object like any other, and externality of objects to it is, therefore, a special case of the mutual externality of presented things. Hence we cannot regard space as giving, primarily at any rate, externality to the Self, but only the mutual externality of the things presented to sense-perception[2].

**186**. This, then, is the kind of externality we are to expect from space, and our question must be: Would the existence of diverse but interrelated things be unknowable, if there were not, in sense-perception, some form of externality? This is the crucial question, on which turns the apriority of our form, and hence of the necessary axioms of Geometry.

**187**. The converse argument to mine, the argument from the spatio-temporal element in perception to a world of inter-related but diverse things, is developed at length in Bradley's Logic. It is put briefly in the following sentence (p. 44, note): "If space and time are continuous, and if all appearance must occupy some time or space—and it is not hard to support both these *theses*—we can at once proceed to the conclusion, no mere particular exists. Every phenomenon will exist in more times or spaces than one; and against that diversity will be itself an universal[3]." The importance of this fact appears, when we

[1] *E.g.* by Caird, *op. cit.* Vol. I. p. 286.

[2] I have no wish to deny, however, that space is essential in the subsequent distinction of Self and not-Self.

[3] See also Book I. Chap II. passim; especially p. 51 ff. and pp. 70–1.

consider that, if any *mere* particular existed, all judgment and inference as to that particular would be impossible, since all judgment and inference necessarily operate by means of universals. But all reality is constructed from the *This* of immediate presentation, from which judgment and inference necessarily spring. Owing, however, to the continuity and relativity of space and time, no *This* can be regarded either as simple or as self-subsistent. Every *This*, on the one hand, can be analyzed into *Thises*, and on the other hand, is found to be necessarily related to other things, outside the limits of the given object of sense-perception. This function of space and time is presupposed in the following statement from Bosanquet's Logic (Vol. I. pp. 77—78): "Reality is given for me *in* present sensuous perception, and *in* the immediate feeling of my own sentient existence that goes with it. The real world, as a definite organized system, is *for me* an extension of this present sensation and self feeling by means of judgment, and it is the essence of judgment to effect and sustain such an extension... The subject in every judgment of Perception is some given spot or point in sensuous contact with the percipient self. But, as all reality is continuous, the subject is not *merely* this given spot or point."

**188.** This doctrine of Bradley and Bosanquet is the converse of the epistemological doctrine I have to advocate. Owing to the continuity and relativity of space and time, they say, we are able to construct a systematic world, by judgment and inference, out of that fragmentary and yet necessarily complex existence which is given in sense-perception. My contention is, conversely, that since all knowledge is necessarily derived by an extension of the *This* of sense-perception, and since such extension is only possible if the *This* has that fragmentary and yet complex character conferred by a form of externality, therefore some form of externality, given with the *This*, is essential to all knowledge, and is thus logically *à priori*. Bradley's argument, if sound, already proves this contention; for while, on the one hand, he uses no properties of space and time but those which belong to every form of externality, he proves, on the other hand, that judgment and inference require the *This* to be neither single nor self-subsistent. But I will endeavour, since the point is of fundamental importance, to reproduce the proof, in a form more suited than Bradley's to the epistemological question.

**189.** The essence of my contention is that, if experience is to be possible, every sensational *This* must, when attended to, be found, on the one hand, resolvable into *Thises,* and on the other hand dependent, for some of its adjectives, on external reference. The second of these theses follows from the first, for if we take one of the *Thises* contained in the first *This*, we get a new *This* necessarily related to the other *Thises* which make up the original *This.* I may, therefore, confine myself to the first proposition, which affirms that the object of perception must contain a diversity, not only of conceptual content, but of existence, and that this can only be known if sense-perception contains, as an element, some form of externality.

My premiss, in this argument, is that all knowledge involves a recognition of diversity in relation, or, if we prefer it, of identity in difference. This premiss I accept from Logic, as resulting from the analysis of judgment and inference. To prove such a premiss, would require a treatise on Logic; I must refer the reader, therefore, to the works of Bradley and Bosanquet on the subject. It follows at once, from my premiss, that knowledge would be impossible, unless the object of attention could be complex, *i.e.* not a *mere* particular. Now could the mental object—*i.e.*, in this connection, the object of a cognition—be complex, if the object of immediate perception were always simple?

**190.** We might be inclined, at first sight, to answer this question affirmatively. But several difficulties, I think, would prevent such an answer. In the first place, knowledge must start from perception. Hence, either we could have no knowledge except of our present perception, or else we must be able to contrast and compare it with some other perception. Now in the first case, since the present perception, by hypothesis, is a mere particular, knowledge of it is impossible, according to our premiss. But in the second case, the other perception, with which we compare our first, must have occurred at some other time, and with time, we have at once a form of externality. But what is more, our present perception is no longer a mere particular. For the power of comparing it with another perception involves a point of identity between the two, and thus renders both complex. Moreover, time must be continuous, and the present, as Bradley points out, is no mere point of time[1]. Thus our present perception contains the complexity involved in duration throughout the specious present: its mere particularity and its simplicity are lost. Its self-subsistence is also lost, for beyond the specious present, lie the past and the future, to which our present perception thus unavoidably refers us. Time at least, therefore, is essential to that identity in difference, which all knowledge postulates.

**191.** But we have derived, from all this, no ground for affirming a multiplicity of real things, or a form of externality of more than one dimension, which, we saw, was necessary for the truth of two out of our three axioms. This brings us to the question: Have we enough, with time alone as a form of externality, for the possibility of knowledge?

This question we must, I think, answer in the negative. With time alone, we have seen, our presented object must be complex, but its complexity must, if I may use such a phrase, be merely adjectival. Without a second form of externality, only one thing can be given at one moment[2], and this one thing, therefore, must constitute the whole of our world. The object of past perception must—since our one thing has nothing external to it, by which it could be created or destroyed—be regarded as the same thing in a different state. The complexity, therefore, will lie only in the changing states of our one thing—it will be adjectival, not substantival. Moreover we have the following dilemma: Either the one thing must be ourselves, or else self-consciousness could never arise. But the chief difficulty of such a world would lie in the changes of the thing. What could cause these changes, since we should know of nothing external to our thing? It would be like a Leibnitzian monad, without any God outside it to prearrange its changes. Causality, in such a world, could not be applied, and change would be wholly inexplicable.

[1] Logic, p. 51 ff.

[2] For the *This*, on such a hypothesis, has a purely temporal complexity, and is not resolvable into coexisting *Thises*.

Hence we require also the possibility of a diversity of simultaneously existing things, not merely of successive adjectives; and this, we have seen, cannot be given by time alone, but only by a form of externality for simultaneous parts of one presentation. We could never, in other words, infer the existence of diverse but interrelated things, unless the object of sense-perception could have substantival complexity, and for such complexity we require a form of externality other than time. Such a form, moreover, as was shown in Chapter III., Section A (§ 135), can only fulfil its functions if it has more than one dimension. In our actual world, this form is given by space; in any world, knowable to beings with our laws of thought, some such form, as we have now seen, must be given in sense-perception.

This argument may be briefly summed up, by assuming the doctrine of Bradley, that all knowledge is obtained by inference from the *This* of sense-perception. For, if this be so, the *This*—in order that inference, which depends on identity in difference, may be possible at all—must itself be complex, and must, on analysis, reveal adjectives having a reference beyond itself. But this, as was shown above, can only happen by means of a form of externality. This establishes the *à priori* axioms of Geometry, as necessarily having existential import and validity in any intelligible world.

**192**. The above argument, I hope, has explained why I hold it possible to deduce, from a mere conception like that of a form of externality, the logical apriority of certain axioms as to experienced space. The Kantian argument—which was correct, if our reasoning has been sound, in asserting that real diversity, in our actual world, could only be known by the help of space—was only mistaken, so far as its purely logical scope extends, in overlooking the possibility of other forms of externality, which could, if they existed, perform the same task with equal efficiency. In so far as space differs, therefore, from these other conceptions of possible intuitional forms, it is a mere experienced fact, while in so far as its properties are those which all such forms must have, it is *à priori* necessary to the possibility of experience.

I cannot hope, however, that no difficulty will remain, for

the reader, in such a deduction, from abstract conceptions, of the properties of an actual *datum* in sense-perception. Let us consider, for example, such a property as impenetrability. To suppose two things simultaneously in the same position in a form of externality, is a logical contradiction; but can we say as much of actual space and time? Is not the impossibility, here, a matter of experience rather than of logic? Not if the above argument has been sound, I reply. For in that case, we infer real diversity, *i.e.* the existence of different things, only from difference of position in space or time. It follows, that to suppose two things in the same point of space and time, is still a logical contradiction: not because we have constructed the data of sense out of logic, but because logic is dependent, as regards its application, on the nature of these data. This instance illustrates, what I am anxious to make plain, that my argument has not attempted to construct the living wealth of sense-perception out of "bloodless categories," but only to point out that, unless sense-perception contained a certain element, these categories would be powerless to grapple with it.

**193.** How we are to account for the fortunate realization of these requirements—whether by a pre-established harmony, by Darwinian adaptation to our environment, by the subjectivity of the necessary element in sense-perception, or by a fundamental identity and unity between ourselves and the rest of reality—is a further question, belonging rather to metaphysics than to our present line of argument. The *à priori*, we have said throughout, is that which is necessary for the possibility of experience, and in this we have a purely logical criterion, giving results which only Logic and Epistemology can prove or disprove. What is subjective in experience, on the contrary, is primarily a question for psychology, and should be decided on psychological grounds alone. When these two questions have been separately answered, but not till then, we may frame theories as to the connection of the *à priori* and the subjective; to allow such theories to influence our decision, on either of the two previous questions, is liable, surely, to confuse the issue, and prevent a clear discrimination between fundamentally different points of view.

**194.** I come now to the second question with which this chapter has to deal, the question, namely: What are we to do with the contradictions which obtruded themselves in Chapter III., whenever we came to a point which seemed fundamental? I shall treat this question briefly, as I have little to add to answers with which we are all familiar. I have only to prove, first, that the contradictions are inevitable, and therefore form no objection to my argument; secondly, that the first step in removing them is to restore the notion of matter, as that which, in the data of sense-perception, is localized and interrelated in space.

**195.** The contradictions in space are an ancient theme—as ancient, in fact, as Zeno's refutation of motion. They are, roughly, of two kinds, though the two kinds cannot be sharply divided. There are the contradictions inherent in the notion of the continuum, and the contradictions which spring from the fact that space, while it must, to be knowable, be pure relativity, must also, it would seem, since it is immediately experienced, be something more than mere relations. The first class of contradictions has been encountered more frequently in this essay, and is also, I think, the more definite, and the more important for our present purpose. I doubt, however, whether the two classes are really distinct; for any continuum, I believe, in which the elements are not data, but intellectual constructions resulting from analysis, can be shown to have the same relational and yet not wholly relational character as belongs to space.

The three following contradictions, which I shall discuss successively, seem to me the most prominent in a theory of Geometry.

(1) Though the parts of space are intuitively distinguished, no conception is adequate to differentiate them. Hence arises a vain search for elements, by which the differentiation could be accomplished, and for a whole, of which the parts of space are to be components. Thus we get the point, or zero extension, as the spatial element, and an infinite regress or a vicious circle in the search for a whole.

(2) All positions being relative, positions can only be defined by their relations, *i.e.* by the straight lines or planes

through them; but straight lines and planes, being all qualitatively similar, can only be defined by the positions they relate. Hence, again, we get a vicious circle.

(3) Spatial figures must be regarded as relations. But a relation is necessarily indivisible, while spatial figures are necessarily divisible *ad infinitum.*

**196.** (1) *Points.* The antinomy of the point—which arises wherever a continuum is given, and elements have to be sought in it—is fundamental to Geometry. It has been given, perhaps unintentionally, by Veronese as the first axiom, in the form: "There are different points. All points are identical" (*op. cit.* p. 226). We saw, in discussing projective Geometry, that straight lines and planes must be regarded, on the one hand as relations between points, and on the other hand as made up of points[1]. We saw again, in dealing with measurement, how space must be regarded as infinitely divisible, and yet as mere relativity. But what is divisible and consists of parts, as space does, must lead at last, by continued analysis, to a simple and unanalyzable part, as the unit of differentiation. For whatever can be divided, and has parts, possesses some thinghood, and must, therefore, contain two ultimate units, the whole namely, and the smallest element possessing thinghood. But in space this is notoriously not the case. After hypostatizing space, as Geometry is compelled to do, the mind imperatively demands elements, and insists on having them, whether possible or not. Of this demand, all the geometrical applications of the infinitesimal calculus are evidence[2]. But what sort of elements do we thus obtain? Analysis, being unable to find any earlier halting-place, finds its elements in points, that is, in zero quanta of space. Such a conception is a palpable contradiction, only rendered tolerable by its necessity and familiarity. A point must be spatial, otherwise it would not fulfil the function of a spatial element; but again it must contain no space, for any finite extension is capable of further analysis. Points can never be given in intuition, which has no concern with the infinitesimal: they are a purely conceptual construction, arising

[1] Chapter III. Section A, (§ 131).

[2] Cf. Hannequin, Essai critique sur l'hypothèse des atomes, Paris 1895, Chap. I. Section III.; especially p. 43.

out of the need of terms between which spatial relations can hold. If space be more than relativity, spatial relations must involve spatial relata; but no relata appear, until we have analyzed our spatial data down to nothing. The contradictory notion of the point, as a thing in space without spatial magnitude, is the only outcome of our search for spatial relata. This *reductio ad absurdum* surely suffices, by itself, to prove the essential relativity of space.

**197.** Thus Geometry is forced, since it wishes to regard space as independent, to hypostatize its abstractions, and therefore to invent a self-contradictory notion as the spatial element. A similar absurdity appears, even more obviously, in the notion of a whole of space. The antinomy may, therefore, be stated thus: Space, as we have seen throughout, must, if knowledge of it is to be possible, be mere relativity; but it must also, if *independent* knowledge of it, such as Geometry seeks, is to be possible, be something more than mere relativity, since it is divisible and has parts. But we saw, in Chap. III., Section A (§ 133) that knowledge of a form of externality must be logically independent of the particular matter filling the form. How then are we to extricate ourselves from this dilemma?

The only way, I think, is, not to make Geometry dependent on Physics, which we have seen to be erroneous[1], but to give every geometrical proposition a certain reference to matter in general. And at this point an important distinction must be made. We have hitherto spoken of space as relational, and of spatial figures as relations. But space, it would seem, is rather relativity than relations—itself not a relation, it gives the bare possibility of relations between diverse things[2]. As applied to a spatial figure, which can only arise by a differentiation of space, and hence by the introduction of some differentiating matter, the word relation is, perhaps, less misleading than any other; as applied to empty undifferentiated space, it seems by no means an accurate description.

But a bare possibility cannot exist, or be given in sense-perception! What becomes, then, of the arguments of the

[1] See Chapter II. § 69 ff.

[2] See third antinomy below, § 201 ff.

first part of this chapter? I reply, it is not empty space, but spatial figures, which sense-perception reveals, and spatial figures, as we have just seen, involve a differentiation of space, and therefore a reference to the matter which is in space. It is spatial figures, also, and not empty space, with which Geometry has to deal. The antinomy discussed above arises then—so it would seem—from the attempt to deal with empty space, rather than with spatial figures and the matter to which they necessarily refer.

**198**. Let us see whether, by this change, we can overcome the antinomy of the point. Spatial figures, we shall now say, are relations between the matter which differentiates empty space. Their divisibility, which seemed to contradict their relational character, may be explained in two ways: first, as holding of the figures considered as parts of empty space, which is itself not a relation; second, as denoting the possibility of continuous change in the relation expressed by the spatial figure. These two ways are, at bottom, the same; for empty space is a possibility of relations, and the figure, when viewed in connection with empty space, thus becomes a *possible* relation, with which other possible relations may be contrasted or compared. But the second way of regarding divisibility is the better way, since it introduces a reference to the matter which differentiates empty space, without which, spatial figures, and therefore Geometry, could not exist. It is empty space, then—so we must conclude—which gives rise to the antinomy in question; for empty space is a bare possibility of relations, undifferentiated and homogeneous, and thus wholly destitute of parts or of thinghood. To speak of parts of a possibility is nonsense; the parts and differentiations arise only through a reference to the matter which is differentiated in space.

**199**. But what nature must we ascribe to this matter, which is to be involved in all geometrical propositions? In criticizing Helmholtz (Chap. II. § 73), it may be remembered, we decided that Geometry refers to a peculiar and abstract kind of matter, which is not regarded as possessing any causal qualities, as exerting or as subject to the action of forces. And this is the matter, I think, which we require for the needs of the moment. Not that we affirm, of course, that actual matter can be destitute of the properties with which Physics is cognizant, but that we abstract from these properties, as being irrelevant to Geometry. All that we require, for our immediate purpose, is a subject of that diversity which space renders possible, or terms for those relations by which empty space, if space is to be studied at all, must be differentiated. But how must a matter, which is to fulfil this function, be regarded?

Empty space, we have said, is a possibility of diversity in relation, but spatial figures, with which Geometry necessarily deals, are the actual relations rendered possible by empty space. Our matter, therefore, must supply the terms for these relations. It must be differentiated, since such differentiation, as we have seen, is the special work of space. We must find, therefore, in our matter, that unit of differentiation, or atom[1], which in space we could not find. This atom must be simple, *i.e.* it must contain no real diversity; it must be a *This* not resolvable into *Thises.* Being simple, it can contain no relations within itself, and consequently, since spatial figures are mere relations, it cannot appear as a spatial figure; for every spatial figure involves some diversity of matter. But our atom must have spatial relations with other atoms, since to supply terms for these relations is its only function. It is also capable of having these relations, since it is differentiated from other atoms. Hence we obtain an unextended term for spatial relations, precisely of the kind we require. So long as we sought this term without reference to anything more than space, the self-contradictory notion of the point was the only outcome of our search; but now that we allow a reference to the matter differentiated by space, we find at once the term which was needed, namely, a non-spatial simple element, with spatial relations to other elements. To Geometry such a term will appear, owing to its spatial relations, as a point; but the contradiction of the point, as we now see, is a result only of the undue abstraction with which Geometry deals.

**200.** (2) *The circle in the definition of straight lines and planes.* This difficulty need not long detain us, since we have already, with the material atom, broken through the relativity which caused our circle. Straight lines, in the purely geometrical

[1] This atom, of course, must not be confounded with the atom of Chemistry.

procedure, are defined only by points, and points only by straight lines. But points, now, are replaced by material atoms: the duality of points and lines, therefore, has disappeared, and the straight line may be defined as the spatial relation between two unextended atoms. These atoms have spatial adjectives, derived from their relations to other atoms; but they have no *intrinsic* spatial adjectives, such as could belong to them if they had extension or figure. Thus straight lines and planes are the true spatial units, and points result only from the attempt to find, within space, those terms for spatial relations which exist only in a more than spatial matter. Straight lines, planes and volumes are the spatial relations between two, three or four unextended atoms, and points are a merely convenient geometrical fiction, by which possible atoms are replaced. For, since space, as we saw, is a possibility, Geometry deals not with actually realized spatial relations, but with the whole scheme of possible relations.

**201.** (3) *Space is at once relational and more than relational.* We have already touched on the question how far space is other than relations, but as this question is quite fundamental, as *relation* is an ambiguous and dangerous word, as I have made constant use of the relativity of space without attempting to define a relation, it will be necessary to discuss this antinomy at length.

**202.** Now for this discussion it is essential to distinguish clearly between empty space and spatial figures. Empty space, as a form of externality, is not actual relations, but the possibility of relations: if we ascribe existential import to it, as the ground, in reality, of all diversity in relation, we at once have space as something not itself relations, though giving the possibility of all relations. In this sense, space is to be distinguished from spatial order. Spatial order, it may be said, presupposes space, as that in which this order is possible. Thus Stumpf says[1]: "There is no order or relation without a positive absolute content, underlying it, and making it possible to order anything in this manner. Why and how should we otherwise distinguish one order from another?...To distinguish different orders from one another, we must everywhere recognize a

[1] Ursprung der Raumvorstellung, p. 15.

particular absolute content, in relation to which the order takes place. And so space, too, is not a mere order, but just that by which the spatial order, side-by-sideness (*Nebeneinander*) distinguishes itself from the rest."

May we not, then, resolve the antinomy very simply, by a reference to this ambiguity of space? Bradley contends (Appearance and Reality, pp. 36–7) that, on the one hand, space has parts, and is therefore not mere relations, while on the other hand, when we try to say what these parts are, we find them after all to be mere relations. But cannot the space which has parts be regarded as empty space, Stumpf's absolute underlying content, which is not mere relations, while the parts, in so far as they turn out to be mere relations, are those relations which constitute spatial order, not empty space? If this can be maintained, the antinomy no longer exists.

But such an explanation, though I believe it to be a first step towards a solution, will, I fear, itself demand almost as much explanation as the original difficulty. For the connection of empty space with spatial order is itself a question full of difficulty, to be answered only after much labour.

**203**. Let us consider what this empty space is. (I speak of "empty" space without necessarily implying the absence of matter, but only to denote a space which is not a mere order of material things.) Stumpf regards it as given in sense; Kant, in the last two arguments of his metaphysical deduction, argues that it is an intuition, not a concept, and must be known before spatial order becomes possible. I wish to maintain, on the contrary, that it is wholly conceptual; that space is given only as spatial order; that spatial relations, being given, appear as more than mere relations, and so become hypostatized; that when hypostatized, the whole collection of them is regarded as contained in empty space; but that this empty space itself, if it means more than the logical possibility of space-relations, is an unnecessary and self-contradictory assumption. Let us begin by considering Kant's arguments on this point.

Leibnitz had affirmed that space was only relations, while Newton had maintained the objective reality of absolute space. Kant adopted a middle course: he asserted absolute space, but regarded it as purely subjective. The assertion of absolute space is the object of his second argument; for if space were mere relations between things, it would necessarily disappear with the disappearance of the things in it; but this the second argument denies[1]. Now spatial order obviously does disappear with matter, but absolute or empty space may be supposed to remain. It is this, then, which Kant is arguing about, and it is this which he affirms to be a pure intuition, necessarily presupposed by spatial order[2].

**204**. But can we agree in regarding empty space, the "infinite given whole," as really given? Must we not, in spite of Kant's argument, regard it as wholly conceptual? It is not required, in the first place, by the argument of the first half of this chapter, which required only that every *This* of sense-perception should be resolvable into *Thises*, and thus involved only an order among *Thises*, not anything given originally without reference to them at all. In the second place, Kant's two arguments[3] designed to prove that empty space is not conceptual, are inadequate to their purpose. The argument that the parts of space are not contained *under* it, but *in* it, proves certainly that space is not a general conception, of which spatial figures are the instances; but it by no means follows that empty space is not a conception. Empty space is undifferentiated and homogenous; parts of space, or spatial figures, arise only by reference to some differentiating matter, and thus belong rather to spatial order than to empty space. If empty space be the pre-condition of spatial order, we cannot expect it to be connected with spatial relations as genus with species. But empty space may nevertheless be a universal conception; it may be related to spatial order as the state to the citizens. These are not instances of the state, but are contained in it; they also, in a sense, presuppose it, for a man can only become a citizen by being related to other citizens in a state[4].

[1] See Vaihinger's Commentar, II. pp. 189—190.

[2] See ibid. p. 224 ff. for Kant's inconsistencies on this point.

[3] The fourth and fifth in the first edition, the third and fourth in the second.

[4] Cf. Vaihinger's Commentar, II. p. 218.

The uniqueness of space, again, seems hardly a valid argument for its intuitional nature; to regard it as an argument implies, indeed, that all conceptions are abstracted from a series of instances—a view which has been criticized in Chapter II. (§ 77), and need not be further discussed here[1]. There is no ground, therefore, in Kant's two arguments for the intuitional nature of empty space, which can be maintained against criticism.

**205.** Another ground for condemning empty space is to be found in the mathematical antinomies. For it is no solution, as Lotze points out (Metaphysik, Bk. II. Chap. I., § 106), to regard empty space as purely subjective: contradictions in a necessary subjective intuition form as great a difficulty as in anything else. But these antinomies arise only in connection with empty space, not with spatial order as an aggregate of relations. For only when space is regarded as possessed of some thinghood, can a whole or a true element be demanded. This we have seen already in connection with the Point. When space is regarded, so far as it is valid, as only spatial order, unbounded extension and infinite divisibility both disappear. What is divided is not spatial relations, but matter; and if matter, as we have seen that Geometry requires, consists of unextended atoms with spatial relations, there is no reason to regard matter either as infinitely divisible, or as consisting of atoms of finite extension.

**206.** But whence arises, on this view, the paradox that we cannot but regard space as having more or less thinghood, and as divisible *ad infinitum*? This must be explained, I think, as a psychological illusion, unavoidably arising from the fact that spatial relations are immediately presented. They thus have a peculiar psychical quality, as immediate experiences, by which quality they can be distinguished from time-relations or any other order in which things may be arranged. To Stumpf, whose problem is psychological, such a psychical quality would constitute an absolute underlying content, and would fully justify his thesis; to us, however, whose problem is epistemological, it would not do so, but would leave the *meaning* of the spatial element in sense-perception free from any implication

[1] Cf. Vaihinger's Commentar, II. p. 207.

of an absolute or empty space[1]. May we not, then, abandon empty space, and say: Spatial order consists of *felt* relations, and *quâ* felt has, for Psychology, an existence not wholly resolvable into relations, and unavoidably *seeming* to be more than mere relations. But when we examine the information, as to space, which we derive from sense-perception, we find ourselves plunged in contradictions, as soon as we allow this information to consist of more than relations. This leaves spatial order alone in the field, and reduces empty space to a mere name for the logical possibility of spatial relations.

**207.** The apparent divisibility of the relations which constitute spatial order, then, may be explained in two ways, though these are at bottom equivalent. We may take the relation as considered in connection with empty space, in which case it becomes more than a relation; but being falsely hypostatized, it appears as a complex thing, necessarily composed of elements, which elements, however, nowhere emerge until we analyze the pseudo-thing down to nothing, and arrive at the point. In this sense, the divisibility of spatial relations is an unavoidable illusion. Or again, we may take the relation in connection with the material atoms it relates. In this case, other atoms may be imagined, differently localized by different spatial relations. If they are localized on the straight line joining two of the original atoms, this straight line appears as divided by them. But the original relation is not really divided: all that has happened is, that two or more equivalent relations have replaced it, as two compounded relations of father and son may replace the equivalent relation of grandfather and grandson. These two ways of viewing the apparent divisibility are equivalent: for empty space, in so far as it is not illusion, is a name for the aggregate of possible space-relations. To regard a figure in empty space as divided, therefore, means, if it means anything, to regard two or more other possible relations as substituted for it, which gives the second way of viewing the question.

The same reference to matter, then, by which the antinomy of the Point was solved, solves also the antinomy as to the relational nature of space. Space, if it is to be freed from

[1] Cf. James, Psychology, Vol. II., p. 148 ff.

contradictions, must be regarded exclusively as spatial order, as relations between unextended material atoms. Empty space, which arises, by an inevitable illusion, out of the spatial element in sense-perception, may be regarded, if we wish to retain it, as the bare principle of relativity, the bare logical possibility of relations between diverse things. In this sense, empty space is wholly conceptual; spatial order alone is immediately experienced.

**208.** But in what sense does spatial order consist of relations? We have hitherto spoken of externality as a relation, and in a sense such a manner of speaking is justified. Externality, when predicated of anything, is an adjective of that thing, and implies a reference to some other thing. To this extent, then, externality is analogous to other relations; and only to this extent, in our previous arguments, has it been regarded as a relation. But when we take account of further qualities of relations, externality begins to appear, not so much as a relation, but rather as a necessary aspect or element in every relation. And this is borne out by the necessity, for the existence of relations, of some given form of externality.

Every relation, we may say, involves a diversity between the related terms, but also some unity. Mere diversity does not give a ground for that interaction, and that interdependence, which a relation requires. Mere unity leaves the terms identical, and thus destroys the reference of one to another required for a relation. Mere externality, taken in abstraction, gives only the element of diversity required for a relation, and is thus more abstract than any actual relation. But mere diversity does not give that indivisible whole of which any actual relation must consist, and is thus, when regarded abstractly, not subject to the restrictions of ordinary relations.

But with mere diversity, we seem to have returned to empty space, and abandoned spatial order. Mere diversity, surely, is either complete or non-existent; degrees of diversity, or a quantitative measure of it, are nonsense. We cannot, therefore, reduce spatial order to mere diversity. Two things, if they occupy different positions in space, are necessarily diverse, but are as necessarily something more; otherwise spatial order becomes unmeaning.

Empty space, then, in the above sense of the possibility of spatial relations, contains only one aspect of a relation, namely the aspect of diversity; but spatial order, by its reference to matter, becomes more concrete, and contains also the element of unity, arising out of the connection of the different material atoms. Spatial order, then, consists of relations in the ordinary sense; its merely spatial element, however—if one may make such a distinction—the element, that is, which can be abstracted from matter and regarded as constituting empty space, is only one aspect of a relation, but an aspect which, in the concrete, must be inseparably bound up with the other aspect. Here, once more, we see the ground of the contradictions in empty space, and the reason why spatial order is free from these contradictions.

### *Conclusion.*

**209.** We have now completed our review of the foundations of Geometry. It will be well, before we take leave of the subject, briefly to review and recapitulate the results we have won.

In the first chapter, we watched the development of a branch of Mathematics designed, at first, only to establish the logical independence of Euclid's axiom of parallels, and the possibility of a self-consistent Geometry which dispensed with it. We found the further development of the subject entangled, for a while, in philosophical controversy; having shown one axiom to be superfluous, the geometers of the second period hoped to prove the same conclusion of all the others, but failed to construct any system free from three fundamental axioms. Being concerned with analytical and metrical Geometry, they tended to regard Algebra as *à priori*, but held that those properties of spatial magnitudes, which were not deducible from the laws of Algebra, must be empirical. In all this, they aimed as much at discrediting Kant as at advancing Mathematics. But with the third period, the interest in Philosophy diminishes, the opposition to Euclid becomes less marked, and most important of all, measurement is no longer regarded as fundamental, and space is dealt with by descriptive rather than quantitative methods. But nevertheless, three axioms, substantially the same as those retained in the second period, are still retained by all geometers.

In the second chapter, we endeavoured, by a criticism of some geometrical philosophies, to prepare the ground for a constructive theory of Geometry. We saw that Kant, in applying the argument of the Transcendental Aesthetic to space, had gone too far, since its logical scope extended only to some form of externality in general. We saw that Riemann, Helmholtz and Erdmann, misled by the quantitative bias, overlooked the qualitative substratum required by all judgments of quantity, and thus mistook the direction in which the necessary axioms of Geometry are to be found. We rejected, also, Helmholtz's view that Geometry depends on Physics, because we found that Physics must assume a knowledge of Geometry before it can become possible. But we admitted, in Geometry, a reference to matter—not, however, to matter as empirically known in Physics, but to a more abstract matter, whose sole function is to appear in space, and supply the terms for spatial relations. We admitted, however, besides this, that all *actual* measurement must be effected by means of *actual* matter, and is only empirically possible, through the empirical knowledge of approximately rigid bodies. In criticizing Lotze, we saw that the most important sense, in which non-Euclidean spaces are possible, is a philosophical sense, namely, that they are not condemned by any *à priori* argument as to the necessity of space for experience, and that consequently, if they are not affirmed, this must be on empirical grounds alone. Lotze's strictures on the mathematical procedure of Metageometry we found to be wholly due to ignorance of the subject.

Proceeding, in the third chapter, to a constructive theory of Geometry, we saw that projective Geometry, which has no reference to quantity, is necessarily true of any form of externality. Its three axioms—homogeneity, dimensions, and the straight line—were all deduced from the conception of a form of externality, and, since some such form is necessary to experience, were all declared *à priori*. In metrical Geometry, on the contrary, we found an empirical element, arising out of the alternatives of Euclidean and non-Euclidean space. Three *à priori* axioms, common to these spaces, and necessary conditions of the possibility of measurement, still remained; these were the axiom of Free Mobility, the axiom that space has a finite integral number of dimensions, and the axiom of distance. Except for the new idea of motion, these were found equivalent to the projective triad, and thus necessarily true of any form of externality. But the remaining axioms of Euclid—the axiom of three dimensions, the axiom that two straight lines can never enclose a space, and the axiom of parallels—were regarded as empirical laws, derived from the investigation and measurement of our actual space, and true only, as far as the last two are concerned, within the limits set by errors of observation.

In the present chapter, we completed our proof of the apriority of the projective and equivalent metrical axioms, by showing the necessity, for experience, of some form of externality, given by sensation or intuition, and not merely inferred from other data. Without this, we said, a knowledge of diverse but interrelated things, the corner-stone of all experience, would be impossible. Finally, we discussed the contradictions arising out of the relativity and continuity of space, and endeavoured to overcome them by a reference to matter. This matter, we found, must consist of unextended atoms, localized by their spatial relations, and appearing, in Geometry, as points. But the non-spatial adjectives of matter, we contended, are irrelevant to Geometry, and its causal properties may be left out of account. To deal with the new contradictions, involved in such a notion of matter, would demand a fresh treatise, leading us, through Kinematics, into the domains of Dynamics and Physics. But to discuss the special difficulties of space is all that is possible in an essay on the Foundations of Geometry.

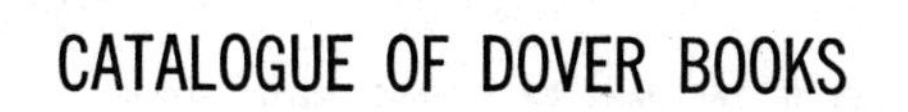

# CATALOGUE OF DOVER BOOKS

# BOOKS EXPLAINING SCIENCE AND MATHEMATICS

## General

**WHAT IS SCIENCE?, Norman Campbell.** This excellent introduction explains scientific method, role of mathematics, types of scientific laws. Contents: 2 aspects of science, science & nature, laws of science, discovery of laws, explanation of laws, measurement & numerical laws, applications of science. 192pp. 5⅜ x 8. S43 Paperbound **$1.25**

**THE COMMON SENSE OF THE EXACT SCIENCES, W. K. Clifford.** Introduction by James Newman, edited by Karl Pearson. For 70 years this has been a guide to classical scientific and mathematical thought. Explains with unusual clarity basic concepts, such as extension of meaning of symbols, characteristics of surface boundaries, properties of plane figures, vectors, Cartesian method of determining position, etc. Long preface by Bertrand Russell. Bibliography of Clifford. Corrected, 130 diagrams redrawn. 249pp. 5⅜ x 8. T61 Paperbound **$1.60**

**SCIENCE THEORY AND MAN, Erwin Schrödinger.** This is a complete and unabridged reissue of SCIENCE AND THE HUMAN TEMPERAMENT plus an additional essay: "What is an Elementary Particle?" Nobel laureate Schrödinger discusses such topics as nature of scientific method, the nature of science, chance and determinism, science and society, conceptual models for physical entities, elementary particles and wave mechanics. Presentation is popular and may be followed by most people with little or no scientific training. "Fine practical preparation for a time when laws of nature, human institutions . . . are undergoing a critical examination without parallel," Waldemar Kaempffert, N. Y. TIMES. 192pp. 5⅜ x 8. T428 Paperbound **$1.35**

**FADS AND FALLACIES IN THE NAME OF SCIENCE, Martin Gardner.** Examines various cults, quack systems, frauds, delusions which at various times have masqueraded as science. Accounts of hollow-earth fanatics like Symmes; Velikovsky and wandering planets; Hoerbiger; Bellamy and the theory of multiple moons; Charles Fort; dowsing, pseudoscientific methods for finding water, ores, oil. Sections on naturopathy, iridiagnosis, zone therapy, food fads, etc. Analytical accounts of Wilhelm Reich and orgone sex energy; L. Ron Hubbard and Dianetics; A. Korzybski and General Semantics; many others. Brought up to date to include Bridey Murphy, others. Not just a collection of anecdotes, but a fair, reasoned appraisal of eccentric theory. Formerly titled IN THE NAME OF SCIENCE. Preface. Index. x + 384pp. 5⅜ x 8. T394 Paperbound **$1.75**

**A DOVER SCIENCE SAMPLER, edited by George Barkin.** 64-page book, sturdily bound, containing excerpts from over 20 Dover books, explaining science. Edwin Hubble, George Sarton, Ernst Mach, A. d'Abro, Galileo, Newton, others, discussing island-universes, scientific truth, biological phenomena, stability in bridges, etc. Copies limited; no more than 1 to a customer, FREE

**POPULAR SCIENTIFIC LECTURES, Hermann von Helmholtz.** Helmholtz was a superb expositor as well as a scientist of genius in many areas. The seven essays in this volume are models of clarity, and even today they rank among the best general descriptions of their subjects ever written. "The Physiological Causes of Harmony in Music" was the first significant physiological explanation of musical consonance and dissonance. Two essays, "On the Interaction of Natural Forces" and "On the Conservation of Force," were of great importance in the history of science, for they firmly established the principle of the conservation of energy. Other lectures include "On the Relation of Optics to Painting," "On Recent Progress in the Theory of Vision," "On Goethe's Scientific Researches," and "On the Origin and Significance of Geometrical Axioms." Selected and edited with an introduction by Professor Morris Kline. xii + 286pp. 5⅜ x 8½. T799 Paperbound **$1.45**

# BOOKS EXPLAINING SCIENCE AND MATHEMATICS

## Physics

**CONCERNING THE NATURE OF THINGS, Sir William Bragg.** Christmas lectures delivered at the Royal Society by Nobel laureate. Why a spinning ball travels in a curved track; how uranium is transmuted to lead, etc. Partial contents: atoms, gases, liquids, crystals, metals, etc. No scientific background needed; wonderful for intelligent child. 32pp. of photos, 57 figures. xii + 232pp. 5⅜ x 8. T31 Paperbound **$1.50**

**THE RESTLESS UNIVERSE, Max Born.** New enlarged version of this remarkably readable account by a Nobel laureate. Moving from sub-atomic particles to universe, the author explains in very simple terms the latest theories of wave mechanics. Partial contents: air and its relatives, electrons & ions, waves & particles, electronic structure of the atom, nuclear physics. Nearly 1000 illustrations, including 7 animated sequences. 325pp. 6 x 9. T412 Paperbound **$2.00**

**FROM EUCLID TO EDDINGTON: A STUDY OF THE CONCEPTIONS OF THE EXTERNAL WORLD, Sir Edmund Whittaker.** A foremost British scientist traces the development of theories of natural philosophy from the western rediscovery of Euclid to Eddington, Einstein, Dirac, etc. The inadequacy of classical physics is contrasted with present day attempts to understand the physical world through relativity, non-Euclidean geometry, space curvature, wave mechanics, etc. 5 major divisions of examination: Space; Time and Movement; the Concepts of Classical Physics; the Concepts of Quantum Mechanics; the Eddington Universe. 212pp. 5⅜ x 8. T491 Paperbound **$1.35**

**PHYSICS, THE PIONEER SCIENCE, L. W. Taylor.** First thorough text to place all important physical phenomena in cultural-historical framework; remains best work of its kind. Exposition of physical laws, theories developed chronologically, with great historical, illustrative experiments diagrammed, described, worked out mathematically. Excellent physics text for self-study as well as class work. Vol. 1: Heat, Sound: motion, acceleration, gravitation, conservation of energy, heat engines, rotation, heat, mechanical energy, etc. 211 illus. 407pp. 5⅜ x 8. Vol. 2: Light, Electricity: images, lenses, prisms, magnetism, Ohm's law, dynamos, telegraph, quantum theory, decline of mechanical view of nature, etc. Bibliography. 13 table appendix. Index. 551 illus. 2 color plates. 508pp. 5⅜ x 8.
Vol. 1 S565 Paperbound **$2.25**
Vol. 2 S566 Paperbound **$2.25**
The set **$4.50**

**A SURVEY OF PHYSICAL THEORY, Max Planck.** One of the greatest scientists of all time, creator of the quantum revolution in physics, writes in non-technical terms of his own discoveries and those of other outstanding creators of modern physics. Planck wrote this book when science had just crossed the threshold of the new physics, and he communicates the excitement felt then as he discusses electromagnetic theories, statistical methods, evolution of the concept of light, a step-by-step description of how he developed his own momentous theory, and many more of the basic ideas behind modern physics. Formerly "A Survey of Physics." Bibliography. Index. 128pp. 5⅜ x 8. S650 Paperbound **$1.15**

**THE ATOMIC NUCLEUS, M. Korsunsky.** The only non-technical comprehensive account of the atomic nucleus in English. For college physics students, etc. Chapters cover: Radioactivity, the Nuclear Model of the Atom, the Mass of Atomic Nuclei, the Disintegration of Atomic Nuclei, the Discovery of the Positron, the Artificial Transformation of Atomic Nuclei, Artificial Radioactivity, Mesons, the Neutrino, the Structure of Atomic Nuclei and Forces Acting Between Nuclear Particles, Nuclear Fission, Chain Reaction, Peaceful Uses, Thermoculear Reactions. Slightly abridged edition. Translated by G. Yankovsky. 65 figures. Appendix includes 45 photographic illustrations. 413 pp. 5⅜ x 8. S1052 Paperbound **$2.00**

**PRINCIPLES OF MECHANICS SIMPLY EXPLAINED, Morton Mott-Smith.** Excellent, highly readable introduction to the theories and discoveries of classical physics. Ideal for the layman who desires a foundation which will enable him to understand and appreciate contemporary developments in the physical sciences. Discusses: Density, The Law of Gravitation, Mass and Weight, Action and Reaction, Kinetic and Potential Energy, The Law of Inertia, Effects of Acceleration, The Independence of Motions, Galileo and the New Science of Dynamics, Newton and the New Cosmos, The Conservation of Momentum, and other topics. Revised edition of "This Mechanical World." Illustrated by E. Kosa, Jr. Bibliography and Chronology. Index. xiv + 171pp. 5⅜ x 8½. T1067 Paperbound **$1.35**

**THE CONCEPT OF ENERGY SIMPLY EXPLAINED, Morton Mott-Smith.** Elementary, non-technical exposition which traces the story of man's conquest of energy, with particular emphasis on the developments during the nineteenth century and the first three decades of our own century. Discusses man's earlier efforts to harness energy, more recent experiments and discoveries relating to the steam engine, the engine indicator, the motive power of heat, the principle of excluded perpetual motion, the bases of the conservation of energy, the concept of entropy, the internal combustion engine, mechanical refrigeration, and many other related topics. Also much biographical material. Index. Bibliography. 33 illustrations. ix + 215pp. 5⅜ x 8½. T1071 Paperbound **$1.25**

**HEAT AND ITS WORKINGS, Morton Mott-Smith.** One of the best elementary introductions to the theory and attributes of heat, covering such matters as the laws governing the effect of heat on solids, liquids and gases, the methods by which heat is measured, the conversion of a substance from one form to another through heating and cooling, evaporation, the effects of pressure on boiling and freezing points, and the three ways in which heat is transmitted (conduction, convection, radiation). Also brief notes on major experiments and discoveries. Concise, but complete, it presents all the essential facts about the subject in readable style. Will give the layman and beginning student a first-rate background in this major topic in physics. Index. Bibliography. 50 illustrations. x + 165pp. 5⅜ x 8½. T978 Paperbound **$1.15**

**THE STORY OF ATOMIC THEORY AND ATOMIC ENERGY, J. G. Feinberg.** Wider range of facts on physical theory, cultural implications, than any other similar source. Completely non-technical. Begins with first atomic theory, 600 B.C., goes through A-bomb, developments to 1959. Avogadro, Rutherford, Bohr, Einstein, radioactive decay, binding energy, radiation danger, future benefits of nuclear power, dozens of other topics, told in lively, related, informal manner. Particular stress on European atomic research. "Deserves special mention . . . authoritative," Saturday Review. Formerly "The Atom Story." New chapter to 1959. Index. 34 illustrations. 251pp. 5⅜ x 8. T625 Paperbound **$1.60**

**THE STRANGE STORY OF THE QUANTUM, AN ACCOUNT FOR THE GENERAL READER OF THE GROWTH OF IDEAS UNDERLYING OUR PRESENT ATOMIC KNOWLEDGE, B. Hoffmann.** Presents lucidly and expertly, with barest amount of mathematics, the problems and theories which led to modern quantum physics. Dr. Hoffmann begins with the closing years of the 19th century, when certain trifling discrepancies were noticed, and with illuminating analogies and examples takes you through the brilliant concepts of Planck, Einstein, Pauli, de Broglie, Bohr, Schroedinger, Heisenberg, Dirac, Sommerfeld, Feynman, etc. This edition includes a new, long postscript carrying the story through 1958. "Of the books attempting an account of the history and contents of our modern atomic physics which have come to my attention, this is the best," H. Margenau, Yale University, in "American Journal of Physics." 32 tables and line illustrations. Index. 275pp. 5⅜ x 8. T518 Paperbound **$1.75**

**THE EVOLUTION OF SCIENTIFIC THOUGHT FROM NEWTON TO EINSTEIN, A. d'Abro.** Einstein's special and general theories of relativity, with their historical implications, are analyzed in non-technical terms. Excellent accounts of the contributions of Newton, Riemann, Weyl, Planck, Eddington, Maxwell, Lorentz and others are treated in terms of space and time, equations of electromagnetics, finiteness of the universe, methodology of science. 21 diagrams. 482pp. 5⅜ x 8. T2 Paperound **$2.25**

**THE RISE OF THE NEW PHYSICS, A. d'Abro.** A half-million word exposition, formerly titled THE DECLINE OF MECHANISM, for readers not versed in higher mathematics. The only thorough explanation, in everyday language, of the central core of modern mathematical physical theory, treating both classical and modern theoretical physics, and presenting in terms almost anyone can understand the equivalent of 5 years of study of mathematical physics. Scientifically impeccable coverage of mathematical-physical thought from the Newtonian system up through the electronic theories of Dirac and Heisenberg and Fermi's statistics. Combines both history and exposition; provides a broad yet unified and detailed view, with constant comparison of classical and modern views on phenomena and theories. "A must for anyone doing serious study in the physical sciences," JOURNAL OF THE FRANKLIN INSTITUTE. "Extraordinary faculty . . . to explain ideas and theories of theoretical physics in the language of daily life," ISIS. First part of set covers philosophy of science, drawing upon the practice of Newton, Maxwell, Poincaré, Einstein, others, discussing modes of thought, experiment, interpretations of causality, etc. In the second part, 100 pages explain grammar and vocabulary of mathematics, with discussions of functions, groups, series, Fourier series, etc. The remainder is devoted to concrete, detailed coverage of both classical and quantum physics, explaining such topics as analytic mechanics, Hamilton's principle, wave theory of light, electromagnetic waves, groups of transformations, thermodynamics, phase rule, Brownian movement, kinetics, special relativity, Planck's original quantum theory, Bohr's atom, Zeeman effect, Broglie's wave mechanics, Heisenberg's uncertainty, Eigen-values, matrices, scores of other important topics. Discoveries and theories are covered for such men as Alembert, Born, Cantor, Debye, Euler, Foucault, Galois, Gauss, Hadamard, Kelvin, Kepler, Laplace, Maxwell, Pauli, Rayleigh, Volterra, Weyl, Young, more than 180 others. Indexed. 97 illustrations. ix + 982pp. 5⅜ x 8. T3 Volume 1, Paperbound **$2.25**
T4 Volume 2, Paperbound **$2.25**

**SPINNING TOPS AND GYROSCOPIC MOTION, John Perry.** Well-known classic of science still unsurpassed for lucid, accurate, delightful exposition. How quasi-rigidity is induced in flexible and fluid bodies by rapid motions; why gyrostat falls, top rises; nature and effect on climatic conditions of earth's precessional movement; effect of internal fluidity on rotating bodies, etc. Appendixes describe practical uses to which gyroscopes have been put in ships, compasses, monorail transportation. 62 figures. 128pp. 5⅜ x 8. T416 Paperbound **$1.25**

**THE UNIVERSE OF LIGHT, Sir William Bragg.** No scientific training needed to read Nobel Prize winner's expansion of his Royal Institute Christmas Lectures. Insight into nature of light, methods and philosophy of science. Explains lenses, reflection, color, resonance, polarization, x-rays, the spectrum, Newton's work with prisms, Huygens' with polarization, Crookes' with cathode ray, etc. Leads into clear statement of 2 major historical theories of light, corpuscle and wave. Dozens of experiments you can do. 199 illus., including 2 full-page color plates. 293pp. 5⅜ x 8. S538 Paperbound **$1.85**

**THE STORY OF X-RAYS FROM RÖNTGEN TO ISOTOPES, A. R. Bleich.** Non-technical history of x-rays, their scientific explanation, their applications in medicine, industry, research, and art, and their effect on the individual and his descendants. Includes amusing early reactions to Röntgen's discovery, cancer therapy, detections of art and stamp forgeries, potential risks to patient and operator, etc. Illustrations show x-rays of flower structure, the gall bladder, gears with hidden defects, etc. Original Dover publication. Glossary. Bibliography. Index. 55 photos and figures. xiv + 186pp. 5⅜ x 8. T662 Paperbound **$1.50**

**ELECTRONS, ATOMS, METALS AND ALLOYS, Wm. Hume-Rothery.** An introductory-level explanation of the application of the electronic theory to the structure and properties of metals and alloys, taking into account the new theoretical work done by mathematical physicists. Material presented in dialogue-form between an "Old Metallurgist" and a "Young Scientist." Their discussion falls into 4 main parts: the nature of an atom, the nature of a metal, the nature of an alloy, and the structure of the nucleus. They cover such topics as the hydrogen atom, electron waves, wave mechanics, Brillouin zones, co-valent bonds, radioactivity and natural disintegration, fundamental particles, structure and fission of the nucleus,etc. Revised, enlarged edition. 177 illustrations. Subject and name indexes. 407pp. 5⅜ x 8½. S1046 Paperbound **$2.25**

**OUT OF THE SKY, H. H. Nininger.** A non-technical but comprehensive introduction to "meteoritics", the young science concerned with all aspects of the arrival of matter from outer space. Written by one of the world's experts on meteorites, this work shows how, despite difficulties of observation and sparseness of data, a considerable body of knowledge has arisen. It defines meteors and meteorites; studies fireball clusters and processions, meteorite composition, size, distribution, showers, explosions, origins, craters, and much more. A true connecting link between astronomy and geology. More than 175 photos, 22 other illustrations. References. Bibliography of author's publications on meteorites. Index. viii + 336pp. 5⅜ x 8. T519 Paperbound **$1.85**

**SATELLITES AND SCIENTIFIC RESEARCH, D. King-Hele.** Non-technical account of the manmade satellites and the discoveries they have yielded up to the autumn of 1961. Brings together information hitherto published only in hard-to-get scientific journals. Includes the life history of a typical satellite, methods of tracking, new information on the shape of the earth, zones of radiation, etc. Over 60 diagrams and 6 photographs. Mathematical appendix. Bibliography of over 100 items. Index. xii + 180pp. 5⅜ x 8½. T703 Paperbound **$2.00**

# BOOKS EXPLAINING SCIENCE AND MATHEMATICS

## Mathematics

**CHANCE, LUCK AND STATISTICS: THE SCIENCE OF CHANCE, Horace C. Levinson.** Theory of probability and science of statistics in simple, non-technical language. Part I deals with theory of probability, covering odd superstitions in regard to "luck," the meaning of betting odds, the law of mathematical expectation, gambling, and applications in poker, roulette, lotteries, dice, bridge, and other games of chance. Part II discusses the misuse of statistics, the concept of statistical probabilities, normal and skew frequency distributions, and statistics applied to various fields—birth rates, stock speculation, insurance rates, advertising, etc. "Presented in an easy humorous style which I consider the best kind of expository writing," Prof. A. C. Cohen, Industry Quality Control. Enlarged revised edition. Formerly titled "The Science of Chance." Preface and two new appendices by the author. Index. xiv + 365pp. 5⅜ x 8. T1007 Paperbound **$1.85**

**PROBABILITIES AND LIFE, Emile Borel.** Translated by M. Baudin. Non-technical, highly readable introduction to the results of probability as applied to everyday situations. Partial contents: Fallacies About Probabilities Concerning Life After Death; Negligible Probabilities and the Probabilities of Everyday Life; Events of Small Probability; Application of Probabilities to Certain Problems of Heredity; Probabilities of Deaths, Diseases, and Accidents; On Poisson's Formula. Index. 3 Appendices of statistical studies and tables. vi + 87pp. 5⅜ x 8½. T121 Paperbound **$1.00**

**GREAT IDEAS OF MODERN MATHEMATICS: THEIR NATURE AND USE, Jagjit Singh.** Reader with only high school math will understand main mathematical ideas of modern physics, astronomy, genetics, psychology, evolution, etc., better than many who use them as tools, but comprehend little of their basic structure. Author uses his wide knowledge of non-mathematical fields in brilliant exposition of differential equations, matrices, group theory, logic, statistics, problems of mathematical foundations, imaginary numbers, vectors, etc. Original publication. 2 appendices. 2 indexes. 65 illustr. 322pp. 5⅜ x 8. S587 Paperbound **$2.00**

**MATHEMATICS IN ACTION, O. G. Sutton.** Everyone with a command of high school algebra will find this book one of the finest possible introductions to the application of mathematics to physical theory. Ballistics, numerical analysis, waves and wavelike phenomena, Fourier series, group concepts, fluid flow and aerodynamics, statistical measures, and meteorology are discussed with unusual clarity. Some calculus and differential equations theory is developed by the author for the reader's help in the more difficult sections. 88 figures. Index. viii + 236pp. 5⅜ x 8. T440 Clothbound **$3.50**

**THE FOURTH DIMENSION SIMPLY EXPLAINED, edited by H. P. Manning.** 22 essays, originally Scientific American contest entries, that use a minimum of mathematics to explain aspects of 4-dimensional geometry: analogues to 3-dimensional space, 4-dimensional absurdities and curiosities (such as removing the contents of an egg without puncturing its shell), possible measurements and forms, etc. Introduction by the editor. Only book of its sort on a truly elementary level, excellent introduction to advanced works. 82 figures. 251pp. 5⅜ x 8. T711 Paperbound **$1.50**

# MATHEMATICS—INTERMEDIATE TO ADVANCED

## General

**INTRODUCTION TO APPLIED MATHEMATICS, Francis D. Murnaghan.** A practical and thoroughly sound introduction to a number of advanced branches of higher mathematics. Among the selected topics covered in detail are: vector and matrix analysis, partial and differential equations, integral equations, calculus of variations, Laplace transform theory, the vector triple product, linear vector functions, quadratic and bilinear forms, Fourier series, spherical harmonics, Bessel functions, the Heaviside expansion formula, and many others. Extremely useful book for graduate students in physics, engineering, chemistry, and mathematics. Index. 111 study exercises with answers. 41 illustrations. ix + 389pp. 5⅜ x 8½.
S1042 Paperbound **$2.25**

**OPERATIONAL METHODS IN APPLIED MATHEMATICS, H. S. Carslaw and J. C. Jaeger.** Explanation of the application of the Laplace Transformation to differential equations, a simple and effective substitute for more difficult and obscure operational methods. Of great practical value to engineers and to all workers in applied mathematics. Chapters on: Ordinary Linear Differential Equations with Constant Coefficients;; Electric Circuit Theory; Dynamical Applications; The Inversion Theorem for the Laplace Transformation; Conduction of Heat; Vibrations of Continuous Mechanical Systems; Hydrodynamics; Impulsive Functions; Chains of Differential Equations; and other related matters. 3 appendices. 153 problems, many with answers. 22 figures. xvi + 359pp. 5⅜ x 8½. S1011 Paperbound **$2.25**

**APPLIED MATHEMATICS FOR RADIO AND COMMUNICATIONS ENGINEERS, C. E. Smith.** No extraneous material here!—only the theories, equations, and operations essential and immediately useful for radio work. Can be used as refresher, as handbook of applications and tables, or as full home-study course. Ranges from simplest arithmetic through calculus, series, and wave forms, hyperbolic trigonometry, simultaneous equations in mesh circuits, etc. Supplies applications right along with each math topic discussed. 22 useful tables of functions, formulas, logs, etc. Index. 166 exercises, 140 examples, all with answers. 95 diagrams. Bibliography. x + 336pp. 5⅜ x 8. S141 Paperbound **$1.75**

## Algebra, group theory, determinants, sets, matrix theory

**ALGEBRAS AND THEIR ARITHMETICS, L. E. Dickson.** Provides the foundation and background necessary to any advanced undergraduate or graduate student studying abstract algebra. Begins with elementary introduction to linear transformations, matrices, field of complex numbers; proceeds to order, basal units, modulus, quaternions, etc.; develops calculus of linears sets, describes various examples of algebras including invariant, difference, nilpotent, semi-simple. "Makes the reader marvel at his genius for clear and profound analysis," Amer. Mathematical Monthly. Index. xii + 241pp. 5⅜ x 8. S616 Paperbound **$1.50**

**THE THEORY OF EQUATIONS WITH AN INTRODUCTION TO THE THEORY OF BINARY ALGEBRAIC FORMS, W. S. Burnside and A. W. Panton.** Extremely thorough and concrete discussion of the theory of equations, with extensive detailed treatment of many topics curtailed in later texts. Covers theory of algebraic equations, properties of polynomials, symmetric functions, derived functions, Horner's process, complex numbers and the complex variable, determinants and methods of elimination, invariant theory (nearly 100 pages), transformations, introduction to Galois theory, Abelian equations, and much more. Invaluable supplementary work for modern students and teachers. 759 examples and exercises. Index in each volume. Two volume set. Total of xxiv + 604pp. 5⅜ x 8.
S714 Vol I Paperbound **$1.85**
S715 Vol II Paperbound **$1.85**
The set **$3.70**

**COMPUTATIONAL METHODS OF LINEAR ALGEBRA, V. N. Faddeeva,** translated by **C. D. Benster.** First English translation of a unique and valuable work, the only work in English presenting a systematic exposition of the most important methods of linear algebra—classical and contemporary. Shows in detail how to derive numerical solutions of problems in mathematical physics which are frequently connected with those of linear algebra. Theory as well as individual practice. Part I surveys the mathematical background that is indispensable to what follows. Parts II and III, the conclusion, set forth the most important methods of solution, for both exact and iterative groups. One of the most outstanding and valuable features of this work is the 23 tables, double and triple checked for accuracy. These tables will not be found elsewhere. Author's preface. Translator's note. New bibliography and index. x + 252pp. 5⅜ x 8. S424 Paperbound **$2.00**

**ALGEBRAIC EQUATIONS, E. Dehn.** Careful and complete presentation of Galois' theory of algebraic equations; theories of Lagrange and Galois developed in logical rather than historical form, with a more thorough exposition than in most modern books. Many concrete applications and fully-worked-out examples. Discusses basic theory (very clear exposition of the symmetric group); isomorphic, transitive, and Abelian groups; applications of Lagrange's and Galois' theories; and much more. Newly revised by the author. Index. List of Theorems. xi + 208pp. 5⅜ x 8. S697 Paperbound **$1.45**

## Differential equations, ordinary and partial; integral equations

**INTRODUCTION TO THE DIFFERENTIAL EQUATIONS OF PHYSICS, L. Hopf.** Especially valuable to the engineer with no math beyond elementary calculus. Emphasizing intuitive rather than formal aspects of concepts, the author covers an extensive territory. Partial contents: Law of causality, energy theorem, damped oscillations, coupling by friction, cylindrical and spherical coordinates, heat source, etc. Index. 48 figures. 160pp. 5⅜ x 8.
S120 Paperbound **$1.35**

**INTRODUCTION TO THE THEORY OF LINEAR DIFFERENTIAL EQUATIONS, E. G. Poole.** Authoritative discussions of important topics, with methods of solution more detailed than usual, for students with background of elementary course in differential equations. Studies existence theorems, linearly independent solutions; equations with constant coefficients; with uniform analytic coefficients; regular singularities; the hypergeometric equation; conformal representation; etc. Exercises. Index. 210pp. 5⅜ x 8. S629 Paperbound **$1.65**

**DIFFERENTIAL EQUATIONS FOR ENGINEERS, P. Franklin.** Outgrowth of a course given 10 years at M. I. T. Makes most useful branch of pure math accessible for practical work. Theoretical basis of D.E.'s; solution of ordinary D.E.'s and partial derivatives arising from heat flow, steady-state temperature of a plate, wave equations; analytic functions; convergence of Fourier Series. 400 problems on electricity, vibratory systems, other topics. Formerly "Differential Equations for Electrical Engineers." Index 41 illus. 307pp. 5⅜ x 8.
S601 Paperbound **$2.00**

**DIFFERENTIAL EQUATIONS, F. R. Moulton.** A detailed, rigorous exposition of all the non-elementary processes of solving ordinary differential equations. Several chapters devoted to the treatment of practical problems, especially those of a physical nature, which are far more advanced than problems usually given as illustrations. Includes analytic differential equations; variations of a parameter; integrals of differential equations; analytic implicit functions; problems of elliptic motion; sine-amplitude functions; deviation of formal bodies; Cauchy-Lipschitz process; linear differential equations with periodic coefficients; differential equations in infinitely many variations; much more. Historical notes. 10 figures. 222 problems. Index. xv + 395pp. 5⅜ x 8. S451 Paperbound **$2.00**

**DIFFERENTIAL AND INTEGRAL EQUATIONS OF MECHANICS AND PHYSICS (DIE DIFFERENTIAL- UND INTEGRALGLEICHUNGEN DER MECHANIK UND PHYSIK), edited by P. Frank and R. von Mises.** Most comprehensive and authoritative work on the mathematics of mathematical physics available today in the United States: the standard, definitive reference for teachers, physicists, engineers, and mathematicians—now published (in the original German) at a relatively inexpensive price for the first time! Every chapter in this 2,000-page set is by an expert in his field: Carathéodory, Courant, Frank, Mises, and a dozen others. Vol I, on mathematics, gives concise but complete coverages of advanced calculus, differential equations, integral equations, and potential, and partial differential equations. Index. xxiii + 916pp. Vol. II (physics): classical mechanics, optics, continuous mechanics, heat conduction and diffusion, the stationary and quasi-stationary electromagnetic field, electromagnetic oscillations, and wave mechanics. Index. xxiv + 1106pp. Two volume set. Each volume available separately. 5⅝ x 8⅜. S787 Vol I Clothbound **$7.50**
S788 Vol II Clothbound **$7.50**
The set **$15.00**

**LECTURES ON CAUCHY'S PROBLEM, J. Hadamard.** Based on lectures given at Columbia, Rome, this discusses work of Riemann, Kirchhoff, Volterra, and the author's own research on the hyperbolic case in linear partial differential equations. It extends spherical and cylindrical waves to apply to all (normal) hyperbolic equations. Partial contents: Cauchy's problem, fundamental formula, equations with odd number, with even number of independent variables; method of descent. 32 figures. Index. iii + 316pp. 5⅜ x 8. S105 Paperbound **$1.75**

**THEORY OF DIFFERENTIAL EQUATIONS, A. R. Forsyth.** Out of print for over a decade, the complete 6 volumes (now bound as 3) of this monumental work represent the most comprehensive treatment of differential equations ever written. Historical presentation includes in 2500 pages every substantial development. Vol. 1, 2: EXACT EQUATIONS, PFAFF'S PROBLEM; ORDINARY EQUATIONS, NOT LINEAR: methods of Grassmann, Clebsch, Lie, Darboux; Cauchy's theorem; branch points; etc. Vol. 3, 4: ORDINARY EQUATIONS, NOT LINEAR; ORDINARY LINEAR EQUATIONS: Zeta Fuchsian functions, general theorems on algebraic integrals, Brun's theorem, equations with uniform periodic coffiecients, etc. Vol. 4, 5: PARTIAL DIFFERENTIAL EQUATIONS: 2 existence-theorems, equations of theoretical dynamics, Laplace transformations, general transformation of equations of the 2nd order, much more. Indexes. Total of 2766pp. 5⅜ x 8. S576-7-8 Clothbound: the set **$15.00**

**PARTIAL DIFFERENTIAL EQUATIONS OF MATHEMATICAL PHYSICS, A. G. Webster.** A keystone work in the library of every mature physicist, engineer, researcher. Valuable sections on elasticity, compression theory, potential theory, theory of sound, heat conduction, wave propagation, vibration theory. Contents include: deduction of differential equations, vibrations, normal functions, Fourier's series, Cauchy's method, boundary problems, method of Riemann-Volterra. Spherical, cylindrical, ellipsoidal harmonics, applications, etc. 97 figures. vii + 440pp. 5⅜ x 8. S263 Paperbound **$2.25**

**ELEMENTARY CONCEPTS OF TOPOLOGY, P. Alexandroff.** First English translation of the famous brief introduction to topology for the beginner or for the mathematician not undertaking extensive study. This unusually useful intuitive approach deals primarily with the concepts of complex, cycle, and homology, and is wholly consistent with current investigations. Ranges from basic concepts of set-theoretic topology to the concept of Betti groups. "Glowing example of harmony between intuition and thcught," David Hilbert. Translated by A. E. Farley. Introduction by D. Hilbert. Index. 25 figures. 73pp. 5⅜ x 8. S747 Paperbound **$1.00**

## Number theory

**INTRODUCTION TO THE THEORY OF NUMBERS, L. E. Dickson.** Thorough, comprehensive approach with adequate coverage of classical literature, an introductory volume beginners can follow. Chapters on divisibility, congruences, quadratic residues & reciprocity, Diophantine equations, etc. Full treatment of binary quadratic forms without usual restriction to integral coefficients. Covers infinitude of primes, least residues, Fermat's theorem, Euler's phi function, Legendre's symbol, Gauss's lemma, automorphs, reduced forms, recent theorems of Thue & Siegel, many more. Much material not readily available elsewhere. 239 problems. Index. I figure. viii + 183pp. 5⅜ x 8. S342 Paperbound **$1.75**

**ELEMENTS OF NUMBER THEORY, I. M. Vinogradov.** Detailed 1st course for persons without advanced mathematics; 95% of this book can be understood by readers who have gone no farther than high school algebra. Partial contents: divisibility theory, important number theoretical functions, congruences, primitive roots and indices, etc. Solutions to both problems and exercises. Tables of primes, indices, etc. Covers almost every essential formula in elementary number theory! Translated from Russian. 233 problems, 104 exercises. viii + 227pp. 5⅜ x 8. S259 Paperbound **$1.75**

**THEORY OF NUMBERS and DIOPHANTINE ANALYSIS, R. D. Carmichael.** These two complete works in one volume form one of the most lucid introductions to number theory, requiring only a firm foundation in high school mathematics. "Theory of Numbers," partial contents: Eratosthenes' sieve, Euclid's fundamental theorem, G.C.F. and L.C.M. of two or more integers, linear congruences, etc "Diophantine Analysis": rational triangles, Pythagorean triangles, equations of third, fourth, higher degrees, method of functional equations, much more. "Theory of Numbers": 76 problems. Index. 94pp. "Diophantine Analysis": 222 problems. Index. 118pp. 5⅜ x 8. S529 Paperbound **$1.35**

## Numerical analysis, tables

**MATHEMATICAL TABLES AND FORMULAS, Compiled by Robert D. Carmichael and Edwin R. Smith.** Valuable collection for students, etc. Contains all tables necessary in college algebra and trigonometry, such as five-place common logarithms, logarithmic sines and tangents of small angles, logarithmic trigonometric functions, natural trigonometric functions, four-place antilogarithms, tables for changing from sexagesimal to circular and from circular to sexagesimal measure of angles, etc. Also many tables and formulas not ordinarily accessible, including powers, roots, and reciprocals, exponential and hyperbolic functions, ten-place logarithms of prime numbers, and formulas and theorems from analytical and elementary geometry and from calculus. Explanatory introduction. viii + 269pp. 5⅜ x 8½. S111 Paperbound **$1.25**

**MATHEMATICAL TABLES, H. B. Dwight.** Unique for its coverage in one volume of almost every function of importance in applied mathematics, engineering, and the physical sciences. Three extremely fine tables of the three trig functions and their inverse functions to thousandths of radians; natural and common logarithms; squares, cubes; hyperbolic functions and the inverse hyperbolic functions; $(a^2 + b^2)$ exp. ½a; complete elliptic integrals of the 1st and 2nd kind; sine and cosine integrals; exponential integrals Ei(x) and Ei( —x); binomial coefficients; factorials to 250; surface zonal harmonics and first derivatives; Bernoulli and Euler numbers and their logs to base of 10; Gamma function; normal probability integral; over 60 pages of Bessel functions; the Riemann Zeta function. Each table with formulae generally used, sources of more extensive tables, interpolation data, etc. Over half have columns of differences, to facilitate interpolation. Introduction. Index. viii + 231pp. 5⅜ x 8. S445 Paperbound **$2.00**

**TABLES OF FUNCTIONS WITH FORMULAE AND CURVES, E. Jahnke & F. Emde.** The world's most comprehensive 1-volume English-text collection of tables, formulae, curves of transcendent functions. 4th corrected edition, new 76-page section giving tables, formulae for elementary functions—not in other English editions. Partial contents: sine, cosine, logarithmic integral; factorial function; error integral; theta functions; elliptic integrals, functions; Legendre, Bessel, Riemann, Mathieu, hypergeometric functions, etc. Supplementary books. Bibliography. Indexed. "Out of the way functions for which we know no other source," SCIENTIFIC COMPUTING SERVICE, Ltd. 212 figures. 400pp. 5⅜ x 8. S133 Paperbound **$2.00**

# CHEMISTRY AND PHYSICAL CHEMISTRY

**ORGANIC CHEMISTRY, F. C. Whitmore.** The entire subject of organic chemistry for the practicing chemist and the advanced student. Storehouse of facts, theories, processes found elsewhere only in specialized journals. Covers aliphatic compounds (500 pages on the properties and synthetic preparation of hydrocarbons, halides, proteins, ketones, etc.), alicyclic compounds, aromatic compounds, heterocyclic compounds, organophosphorus and organometallic compounds. Methods of synthetic preparation analyzed critically throughout. Includes much of biochemical interest. "The scope of this volume is astonishing," INDUSTRIAL AND ENGINEERING CHEMISTRY. 12,000-reference index. 2387-item bibliography. Total of x + 1005pp. 5⅜ x 8. Two volume set.
S700 Vol I Paperbound **$2.25**
S701 Vol II Paperbound **$2.25**
The set **$4.50**

**THE MODERN THEORY OF MOLECULAR STRUCTURE, Bernard Pullman.** A reasonably popular account of recent developments in atomic and molecular theory. Contents: The Wave Function and Wave Equations (history and bases of present theories of molecular structure); The Electronic Structure of Atoms (Description and classification of atomic wave functions, etc.); Diatomic Molecules; Non-Conjugated Polyatomic Molecules; Conjugated Polyatomic Molecules; The Structure of Complexes. Minimum of mathematical background needed. New translation by David Antin of "La Structure Moleculaire." Index. Bibliography. vii + 87pp. 5⅜ x 8½.
S987 Paperbound **$1.00**

**CATALYSIS AND CATALYSTS, Marcel Prettre,** Director, Research Institute on Catalysis. This brief book, translated into English for the first time, is the finest summary of the principal modern concepts, methods, and results of catalysis. Ideal introduction for beginning chemistry and physics students. Chapters: Basic Definitions of Catalysis (true catalysis and generalization of the concept of catalysis); The Scientific Bases of Catalysis (Catalysis and chemical thermodynamics, catalysis and chemical kinetics); Homogeneous Catalysis (acid-base catalysis, etc.); Chain Reactions; Contact Masses; Heterogeneous Catalysis (Mechanisms of contact catalyses, etc.); and Industrial Applications (acids and fertilizers, petroleum and petroleum chemistry, rubber, plastics, synthetic resins, and fibers). Translated by David Antin. Index. vi + 88pp. 5⅜ x 8½.
S998 Paperbound **$1.00**

**POLAR MOLECULES, Pieter Debye.** This work by Nobel laureate Debye offers a complete guide to fundamental electrostatic field relations, polarizability, molecular structure. Partial contents: electric intensity, displacement and force, polarization by orientation, molar polarization and molar refraction, halogen-hydrides, polar liquids, ionic saturation, dielectric constant, etc. Special chapter considers quantum theory. Indexed. 172pp. 5⅜ x 8.
S64 Paperbound **$1.65**

**THE ELECTRONIC THEORY OF ACIDS AND BASES, W. F. Luder and Saverio Zuffanti.** The first full systematic presentation of the electronic theory of acids and bases—treating the theory and its ramifications in an uncomplicated manner. Chapters: Historical Background; Atomic Orbitals and Valence; The Electronic Theory of Acids and Bases; Electrophilic and Electrodotic Reagents; Acidic and Basic Radicals; Neutralization; Titrations with Indicators; Displacement; Catalysis; Acid Catalysis; Base Catalysis; Alkoxides and Catalysts; Conclusion. Required reading for all chemists. Second revised (1961) eidtion, with additional examples and references. 3 figures. 9 tables. Index. Bibliography xii + 165pp. 5⅜ x 8.
S201 Paperbound **$1.50**

**KINETIC THEORY OF LIQUIDS, J. Frenkel.** Regarding the kinetic theory of liquids as a generalization and extension of the theory of solid bodies, this volume covers all types of arrangements of solids, thermal displacements of atoms, interstitial atoms and ions, orientational and rotational motion of molecules, and transition between states of matter. Mathematical theory is developed close to the physical subject matter. 216 bibliographical footnotes. 55 figures. xi + 485pp. 5⅜ x 8.
S95 Paperbound **$2.55**

**THE PRINCIPLES OF ELECTROCHEMISTRY, D. A. MacInnes.** Basic equations for almost every subfield of electrochemistry from first principles, referring at all times to the soundest and most recent theories and results; unusually useful as text or as reference. Covers coulometers and Faraday's Law, electrolytic conductance, the Debye-Hueckel method for the theoretical calculation of activity coefficients, concentration cells, standard electrode potentials, thermodynamic ionization constants, pH, potentiometric titrations, irreversible phenomena, Planck's equation, and much more. "Excellent treatise," AMERICAN CHEMICAL SOCIETY JOURNAL. "Highly recommended," CHEMICAL AND METALLURGICAL ENGINEERING. 2 Indices. Appendix. 585-item bibliography. 137 figures. 94 tables. ii + 478pp. 5⅝ x 8⅜.
S52 Paperbound **$2.75**

**THE PHASE RULE AND ITS APPLICATION, Alexander Findlay.** Covering chemical phenomena of 1, 2, 3, 4, and multiple component systems, this "standard work on the subject" (NATURE, London), has been completely revised and brought up to date by A. N. Campbell and N. O. Smith. Brand new material has been added on such matters as binary, tertiary liquid equilibria, solid solutions in ternary systems, quinary systems of salts and water. Completely revised to triangular coordinates in ternary systems, clarified graphic representation, solid models, etc. 9th revised edition. Author, subject indexes. 236 figures. 505 footnotes, mostly bibliographic. xii + 494pp. 5⅜ x 8.
S91 Paperbound **$2.50**

# PHYSICS

## General physics

**FOUNDATIONS OF PHYSICS, R. B. Lindsay & H. Margenau.** Excellent bridge between semi-popular works & technical treatises. A discussion of methods of physical description, construction of theory; valuable for physicist with elementary calculus who is interested in ideas that give meaning to data, tools of modern physics. Contents include symbolism, mathematical equations; space & time foundations of mechanics; probability; physics & continua; electron theory; special & general relativity; quantum mechanics; causality. "Thorough and yet not overdetailed. Unreservedly recommended," NATURE (London). Unabridged, corrected edition. List of recommended readings. 35 illustrations. xi + 537pp. 5⅜ x 8.
S377 Paperbound **$3.00**

**FUNDAMENTAL FORMULAS OF PHYSICS, ed. by D. H. Menzel.** Highly useful, fully inexpensive reference and study text, ranging from simple to highly sophisticated operations. Mathematics integrated into text—each chapter stands as short textbook of field represented. Vol. 1: Statistics, Physical Constants, Special Theory of Relativity, Hydrodynamics, Aerodynamics, Boundary Value Problems in Math. Physics; Viscosity, Electromagnetic Theory, etc. Vol. 2: Sound, Acoustics, Geometrical Optics, Electron Optics, High-Energy Phenomena, Magnetism, Biophysics, much more. Index. Total of 800pp. 5⅜ x 8.
Vol. 1 S595 Paperbound **$2.25**
Vol. 2 S596 Paperbound **$2.25**

**MATHEMATICAL PHYSICS, D. H. Menzel.** Thorough one-volume treatment of the mathematical techniques vital for classic mechanics, electromagnetic theory, quantum theory, and relativity. Written by the Harvard Professor of Astrophysics for junior, senior, and graduate courses, it gives clear explanations of all those aspects of function theory, vectors, matrices, dyadics, tensors, partial differential equations, etc., necessary for the understanding of the various physical theories. Electron theory, relativity, and other topics seldom presented appear here in considerable detail. Scores of definitions, conversion factors, dimensional constants, etc. "More detailed than normal for an advanced text . . . excellent set of sections on Dyadics, Matrices, and Tensors," JOURNAL OF THE FRANKLIN INSTITUTE. Index. 193 problems, with answers. x + 412pp. 5⅜ x 8.
S56 Paperbound **$2.50**

**THE SCIENTIFIC PAPERS OF J. WILLARD GIBBS.** All the published papers of America's outstanding theoretical scientist (except for "Statistical Mechanics" and "Vector Analysis"). Vol I (thermodynamics) contains one of the most brilliant of all 19th-century scientific papers—the 300-page "On the Equilibrium of Heterogeneous Substances," which founded the science of physical chemistry, and clearly stated a number of highly important natural laws for the first time; 8 other papers complete the first volume. Vol II includes 2 papers on dynamics, 8 on vector analysis and multiple algebra, 5 on the electromagnetic theory of light, and 6 miscellaneous papers. Biographical sketch by H. A. Bumstead. Total of xxxvi + 718pp. 5⅝ x 8⅜.
S721 Vol I Paperbound **$2.50**
S722 Vol II Paperbound **$2.25**
The set **$4.75**

**BASIC THEORIES OF PHYSICS, Peter Gabriel Bergmann.** Two-volume set which presents a critical examination of important topics in the major subdivisions of classical and modern physics. The first volume is concerned with classical mechanics and electrodynamics: mechanics of mass points, analytical mechanics, matter in bulk, electrostatics and magnetostatics, electromagnetic interaction, the field waves, special relativity, and waves. The second volume (Heat and Quanta) contains discussions of the kinetic hypothesis, physics and statistics, stationary ensembles, laws of thermodynamics, early quantum theories, atomic spectra, probability waves, quantization in wave mechanics, approximation methods, and abstract quantum theory. A valuable supplement to any thorough course or text.
Heat and Quanta: Index. 8 figures. x + 300pp. 5⅜ x 8½. S968 Paperbound **$2.00**
Mechanics and Electrodynamics: Index. 14 figures. vii + 280pp. 5⅜ x 8½.
S969 Paperbound **$1.85**

**THEORETICAL PHYSICS, A. S. Kompaneyets.** One of the very few thorough studies of the subject in this price range. Provides advanced students with a comprehensive theoretical background. Especially strong on recent experimentation and developments in quantum theory. Contents: Mechanics (Generalized Coordinates, Lagrange's Equation, Collision of Particles, etc.), Electrodynamics (Vector Analysis, Maxwell's equations, Transmission of Signals, Theory of Relativity, etc.), Quantum Mechanics (the Inadequacy of Classical Mechanics, the Wave Equation, Motion in a Central Field, Quantum Theory of Radiation, Quantum Theories of Dispersion and Scattering, etc.), and Statistical Physics (Equilibrium Distribution of Molecules in an Ideal Gas, Boltzmann statistics, Bose and Fermi Distribution, Thermodynamic Quantities, etc.). Revised to 1961. Translated by George Yankovsky, authorized by Kompaneyets. 137 exercises. 56 figures. 529pp. 5⅜ x 8½. S972 Paperbound **$2.50**

**ANALYTICAL AND CANONICAL FORMALISM IN PHYSICS, André Mercier.** A survey, in one volume, of the variational principles (the key principles—in mathematical form—from which the basic laws of any one branch of physics can be derived) of the several branches of physical theory, together with an examination of the relationships among them. Contents: the Lagrangian Formalism, Lagrangian Densities, Canonical Formalism, Canonical Form of Electrodynamics, Hamiltonian Densities, Transformations, and Canonical Form with Vanishing Jacobian Determinant. Numerous examples and exercises. For advanced students, teachers, etc. 6 figures. Index. viii + 222pp. 5⅜ x 8½. S1077 Paperbound **$1.75**

# MATHEMATICAL PUZZLES AND RECREATIONS

**AMUSEMENTS IN MATHEMATICS, Henry Ernest Dudeney.** The foremost British originator of mathematical puzzles is always intriguing, witty, and paradoxical in this classic, one of the largest collections of mathematical amusements. More than 430 puzzles, problems, and paradoxes. Mazes and games, problems on number manipulation, unicursal and other route problems, puzzles on measuring, weighing, packing, age, kinship, chessboards, joining, crossing river, plane figure dissection, and many others. Solutions. More than 450 illustrations. vii + 258pp. 5⅜ x 8. T473 Paperbound **$1.25**

**SYMBOLIC LOGIC and THE GAME OF LOGIC, Lewis Carroll.** "Symbolic Logic" is not concerned with modern symbolic logic, but is instead a collection of over 380 problems posed with charm and imagination, using the syllogism, and a fascinating diagrammatic method of drawing conclusions. In "The Game of Logic," Carroll's whimsical imagination devises a logical game played with 2 diagrams and counters (included) to manipulate hundreds of tricky syllogisms. The final section, "Hit or Miss" is a lagniappe of 101 additional puzzles in the delightful Carroll manner. Until this reprint edition, both of these books were rarities costing up to $15 each. Symbolic Logic: Index, xxxi + 199pp. The Game of Logic: 96pp. Two vols. bound as one. 5⅜ x 8. T492 Paperbound **$1.75**

**MAZES AND LABYRINTHS: A BOOK OF PUZZLES, W. Shepherd.** Mazes, formerly associated with mystery and ritual, are still among the most intriguing of intellectual puzzles. This is a novel and different collection of 50 amusements that embody the principle of the maze: mazes in the classical tradition; 3-dimensional, ribbon, and Möbius-strip mazes; hidden messages; spatial arrangements; etc.—almost all built on amusing story situations. 84 illustrations. Essay on maze psychology. Solutions. xv + 122pp. 5⅜ x 8. T731 Paperbound **$1.00**

**MATHEMATICAL RECREATIONS, M. Kraitchik.** Some 250 puzzles, problems, demonstrations of recreational mathematics for beginners & advanced mathematicians. Unusual historical problems from Greek, Medieval, Arabic, Hindu sources: modern problems based on "mathematics without numbers," geometry, topology, arithmetic, etc. Pastimes derived from figurative numbers, Mersenne numbers, Fermat numbers; fairy chess, latruncles, reversi, many topics. Full solutions. Excellent for insights into special fields of math. 181 illustrations. 330pp. 5⅜ x 8. T163 Paperbound **$1.75**

**MATHEMATICAL PUZZLES OF SAM LOYD, Vol. I, selected and edited by M. Gardner.** Puzzles by the greatest puzzle creator and innovator. Selected from his famous "Cyclopedia of Puzzles," they retain the unique style and historical flavor of the originals. There are posers based on arithmetic, algebra, probability, game theory, route tracing, topology, counter, sliding block, operations research, geometrical dissection. Includes his famous "14-15" puzzle which was a national craze, and his "Horse of a Different Color" which sold millions of copies. 117 of his most ingenious puzzles in all, 120 line drawings and diagrams. Solutions. Selected references. xx + 167pp. 5⅜ x 8. T498 Paperbound **$1.00**

**MY BEST PUZZLES IN MATHEMATICS, Hubert Phillips ("Caliban").** Caliban is generally considered the best of the modern problemists. Here are 100 of his best and wittiest puzzles, selected by the author himself from such publications as the London Daily Telegraph, and each puzzle is guaranteed to put even the sharpest puzzle detective through his paces. Perfect for the development of clear thinking and a logical mind. Complete solutions are provided for every puzzle. x + 107pp. 5⅜ x 8½. T91 Paperbound **$1.00**

**MY BEST PUZZLES IN LOGIC AND REASONING, H. Phillips ("Caliban").** 100 choice, hitherto unavailable puzzles by England's best-known problemist. No special knowledge needed to solve these logical or inferential problems, just an unclouded mind, nerves of steel, and fast reflexes. Data presented are both necessary and just sufficient to allow one unambiguous answer. More than 30 different types of puzzles, all ingenious and varied, many one of a kind, that will challenge the expert, please the beginner. Original publication. 100 puzzles, full solutions. x + 107pp. 5⅜ x 8½. T119 Paperbound **$1.00**

**MATHEMATICAL PUZZLES FOR BEGINNERS AND ENTHUSIASTS, G. Mott-Smith.** 188 mathematical puzzles to test mental agility. Inference, interpretation, algebra, dissection of plane figures, geometry, properties of numbers, decimation, permutations, probability, all enter these delightful problems. Puzzles like the Odic Force, How to Draw an Ellipse, Spider's Cousin, more than 180 others. Detailed solutions. Appendix with square roots, triangular numbers, primes, etc. 135 illustrations. 2nd revised edition. 248pp. 5⅜ x 8. T198 Paperbound **$1.25**

**MATHEMATICS, MAGIC AND MYSTERY, Martin Gardner.** Card tricks, feats of mental mathematics, stage mind-reading, other "magic" explained as applications of probability, sets, theory of numbers, topology, various branches of mathematics. Creative examination of laws and their applications with scores of new tricks and insights. 115 sections discuss tricks wtih cards, dice, coins; geometrical vanishing tricks, dozens of others. No sleight of hand needed; mathematics guarantees success. 115 illustrations. xii + 174pp. 5⅜ x 8. T335 Paperbound **$1.00**

**RECREATIONS IN THE THEORY OF NUMBERS: THE QUEEN OF MATHEMATICS ENTERTAINS, Albert H. Beiler.** The theory of numbers is often referred to as the "Queen of Mathematics." In this book Mr. Beiler has compiled the first English volume to deal exclusively with the recreational aspects of number theory, an inherently recreational branch of mathematics. The author's clear style makes for enjoyable reading as he deals with such topics as: perfect numbers, amicable numbers, Fermat's theorem, Wilson's theorem, interesting properties of digits, methods of factoring, primitive roots, Euler's function, polygonal and figurate numbers, Mersenne numbers, congruence, repeating decimals, etc. Countless puzzle problems, with full answers and explanations. For mathematicians and mathematically-inclined laymen, etc. New publication. 28 figures. 9 illustrations. 103 tables. Bibliography at chapter ends. vi + 247pp. 5⅜ x 8½. T1096 Paperbound **$2.00**

**PAPER FOLDING FOR BEGINNERS, W. D. Murray and F. J. Rigney.** A delightful introduction to the varied and entertaining Japanese art of origami (paper folding), with a full crystal-clear text that anticipates every difficulty; over 275 clearly labeled diagrams of all important stages in creation. You get results at each stage, since complex figures are logically developed from simpler ones. 43 different pieces are explained: place mats, drinking cups, bonbon boxes, sailboats, frogs, roosters, etc. 6 photographic plates. 279 diagrams. 95pp. 5⅝ x 8⅜. T713 Paperbound **$1.00**

**1800 RIDDLES, ENIGMAS AND CONUNDRUMS, Darwin A. Hindman.** Entertaining collection ranging from hilarious gags to outrageous puns to sheer nonsense—a welcome respite from sophisticated humor. Children, toastmasters, and practically anyone with a funny bone will find these zany riddles tickling and eminently repeatable. Sample: "Why does Santa Claus always go down the chimney?" "Because it soots him." Some old, some new—covering a wide variety of subjects. New publication. iii + 154pp. 5⅜ x 8½. T1059 Paperbound **$1.00**

**EASY-TO-DO ENTERTAINMENTS AND DIVERSIONS WITH CARDS, STRING, COINS, PAPER AND MATCHES, R. M. Abraham.** Over 300 entertaining games, tricks, puzzles, and pastimes for children and adults. Invaluable to anyone in charge of groups of youngsters, for party givers, etc. Contains sections on card tricks and games, making things by paperfolding—toys, decorations, and the like; tricks with coins, matches, and pieces of string; descriptions of games; toys that can be made from common household objects; mathematical recreations; word games; and 50 miscellaneous entertainments. Formerly "Winter Nights Entertainments." Introduction by Lord Baden Powell. 329 illustrations. v + 186pp. 5⅜ x 8. T921 Paperbound **$1.00**

**DIVERSIONS AND PASTIMES WITH CARDS, STRING, PAPER AND MATCHES, R. M. Abraham.** Another collection of amusements and diversion for game and puzzle fans of all ages. Many new paperfolding ideas and tricks, an extensive section on amusements with knots and splices, two chapters of easy and not-so-easy problems, coin and match tricks, and lots of other parlor pastimes from the agile mind of the late British problemist and gamester. Corrected and revised version. Illustrations. 160pp. 5⅜ x 8½. T1127 Paperbound **$1.00**

**STRING FIGURES AND HOW TO MAKE THEM: A STUDY OF CAT'S-CRADLE IN MANY LANDS, Caroline Furness Jayne.** In a simple and easy-to-follow manner, this book describes how to make 107 different string figures. Not only is looping and crossing string between the fingers a common youthful diversion, but it is an ancient form of amusement practiced in all parts of the globe, especially popular among primitive tribes. These games are fun for all ages and offer an excellent means for developing manual dexterity and coordination. Much insight also for the anthropological observer on games and diversions in many different cultures. Index. Bibliography. Introduction by A. C. Haddon, Cambridge University. 17 full-page plates. 950 illustrations. xxiii + 407pp. 5⅜ x 8½. T152 Paperbound **$2.00**

**CRYPTANALYSIS, Helen F. Gaines.** (Formerly ELEMENTARY CRYPTANALYSIS.) A standard elementary and intermediate text for serious students. It does not confine itself to old material, but contains much that is not generally known, except to experts. Concealment, Transposition, Substitution ciphers; Vigenere, Kasiski, Playfair, multafid, dozens of other techniques. Appendix with sequence charts, letter frequencies in English, 5 other languages, English word frequencies. Bibliography. 167 codes. New to this edition: solution to codes. vi + 230pp. 5⅜ x 8. T97 Paperbound **$2.25**

**MAGIC SQUARES AND CUBES, W. S. Andrews.** Only book-length treatment in English, a thorough non-technical description and analysis. Here are nasik, overlapping, pandiagonal, serrated squares; magic circles, cubes, spheres, rhombuses. Try your hand at 4-dimensional magical figures! Much unusual folklore and tradition included. High school algebra is sufficient. 754 diagrams and illustrations. viii + 419pp. 5⅜ x 8. T658 Paperbound **$1.85**

**CALIBAN'S PROBLEM BOOK: MATHEMATICAL, INFERENTIAL, AND CRYPTOGRAPHIC PUZZLES, H. Phillips ("Caliban"), S. T. Shovelton, G. S. Marshall.** 105 ingenious problems by the greatest living creator of puzzles based on logic and inference. Rigorous, modern, piquant, and reflecting their author's unusual personality, these intermediate and advanced puzzles all involve the ability to reason clearly through complex situations; some call for mathematical knowledge, ranging from algebra to number theory. Solutions. xi + 180pp. 5⅜ x 8. T736 Paperbound **$1.25**

# FICTION

**THE LAND THAT TIME FORGOT and THE MOON MAID, Edgar Rice Burrougns.** In the opinion of many, Burroughs' best work. The first concerns a strange island where evolution is individual rather than phylogenetic. Speechless anthropoids develop into intelligent human beings within a single generation. The second projects the reader far into the future and describes the first voyage to the Moon (in the year 2025), the conquest of the Earth by the Moon, and years of violence and adventure as the enslaved Earthmen try to regain possession of their planet. "An imaginative tour de force that keeps the reader keyed up and expectant," NEW YORK TIMES. Complete, unabridged text of the original two novels (three parts in each). 5 illustrations by J. Allen St. John. vi + 552pp. 5⅜ x 8½.
T1020 Clothbound **$3.75**
T358 Paperbound **$2.00**

**AT THE EARTH'S CORE, PELLUCIDAR, TANAR OF PELLUCIDAR: THREE SCIENCE FICTION NOVELS BY EDGAR RICE BURROUGHS.** Complete, unabridged texts of the first three Pellucidar novels. Tales of derring-do by the famous master of science fiction. The locale for these three related stories is the inner surface of the hollow Earth where we discover the world of Pellucidar, complete with all types of bizarre, menacing creatures, strange peoples, and alluring maidens—guaranteed to delight all Burroughs fans and a wide circle of advenutre lovers. Illustrated by J. Allen St. John and P. F. Berdanier. vi + 433pp. 5⅜ x 8½.
T1051 Paperbound **$2.00**

**THE PIRATES OF VENUS and LOST ON VENUS: TWO VENUS NOVELS BY EDGAR RICE BURROUGHS.** Two related novels, complete and unabridged. Exciting adventure on the planet Venus with Earthman Carson Napier broken-field running through one dangerous episode after another. All lovers of swashbuckling science fiction will enjoy these two stories set in a world of fascinating societies, fierce beasts, 5000-ft. trees, lush vegetation, and wide seas. Illustrations by Fortunino Matania. Total of vi + 340pp. 5⅜ x 8½. T1053 Paperbound **$1.75**

**A PRINCESS OF MARS and A FIGHTING MAN OF MARS: TWO MARTIAN NOVELS BY EDGAR RICE BURROUGHS.** "Princess of Mars" is the very first of the great Martian novels written by Burroughs, and it is probably the best of them all; it set the pattern for all of his later fantasy novels and contains a thrilling cast of strange peoples and creatures and the formula of Olympian heroism amidst ever-fluctuating fortunes which Burroughs carries off so successfully. "Fighting Man" returns to the same scenes and cities—many years later. A mad scientist, a degenerate dictator, and an indomitable defender of the right clash—with the fate of the Red Planet at stake! Complete, unabridged reprinting of original editions. Illustrations by F. E. Schoonover and Hugh Hutton. v + 356pp. 5⅜ x 8½.
T1140 Paperbound **$1.75**

**THREE MARTIAN NOVELS, Edgar Rice Burroughs.** Contains: Thuvia, Maid of Mars; The Chessmen of Mars; and The Master Mind of Mars. High adventure set in an imaginative and intricate conception of the Red Planet. Mars is peopled with an intelligent, heroic human race which lives in densely populated cities and with fierce barbarians who inhabit dead sea bottoms. Other exciting creatures abound amidst an inventive framework of Martian history and geography. Complete unabridged reprintings of the first edition. 16 illustrations by J. Allen St. John. vi + 499pp. 5⅜ x 8½. T39 Paperbound **$1.85**

**THREE PROPHETIC NOVELS BY H. G. WELLS, edited by E. F. Bleiler.** Complete texts of "When the Sleeper Wakes" (1st book printing in 50 years), "A Story of the Days to Come," "The Time Machine" (1st complete printing in book form). Exciting adventures in the future are as enjoyable today as 50 years ago when first printed. Predict TV, movies, intercontinental airplanes, prefabricated houses, air-conditioned cities, etc. First important author to foresee problems of mind control, technological dictatorships. "Absolute best of imaginative fiction," N. Y. Times. Introduction. 335pp. 5⅜ x 8. T605 Paperbound **$1.50**

**28 SCIENCE FICTION STORIES OF H. G. WELLS.** Two full unabridged novels, MEN LIKE GODS and STAR BEGOTTEN, plus 26 short stories by the master science-fiction writer of all time. Stories of space, time, invention, exploration, future adventure—an indispensable part of the library of everyone interested in science and adventure. PARTIAL CONTENTS: Men Like Gods, The Country of the Blind, In the Abyss, The Crystal Egg, The Man Who Could Work Miracles, A Story of the Days to Come, The Valley of Spiders, and 21 more! 928pp. 5⅜ x 8.
T265 Clothbound **$4.50**

**THE WAR IN THE AIR, IN THE DAYS OF THE COMET, THE FOOD OF THE GODS: THREE SCIENCE FICTION NOVELS BY H. G. WELLS.** Three exciting Wells offerings bearing on vital social and philosophical issues of his and our own day. Here are tales of air power, strategic bombing,, East vs. West, the potential miracles of science, the potential disasters from outer space, the relationship between scientific advancement and moral progress, etc. First reprinting of "War in the Air" in almost 50 years. An excellent sampling of Wells at his storytelling best. Complete, unabridged reprintings. 16 illustrations. 645pp. 5⅜ x 8½.
T1135 Paperbound **$2.00**

**SEVEN SCIENCE FICTION NOVELS, H. G. Wells.** Full unabridged texts of 7 science-fiction novels of the master. Ranging from biology, physics, chemistry, astronomy to sociology and other studies, Mr. Wells extrapolates whole worlds of strange and intriguing character. "One will have to go far to match this for entertainment, excitement, and sheer pleasure . . . ," NEW YORK TIMES. Contents: The Time Machine, The Island of Dr. Moreau, First Men in the Moon, The Invisible Man, The War of the Worlds, The Food of the Gods, In the Days of the Comet. 1015pp. 5⅜ x 8. T264 Clothbound **$4.50**

**BEST GHOST STORIES OF J. S. LE FANU, Selected and introduced by E. F. Bleiler.** LeFanu is deemed the greatest name in Victorian supernatural fiction. Here are 16 of his best horror stories, including 2 nouvelles: "Carmilla," a classic vampire tale couched in a perverse eroticism, and "The Haunted Baronet." Also: "Sir Toby's Will," "Green Tea," "Schalken the Painter," "Ultor de Lacy," "The Familiar," etc. The first American publication of about half of this material: a long-overdue opportunity to get a choice sampling of LeFanu's work. New selection (1964). 8 illustrations. 5⅜ x 8⅜. T415 Paperbound **$1.85**

**THE WONDERFUL WIZARD OF OZ, L. F. Baum.** Only edition in print with all the original W. W. Denslow illustrations in full color—as much a part of "The Wizard" as Tenniel's drawings are for "Alice in Wonderland." "The Wizard" is still America's best-loved fairy tale, in which, as the author expresses it, "The wonderment and joy are retained and the heartaches and nightmares left out." Now today's young readers can enjoy every word and wonderful picture of the original book. New introduction by Martin Gardner. A Baum bibliography. 23 full-page color plates. viii + 268pp. 5⅜ x 8. T691 Paperbound **$1.50**

**GHOST AND HORROR STORIES OF AMBROSE BIERCE, Selected and introduced by E. F. Bleiler.** 24 morbid, eerie tales—the cream of Bierce's fiction output. Contains such memorable pieces as "The Moonlit Road," "The Damned Thing," "An Inhabitant of Carcosa," "The Eyes of the Panther," "The Famous Gilson Bequest," "The Middle Toe of the Right Foot," and other chilling stories, plus the essay, "Visions of the Night" in which Bierce gives us a kind of rationale for his aesthetic of horror. New collection (1964). xxii + 199pp. 5⅜ x 8⅜. T767 Paperbound **$1.00**

## HUMOR

**MR. DOOLEY ON IVRYTHING AND IVRYBODY, Finley Peter Dunne.** Since the time of his appearance in 1893, "Mr. Dooley," the fictitious Chicago bartender, has been recognized as America's most humorous social and political commentator. Collected in this volume are 102 of the best Dooley pieces—all written around the turn of the century, the height of his popularity. Mr. Dooley's Irish brogue is employed wittily and penetratingly on subjects which are just as fresh and relevant today as they were then: corruption and hypocrisy of politicans, war preparations and chauvinism, automation, Latin American affairs, superbombs, etc. Other articles range from Rudyard Kipling to football. Selected with an introduction by Robert Hutchinson. xii + 244pp. 5⅜ x 8½. T626 Paperbound **$1.00**

**RUTHLESS RHYMES FOR HEARTLESS HOMES and MORE RUTHLESS RHYMES FOR HEARTLESS HOMES, Harry Graham ("Col. D. Streamer").** A collection of Little Willy and 48 other poetic "disasters." Graham's funniest and most disrespectful verse, accompanied by original illustrations. Nonsensical, wry humor which employs stern parents, careless nurses, uninhibited children, practical jokers, single-minded golfers, Scottish lairds, etc. in the leading roles. A precursor of the "sick joke" school of today. This volume contains, bound together for the first time, two of the most perennially popular books of humor in England and America. Index. vi + 69pp. 5⅜ x 8. T930 Paperbound **75¢**

**A WHIMSEY ANTHOLOGY, Collected by Carolyn Wells.** 250 of the most amusing rhymes ever written. Acrostics, anagrams, palindromes, alphabetical jingles, tongue twisters, echo verses, alliterative verses, riddles, mnemonic rhymes, interior rhymes, over 40 limericks, etc. by Lewis Carroll, Edward Lear, Joseph Addison, W. S. Gilbert, Christina Rossetti, Chas. Lamb, James Boswell, Hood, Dickens, Swinburne, Leigh Hunt, Harry Graham, Poe, Eugene Field, and many others. xiv + 221pp. 5⅜ x 8½. T195 Paperbound **$1.25**

**MY PIOUS FRIENDS AND DRUNKEN COMPANIONS and MORE PIOUS FRIENDS AND DRUNKEN COMPANIONS, Songs and ballads of Conviviality Collected by Frank Shay. Magnificently illuminated by John Held, Jr.** 132 ballads, blues, vaudeville numbers, drinking songs, cowboy songs, sea chanties, comedy songs, etc. of the Naughty Nineties and early 20th century. Over a third are reprinted with music. Many perennial favorites such as: The Band Played On, Frankie and Johnnie, The Old Grey Mare, The Face on the Bar-room Floor, etc. Many others unlocatable elsewhere: The Dog-Catcher's Child, The Cannibal Maiden, Don't Go in the Lion's Cage Tonight, Mother, etc. Complete verses and introductions to songs. Unabridged republication of first editions, 2 Indexes (song titles and first lines and choruses). Introduction by Frank Shay. 2 volumes bounds as 1. Total of xvi + 235pp. 5⅜ x 8½. T946 Paperbound **$1.25**

**MAX AND MORITZ, Wilhelm Busch. Edited and annotated by H. Arthur Klein. Translated by H. Arthur Klein, M. C. Klein, and others.** The mischievous high jinks of Max and Moritz, Peter and Paul, Ker and Plunk, etc. are delightfully captured in sketch and rhyme. (Companion volume to "Hypocritical Helena.") In addition to the title piece, it contians: Ker and Plunk; Two Dogs and Two Boys; The Egghead and the Two Cut-ups of Corinth; Deceitful Henry; The Boys and the Pipe; Cat and Mouse; and others. (Original German text with accompanying English translations.) Afterword by H. A. Klein. vi + 216pp. 5⅜ x 8½.
T181 Paperbound **$1.15**

**THROUGH THE ALIMENTARY CANAL WITH GUN AND CAMERA: A FASCINATING TRIP TO THE INTERIOR, Personally Conducted by George S. Chappell.** In mock-travelogue style, the amusing account of an imaginative journey down the alimentary canal. The "explorers" enter the esophagus, round the Adam's Apple, narrowly escape from a fierce Amoeba, struggle through the impenetrable Nerve Forests of the Lumbar Region, etc. Illustrated by the famous cartoonist, Otto Soglow, the book is as much a brilliant satire of academic pomposity and professional travel literature as it is a clever use of the facts of physiology for supremely comic purposes. Preface by Robert Benchley. Author's Foreword. 1 Photograph. 17 illustrations by O. Soglow. xii + 114pp. 5⅜ x 8½. T376 Paperbound **$1.00**

**THE BAD CHILD'S BOOK OF BEASTS, MORE BEASTS FOR WORSE CHILDREN, and A MORAL ALPHABET, H. Belloc.** Hardly an anthology of humorous verse has appeared in the last 50 years without at least a couple of these famous nonsense verses. But one must see the entire volumes—with all the delightful original illustrations by Sir Basil Blackwood—to appreciate fully Belloc's charming and witty verses that play so subacidly on the platitudes of life and morals that beset his day—and ours. A great humor classic. Three books in one. Total of 157pp. 5⅜ x 8. T749 Paperbound **$1.00**

**THE DEVIL'S DICTIONARY, Ambrose Bierce.** Sardonic and irreverent barbs puncturing the pomposities and absurdities of American politics, business, religion, literature, and arts, by the country's greatest satirist in the classic tradition. Epigrammatic as Shaw, piercing as Swift, American as Mark Twain, Will Rogers, and Fred Allen. Bierce will always remain the favorite of a small coterie of enthusiasts, and of writers and speakers whom he supplies with "some of the most gorgeous witticisms of the English language." (H. L. Mencken) Over 1000 entries in alphabetical order. 144pp. 5⅜ x 8. T487 Paperbound **$1.00**

**THE COMPLETE NONSENSE OF EDWARD LEAR.** This is the only complete edition of this master of gentle madness available at a popular price. A BOOK OF NONSENSE, NONSENSE SONGS, MORE NONSENSE SONGS AND STORIES in their entirety with all the old favorites that have delighted children and adults for years. The Dong With A Luminous Nose, The Jumblies, The Owl and the Pussycat, and hundreds of other bits of wonderful nonsense. 214 limericks, 3 sets of Nonsense Botany, 5 Nonsense Alphabets. 546 drawings by Lear himself, and much more. 320pp. 5⅜ x 8. T167 Paperbound **$1.00**

**SINGULAR TRAVELS, CAMPAIGNS, AND ADVENTURES OF BARON MUNCHAUSEN, R. E. Raspe, with 90 illustrations by Gustave Doré.** The first edition in over 150 years to reestablish the deeds of the Prince of Liars exactly as Raspe first recorded them in 1785—the genuine Baron Munchausen, one of the most popular personalities in English literature. Included also are the best of the many sequels, written by other hands. Introduction on Raspe by J. Carswell. Bibliography of early editions. xliv + 192pp. 5⅜ x 8. T698 Paperbound **$1.00**

**HOW TO TELL THE BIRDS FROM THE FLOWERS, R. W. Wood.** How not to confuse a carrot with a parrot, a grape with an ape, a puffin with nuffin. Delightful drawings, clever puns, absurd little poems point out farfetched resemblances in nature. The author was a leading physicist. Introduction by Margaret Wood White. 106 illus. 60pp. 5⅜ x 8.
T523 Paperbound **75¢**

**JOE MILLER'S JESTS OR, THE WITS VADE-MECUM.** The original Joe Miller jest book. Gives a keen and pungent impression of life in 18th-century England. Many are somewhat on the bawdy side and they are still capable of provoking amusement and good fun. This volume is a facsimile of the original "Joe Miller" first published in 1739. It remains the most popular and influential humor book of all time. New introduction by Robert Hutchinson. xxi + 70pp. 5⅜ x 8½. T423 Paperbound **$1.00**

*Prices subject to change without notice.*

*Dover publishes books on art, music, philosophy, literature, languages, history, social sciences, psychology, handcrafts, orientalia, puzzles and entertainments, chess, pets and gardens, books explaining science, intermediate and higher mathematics, mathematical physics, engineering, biological sciences, earth sciences, classics of science, etc. Write to:*

*Dept. catrr.*
*Dover Publications, Inc.*
*180 Varick Street, N.Y. 14, N.Y.*